MAN, CULTURE, AND ANIMALS

The Role of Animals in Human Ecological Adjustments

Based on a symposium presented at the Denver meeting of the American Association for the Advancement of Science 30 December 1961

Edited by ANTHONY LEEDS
ANDREW P. VAYDA

Publication No. 78 of the

AMERICAN ASSOCIATION FOR THE ADVANCEMENT OF SCIENCE

WASHINGTON, D. C.   1965

Preface

Man, Culture, and Animals is based on a symposium entitled "The Role of Animals in Human Ecological Adjustments," held during the 128th annual meeting of the American Association for the Advancement of Science at Denver, Colorado, in December 1961.

The symposium grew out of the editors' earlier work on the role of pigs in Melanesian economies,[1] an investigation that led to a recognition of the need for additional data and for new analyses pertaining to the relation between man and animals in other parts of the world.

The original participants in the symposium were Vayda (Introduction) ; Kunstadter (Apache cattle and Navaho sheep) ; Leeds (Chukchi reindeer) ; Ann Chowning (Melanesian pigs and dogs) ; Harold Schneider (East African cattle) ; Murra (Inca llamas) ; Sweet (Bedouin camels) ; and Aschmann (Comments) . Chowning and Schneider preferred not to publish their papers.

After the Denver meeting, the editors became aware of work being done by other anthropologists and geographers in line with the symposium theme. Papers were solicited from such persons, especially if their research dealt with animals not included in the original roster of the symposium. An attempt was made also to widen the range of cultures and animal "roles" represented. Thus, consideration of the role of nondomesticated animals was broadened by including the papers by Meggitt, Knight, and Hickerson. Coverage of the use of animals in relatively complex, agrarian, state-organized societies was extended by adding the papers of Downs and Ekvall and of Harris. Finally, the range of cultures was extended to "modern" industrializing societies by the inclu-

[1] A. P. Vayda, A. Leeds, and D. B. Smith, The place of pigs in Melanesian subsistence, *Proceedings of the 1961 Annual Spring Meeting of the American Ethnological Society* (Viola E. Garfield, editor) , pp. 69–77. University of Washington Press, Seattle, 1961.

sion of Strickon's paper. Deshler's paper was substituted for Schneider's on East African cattle, and Collins' comments, from the standpoint of the philosophy of science, were added.

In spite of the range of cultures, animals, and animal roles represented, it should be obvious that, in soliciting papers, the editors attempted nothing so rigorous (and so impractical) as getting a sample of human ecological adjustments that could be used for testing carefully defined hypotheses. Rather, some anthropologists and geographers who had done research on human populations utilizing certain animals were simply asked to prepare papers in which at least the following points would receive consideration: the uses that the people make of particular animals and their products; the characteristics of the animals upon which such uses depend (e.g., the animals' population dynamics, their diet, their mobility) ; and the effects that using or having to use the animals has upon cultural patterns and social organization. Despite the omission of papers on certain aspects of the influence of animals —for example, their role as carriers and reservoirs of disease—the editors believe that these collected papers can lead to the recognition of some regularities in roles played by animals in human ecological adjustments; that they can lead to the formulation of new hypotheses; and that they can provide a stimulus to future field work by pointing up lacunae in the ethnographic record and the need for additional quantitative data. Further, the editors believe that the papers indicate the possibility and also the fruitfulness of functional analyses concerned not only with the interrelation of sociological variables but also with the operation of mechanisms maintaining environmental variables at values conducive to the survival or expansion of human populations.

The editors would like to thank the many people who made possible the original symposium and its adaptation into a book. Special thanks are due to Mrs. Jean Henry Champ, who helped indefatigably with the preparation of the index.

ANTHONY LEEDS
The University of Texas
ANDREW P. VAYDA
Columbia University

Contributors

HOMER ASCHMANN, Department of Geography, University of California, Riverside, California.

PAUL W. COLLINS, Department of Philosophy, State University of New York, Stony Brook, Long Island, New York

W. W. DESHLER, Department of Geography, University of Maryland, College Park, Maryland

JAMES F. DOWNS, Department of Anthropology, California State College at Los Angeles, Los Angeles, California

ROBERT B. EKVALL, Burke Memorial Museum, University of Washington, Seattle, Washington

MARVIN HARRIS, Department of Anthropology, Columbia University, New York, New York

HAROLD HICKERSON, Department of Anthropology, State University of New York at Buffalo, Buffalo, New York

ROLF KNIGHT, Department of Anthropology, Columbia University, New York, New York

PETER KUNSTADTER, Department of Sociology and Anthropology, Princeton University, Princeton, New Jersey

ANTHONY LEEDS, Department of Anthropology, The University of Texas, Austin, Texas

M. J. MEGGITT, Department of Anthropology, University of Sydney, Sydney, Australia

JOHN V. MURRA, Institute of Andean Research, Huánuco, Perú

ARNOLD STRICKON, Department of Anthropology, Brandeis University, Waltham, Massachusetts

LOUISE E. SWEET, Department of Anthropology, State University of New York, Harpur College, Binghamton, New York

ANDREW P. VAYDA, Department of Anthropology, Columbia University, New York, New York

Contents

Anthropologists and Ecological Problems

ANDREW P. VAYDA

Department of Anthropology, Columbia University, New York, New York

SINCE THIS VOLUME consists predominantly of papers by anthropologists, it may perhaps be asked why the role of animals in human ecological adjustments should be a matter of anthropological concern. One possible answer is that anything at all which relates to man is within the purview of the anthropologist. On the other hand, it might also be argued that anthropologists, as social scientists, may not properly venture outside the realm of the social or cultural, at least not when they are attempting to give explanations of social or cultural phenomena. This latter position may have two different bases. One of them is to be found in White's argument that culture is "a thing sui generis" and can be explained only in terms of itself (White, 1949, p. 78). This argument assumes, first of all, that biological variations and variability in mankind are limited enough to be treated as constant factors and ignored in explanations of cultural phenomena (White, 1959, p. 12). The argument further assumes that it is not necessary to consider the physical environment in order to provide adequate answers to such questions as how and why social systems change (*ibid.*, pp. 50–51). In the light of some of the recent research to be referred to below, these assumptions are difficult to justify.

A different basis from White's for keeping the anthropologist within the cultural or social realm is provided by professional division of labor. Quite apart from the empirical question whether or

1

not noncultural phenomena may significantly influence culture, the fact remains that cultural anthropologists are trained to study culture rather than to study plants and animals and soils and winds. In the light of this fact, it can be argued that although it may well be that an explanation of some cultural phenomena requires reference to noncultural variables, it is not the job of the cultural anthropologist to deal with these variables. In this view, the cultural anthropologist reaches his ultimate explanation of some particular phenomena when he can no longer present any further explanation in terms of cultural variables alone (cf. Brown, 1963, p. 189).

As far as White's argument is concerned, we may be quite peremptory in dismissing it at the present stage of inquiry in anthropology. In the absence of firmly established principles or laws of human behavior, *a priori* restrictions on the variables suitable for study can only hold back the progress of science. Furthermore, recent work has been indicating that the consideration of biological and environmental factors can, in fact, add greatly to our understanding of cultural phenomena (Baker, 1962; Dobzhansky, 1962; Wallace, 1961).

But is it the anthropologist's job to consider these factors? This is the question that brings to the fore the issue of professional division of labor. A possible answer is that a new division of labor is needed. This, in effect, has been suggested by Wallace. He has stated that ignoring biology and the physical environment will leave us with a "sterile catalogue of cultural forms" rather than with a *science* of culture (Wallace, 1961, p. 22), and he looks to the next generation of students in cultural anthropology to recognize and deal with biological and environmental variables (*ibid.*, p. 200).

Of course, it may be that the future students who do this work and are trained to do it will, in fact, be called not "cultural anthropologists" but rather something else, in explicit recognition of change in the professional division of labor. The point is worth making only in order to remind us that disciplinary boundaries are not immutable. Right now, the crossing of extant boundaries by scientists formally identified with one discipline or another can prepare the way for a redrawing of disciplinary boundaries so as to enhance future scientific productivity. And if the boundary crossing does not succeed in accomplishing this, it might still effect at least an increase in interaction, communication, and collaboration among workers in the different disciplines. This result too could be a means for new achievements in understanding and scholarship.

Whether by individual scientists crossing disciplinary boundaries or by collaborators from different disciplines, the attack on the problem of the interaction of cultural, biological, and environmental variables may be made in a number of different ways. It is appropriate to consider some of the possibilities here.

One approach, already aptly criticized by Geertz (1963, pp. 1–3), treats the variables as belonging to different spheres (e.g., "culture" and "environment") and asks how the different spheres, regarded as independent wholes, influence one another. To such gross questions, only gross answers can be given (e.g., the often cited, but rarely analyzed, dictum that environment "limits but does not determine" culture).

Regarding such answers as inadequate, Geertz himself (1963, p. 3) advocates an approach that places the different variables within a single analytical system. The necessary conceptual framework is provided, for him, by the concept of the *ecosystem*, borrowed from plant and animal ecologists, who use it to refer to any functioning, interacting system composed of one or more living organisms and their effective environment (Fosberg, 1963, p. 2). Geertz' procedure is to delineate an "ecosystem within which certain selected cultural, biological, and physical variables are determinately interrelated" and then to analyze the operation of and changes in this system.

The approach differs from ecological approaches to biotic phenomena in general in that it allows for the inclusion of ideologies, moral valuations, and similar cultural phenomena among the variables to be dealt with. In the present volume a number of authors —for example, Kunstadter and Murra—are concerned with the influence of such phenomena upon the uses to which animals are put by human beings.

These phenomena are of course legitimate and significant subjects of investigation. Attention to cultural ideas, values, or concepts cannot, however, be said to be a *sine qua non* of the analysis of ecosystems including man. One may choose rather to place emphasis upon the actual physical behavior or bodily movements through which man directly effects alterations in his environment (cf. Harris, 1964, pp. 29–30, 169–170; Wagner, 1960, pp. 26–27). Indeed, a possible approach, suggested by Simpson (1962, p. 106) among others, is to regard human culture simply as the behavior or part of the behavior of a particular species of primates. By so regarding it, we are enabled to study and interpret it as we do the behavior of any other species; for example, with respect not only to its interaction with environmental variables but also to the effect of this interaction upon natural selection. The fact that human behavior is complex, varied, variable, and, to a considerable extent, population-specific may make observation and description formidable tasks, but it does not mean that basically different principles must be used in the study of human behavior and the study of behavior in other animal species (cf. Harris, 1964, p. 173; Rappaport, 1963, pp. 168–169).

In the present volume a number of authors—for example, Deshler, Harris, Hickerson, Knight, Leeds, and Sweet—do in fact (even if not explicitly) appear to utilize this last mentioned approach and to focus upon the biologically adaptive aspects of socially standardized human behavior ranging from the use of cow dung as a cooking fuel to intertribal fighting and raiding. It seems significant that these authors are successful in applying in their analyses such general ecological principles and concepts as Liebig's law of the minimum and other principles pertaining to limiting factors (Odum, 1959, chap. 4). If the same principles can be applied in illuminating fashion not only to ecosystems involving fishes, reptiles, and rodents but also to ecosystems involving Indian hunters, Siberian reindeer herders, Arabian nomads, and South Asian peasants, then it may be suggested that the prospects are promising for the further development of a science of ecology with laws and principles that apply to man as they do to other species.

REFERENCES

BAKER, P. T. 1962. The application of ecological theory to anthropology. *Am. Anthropologist, 64,* 15–22.

BROWN, R. 1963. *Explanation in Social Science.* Aldine Publishing Co., Chicago, Ill.

DOBZHANSKY, T. 1962. *Mankind Evolving; The Evolution of the Human Species.* Yale University Press, New Haven, Conn.

FOSBERG, F. R. 1963. The island ecosystem. In *Man's Place in the Island Ecosystem* (F. R. Fosberg, editor), pp. 1–6. Bishop Museum Press, Honolulu, Hawaii.

GEERTZ, C. 1963. *Agricultural Involution; The Process of Ecological Change in Indonesia.* University of California Press, Berkeley, Calif.

HARRIS, M. 1964. *The Nature of Cultural Things.* Random House, New York, N. Y.

ODUM, E. P. 1959. *Fundamentals of Ecology,* 2nd edition. W. B. Saunders Co., Philadelphia, Pa.

RAPPAPORT, R. A. 1963. Aspects of man's influence upon island ecosystems: Alteration and control. In *Man's Place in the Island Ecosystem* (F. R. Fosberg, editor), pp. 155–174. Bishop Museum Press, Honolulu, Hawaii.

SIMPSON, G. G. 1962. Comments on cultural evolution. In *Evolution and Man's Progress* (H. Hoagland and R. W. Burhoe, editors), pp. 104–108. Columbia University Press, New York, N. Y.

WAGNER, P. L. 1960. *The Human Use of the Earth.* Free Press of Glencoe, Ill.

WALLACE, A. F. C. 1961. *Culture and Personality.* Random House, New York, N. Y.

WHITE, L. A. 1949. *The Science of Culture.* Farrar, Straus and Co., New York, N. Y.

WHITE, L. A. 1959. *The Evolution of Culture.* McGraw-Hill Book Co., New York, N. Y.

The Association between Australian Aborigines and Dingoes

M. J. MEGGITT

Department of Anthropology, University of Sydney, Sydney, Australia

Downs, in a paper entitled "Domestication; An Examination of the Changing Social Relationships between Men and Animals" (1960), treats (under the heading "Pack Scavengers") man's association with, and domestication of, the dog—not only *Canis familiaris,* but also other species of *Canis.*

I shall indicate the main points of Downs' discussion (1960, pp. 45–47) and then, in the light of his argument, take up the question of the association between the Australian Aborigines and *Canis dingo,* the Australian wild dog, often called the dingo or the warrigal. I shall examine the ways in which Aborigines have exploited dingoes and shall try to estimate the utility of the animals as hunting aids. In particular, I want to point to a hitherto little-publicized conservational aspect of Aboriginal hunting behavior.

Downs begins by questioning the assumption that traces the present distribution of domesticated canines to one point of origin in a single, prototypic domestication of the dog in mesolithic Europe. He asserts that there is a dichotomy between "European" and "Asian" attitudes toward the dog, one congruent with the difference in relationships that exist between nomadic hunters and dogs, on the one hand, and between sedentary agriculturalists and dogs, on the other. Moreover, he believes the dichotomy is intelligible in the light of differences between prehistoric sequences in Europe and those in southern Asia and the Orient. In Europe

7

there was a distinctive "mesolithic" age, a long period during which men gave up purely nomadic hunting for a combination of semisedentary hunting and gathering before developing semisedentary agriculture. This was apparently not the case in the East, where there seems to have been a relatively abrupt and rapid transition from hunting to sedentary agriculture.[1]

Downs then sketches a putative history of the association of man and dog in early Europe. Paleolithic hunters, he says, were commonly nomads or seminomads who conducted large-scale drives of the bigger animals which at that time roamed the plains and tundras. In the massive slaughter that ensued, as, for instance, at Dordogne, where herds of horses were driven over cliffs, a considerable residue of bones and offal was left; this encouraged scavenging wild dogs to follow the movements of the hunting parties.

This kind of subsistence pattern altered with the climatic changes of the late Pleistocene and early Holocene, changes which greatly affected the flora and fauna of Europe. Dense forest replaced much of the open plain and tundra, and men now had to stalk more solitary and elusive species of beasts in relatively restricted areas. An increasing dependence on fishing and the gathering of shellfish also facilitated the development of more or less stable habitations, marked by huge middens. Wild dogs wanting to scavenge among man's refuse now had to remain much nearer his semipermanent camps.

Downs hypothesizes that, as packs of dogs ran down their own game in the dense forests, hunters armed with spears or bows occasionally followed the dogs in order to take the catch from them. "One can envision, although perhaps never prove, a symbiotic hunting partnership between these wild dogs who located, pursued and brought to bay game, and man who could despatch beasts effectively with his weapons. . . . The percentage of kills made in such a way must have been higher than could have been made by either species, man or dog, hunting alone. . . . We can assume that these variations [in the dogs' traits or qualities] provided a basis for an unconscious selection on the part of man" (1960, p.

---

[1] As I am neither a prehistorian nor an archeologist, I am not competent to assess the validity of such general propositions.

46). It was this kind of association, Downs asserts, that was absent in the Orient.

Finally, he suggests that an examination of "the attitudes toward dogs among peoples who use them in hunting might shed further light on the postulate that this relationship does in fact engender certain attitudes toward canines and thus open the way to a wider use of the species" (1960, p. 47).

It is unfortunate that Downs does not refer at all in his argument to the place of the dingo in the culture of the Australian Aboriginal hunters, for, until Europeans brought horses, donkeys, and camels to run wild in the bush,[2] this was the only animal that the Aborigines in any way tried to tame (see, for instance, Spencer and Gillen, 1898, p. 18). His omission led me to examine the literature on the Aborigines in search of pertinent data, in order to ascertain what in fact was the relationship between Aborigines and dingoes and to see if the evidence was compatible with Downs' hypotheses. Somewhat to my surprise, my survey revealed the existence of few useful data. These I shall present here, together with observations of my own made during three periods of anthropological field work among the Walbiri of the Northern Territory of Australia between 1953 and 1960.

The Dingoes

We do not know with any certainty the place of origin of the dingo or the time of its arrival in Australia (Macintosh, 1956, p. 12; Tindale, 1959, pp. 44–46; Troughton, 1951, pp. 235–236;

---

[2] Private citizens and governmental agencies first brought Asian camels and camel drivers to Australia in the 1860's and 1870's to assist in the exploration of the arid inland regions (see Calvert, 1901, 2, 258 f.). Later, these so-called Afghans (actually Pathans) used their camels to carry supplies to cattle stations in the outback. By the 1930's, however, rail and motor transport had supplanted pack camels, many of which escaped to the bush, where their progeny still roam. Donkeys, introduced to haul wagons on cattle and sheep stations, also run wild in the bush today; in some areas they are a major pest, destroying stock feed, and have to be systematically shot out. Desert Aborigines occasionally catch and use camels and donkeys as pack animals when walking long distances through waterless areas, but they are rarely able to use the many brumbies or wild horses in this way. Aborigines say that, if they are hard pressed, they will eat camels and donkeys, but I have no firsthand evidence of their doing so.

Wood Jones, 1925, *3*, 348–356, who also summarizes earlier opinions) .[3] It is generally agreed that the animal, like the Aborigines, came from somewhere in south or southeast Asia and that it reached Australia during the migrations of the Aborigines. Earlier writers such as Basedow (1925, p. 119), Etheridge (1916), and Smyth (1878, *1*, 149) were inclined to attribute a relatively long history of occupation in Australia to the dingo, of the order of 8000 or 9000 years; but present-day opinion is that recent archeological findings (as negative evidence) substantially reduce this estimate (Tindale, 1959, pp. 44–46). Nevertheless, even on current assumptions, it must be taken that Aborigines and dingoes have been in intermittent contact in Australia for some 3000 to 4000 years. This long duration is, I think, worth bearing in mind when examining the form the association has taken and when assessing its relative inefficacy as a means of domestication.[4]

The dingo is, from one point of view, a highly adaptable animal, being distributed throughout Australia from the southern Alps to the central deserts and to the northern rain forests, although it seems to have been relatively less numerous in the wetter regions (see Lumholtz, 1889, pp. 38, 178). Nevertheless, it is not a true vagrant or nomad. Rather, particular populations of dingoes are seasonally migratory within defined environments to which they have become adapted. There is, moreover, a subdivision of such areas into a mosaic of fairly clearly delimited hunting territories, each of which is exploited by a single dingo, by a pair, or by a small family (Macintosh, 1956, 1961).

In the region with which I am especially concerned, the desert and semidesert country of Central Australia, the need of the dingo to drink often (more often, for instance, than do most marsu-

---

[3] As yet nobody has tried to relate systematically to the dingo data the recent verification of the existence in the highlands of Australian New Guinea of an indigenous dog, *Canis hallstromii*, a nonbarking dog which is partly if not wholly domesticated by the natives, yet looks very like a smaller version of *Canis dingo*. Nor do I know of any attempt to fit into this picture evidence concerning the indigenous Polynesian dogs, of which at least one breed appears to have closely resembled the dingo (Luomala, 1960, p. 191).

[4] Indeed, as Leeds has suggested to me, it may seem remarkable that a people could associate for several millennia with an economically and ritually significant species without domesticating it completely.

pials) is an important factor in determining its seasonal movements (Finlayson, 1952, p. 116). Thus, although in the winter months the dog may frequent the open sandy country, in the summer heat it does not venture far from the rough hill country where water is more abundant and rock shelters are available (cf. Spencer, 1896, p. 2). Desert Aborigines, such as the Walbiri and their congeners, are aware of this seasonal pattern of movement among dingoes and adjust their hunting itineraries accordingly.

Contrary to the widespread belief among white Australians that the dingo is a typical carnivore, the animal is actually a mixed feeder when conditions warrant it (see Lumholtz, 1889, pp. 178–179). For instance, when small game is scarce in the desert, the dingo can subsist for long periods on the succulent fruits of solanums and other xerophilous plants (see Finlayson, 1952, p. 115). It is also a great scavenger in and around Aborigines' and Europeans' camps (see, for instance, Horne and Aiston, 1924, pp. 57–58; Lumholtz, 1889, p. 190). Not only does it forage round those which are permanently or temporarily vacated, but it may also visit occupied camps at dawn before the residents are abroad. (Desert Aborigines have no greater love of early rising than have Europeans.) I have observed such behavior of dingoes both in Central Australia and on Fraser Island, off the coast of Queensland; in the latter case the dingoes' objective was fish.

It is true, however, that the dingo is carnivorous by preference, and, by virtue of its size and equipment, it is the most efficient killer to be found among the Australian land animals. In its natural state in the bush, the dingo does not prey only on the smaller creatures, but also successfully attacks game much larger than itself, such as the kangaroo and euro, the cassowary and emu.[5] Moreover, in areas where Europeans have introduced sheep and cattle, the depredations of dingoes may reach such propor-

[5] The kangaroo commonly found in eastern Australia is the forester or great grey (*Macropus giganteus*), a magnificent animal that stands between six and seven feet tall; the common inland kangaroo is the red (*M. rufus*), another handsome beast, which stands about five feet; the euro (*M. robustus*) is a heavy-set kangaroo of great strength, which frequents the rough hills of Central Australia. The emu (*Dromiceius novae-hollandiae*) is a large, flightless bird, sometimes five feet tall, which abounds in inland Australia; the cassowary (*Casuarius casuarius*), which somewhat resembles the emu, is confined to the tropical rain forests.

tions as to cause pastoralists considerable economic loss (see Macintosh, 1956). There are also occasional reports of hungry dingoes' pursuing a man riding a horse or a camel and eventually
killing the animal while the rider takes refuge in a tree (see, for
instance, Duncan-Kemp, 1933, p. 38). However, as such stories
(which are usually retailed at second or third hand) presuppose
the presence of large packs of dingoes, they are better treated with
reserve.

The following excerpt from Mrs. Hassell's unpublished reminiscences of life in southwestern Australia in the 1860's gives a
clear and accurate picture of the hunting techniques of wild
dingoes.

We were driving along a low ridge of hills and the valley below was
clear and grassy, with a few tall trees from which the afternoon sun
threw long shadows, when we caught sight of two wild dogs chasing
a large kangaroo. The poor hunted brown kangaroo hopped first one
way, then another, while the two dogs, which were of a beautiful
golden sable colour, seemed to be acting on a settled plan. They kept
heading the kangaroo off as it ran. At last it could hop no longer, so
stood with its back to a big tree and tried to fight off its enemies with
its feet, but they were too wary to go too close. One would lie down
some distance away, while the other worried and snapped at the kangaroo. When it was tired, the one lying down took its place. . . . At
last the dog caught the kangaroo off its guard, and made a spring at
its neck; in a second the other dog rushed up and attacked on the
other side and the poor beast was pulled struggling to the ground,
and in a few moments was dead. I think the combat must have lasted
quite half an hour (Hassell, n.d.).

What evidence there is suggests that dingoes rarely congregate
in packs of any size except in certain atypical environments, such
as the snow country (see Smyth, 1878, *1*, 148), or as the result of
abnormal seasonal conditions or of extreme fluctuations of food
supplies in a given region. For instance, a drought may force a
number of dingoes to live near the one water hole and to combine
in exploiting the dwindling game, or the first appearance of stock
in a locality may attract many outlying dingoes to it. Normally,
however, each dog occupies a specific territory of no great extent,

from which it tries to exclude other dogs. A male and a female that live nearby and commonly mate may regularly join forces to hunt larger game, afterward going off to their separate lairs. In the desert region, for instance, one frequently sees a pair of dingoes on the move (see also Horne and Aiston, 1924, p. 58).

Similarly, although the male dog visits the female's domain to engage in characteristically aggressive courting behavior, he returns to his own territory after the mating. The bitch whelps in winter. There may be as many as eight pups in a litter, but the mortality rate is high; the average number of each litter surviving is probably no more than three (Finlayson, 1952, p. 116; Horne and Aiston, 1924, p. 58; Macintosh, 1961). The bitch cares for the pups for some months, after which they not only have to fend for themselves but must also find a new home.

There is thus in normal seasons and circumstances a tendency toward the restriction of dingo numbers in given localities, a state of affairs commented on in a number of Aboriginal myths. For instance, the myths of the Walbiri in which dingoes figure usually refer only to the actions of individual animals or of pairs of dingoes; larger groups are rarely mentioned.

THE ABORIGINES

As is well known, the Australian Aborigines, despite their limited material equipment, were able to exploit in a remarkable way the food resources of their physical environments (see, for instance, Irvine, 1958; Roth, 1901), and indeed many still do so today when European foodstuffs are not available. Even in the arid inland regions Aborigines may utilize a great variety of commodities, ranging from the sugary secretions of honey ants to the flesh of kangaroos, from grass seeds to wild figs and grevillea flowers (see Meggitt, 1958, 1962; Sweeney, 1947). Nevertheless, despite the apparent omnivorousness of the Aborigines, observers are generally agreed that, with few exceptions, they ate dingo meat only when other food was relatively scarce (see, for instance, Beveridge, 1883, p. 59; Helms, 1896, p. 259; Petrie, 1940, p. 89; Roth, 1901, p. 30; Smyth, 1878, *1*, 148). None of the writers, however, suggests any reason for this dietetic selectivity. My own inquiries among the Walbiri simply elicited the response that, as compared with almost any other meat (including that of feral cats), the flesh of dingoes (and dogs) is unpalatable and therefore a second choice.

The preference of Aborigines for other meat should not be taken to imply that they were unable to hunt dingoes successfully or were reluctant to do so.[6] Among the Walbiri, for instance, it was common toward the end of winter for hunters to seek out the lairs of the bitches in order to capture the pups. Although the men might kill and eat any deformed or weak pups of either sex that they found, they kept unharmed the sound pups. Moreover, they made little serious attempt (so the Walbiri assert) to capture the dams, which thus escaped to breed again.

It is usually assumed in the literature that the main, if not the sole, reason for taking dingo pups alive was that they could be reared to be efficient hunting dogs. Thus, Petrie reports that the Moreton Bay natives of southern Queensland caught dingo pups which they tamed and then taught to hunt (1904, pp. 61, 89). Horne and Aiston say that the Dieri and Wonkonguru of South Australia taught their dogs not only to run down game, but also to drop their catch on command (1924, pp. 30–31). Curr remarks that the dogs of the Dieri are "of great service to them, assisting them to find snakes, rats, etc." (1886, p. 47). Smyth asserts that the Victorian Aborigines employed their dogs to find possums, snakes, rats, and lizards (1878, *1*, 147). In southern New South Wales, according to Kreft, "the large kangaroos are generally hunted by a number of men with their dogs, the time chosen being after a heavy shower of rain, when the large animals sink deep into the chalky soil of the mallee scrub" (1862–1865, p. 370).

Chewings, speaking of "pure dingo dogs" he saw in Central Australia round about 1909, states that they were of service for

---

[6] A minor reason for hunting dingoes, one operative in localities as widely separated as Moreton Bay, Port Lincoln, Esperance Bay, and Alice Springs, was the desire to obtain the animals' tails to wear as headdresses (Hassell, n.d.; Petrie, 1904, p. 20; Spencer and Gillen, 1904, p. 690; Wilhelmi, 1860, p. 167).

following trails by scent and consequently were highly prized (1936, p. 12). Stirling also says of Central Australian Aborigines that, although they usually captured large marsupials by lying in wait and spearing them as they came to drink, they sometimes ran them down with packs of dogs (1896, p. 51). Lumholtz says of the dingo in northern Queensland that it "is very useful to the natives, for it has a keen scent and traces every kind of game; it never barks, and hunts less wildly than our dogs, but very rapidly, frequently capturing the game on the run. Sometimes it refuses to go any further, and its owner has then to carry it on his shoulders, a luxury of which it is very fond" (1889, p. 179).

Berndt and Berndt report that tribesmen at Ooldea in South Australia, who commonly used dogs for hunting, prized those of the dingo type most highly. Such dogs received individual names, slept with their masters, and were regularly fed (1945, p. 66). Sometimes women suckled the pups, a practice also observed years ago in western and southern New South Wales by Mitchell (1839, 2, 347) and by Kreft (1862–1865, p. 370). In southwestern Queensland, according to Duncan-Kemp, Aboriginal women not only reared dingo pups in the camp, but also broke the forelegs to cripple those which were intended to remain with the women. She also remarks on the extent to which old and decrepit women became dependent on their lame dogs (1933, pp. 24–25).[7]

Unfortunately, in none of these early accounts (with the exception of that by Lumholtz, who was a professional naturalist) do we find more than brief, passing, and dogmatic statements about the training and use of dingoes; I have quoted or paraphrased most of these in their entirety. Thus, there is little we can construe as real evidence of the effectiveness or otherwise of such training, of the efficiency of dingoes as hunting aids, or of the amount of game they brought in to the camps. As I shall point out again later, my own observations make me skeptical of the

[7] Beveridge says of the Aborigines of southwestern New South Wales that on cold nights they slept with their dingoes to keep warm, a custom to which the old women were particularly attached (1883, p. 58). My experience in the bitter Central Australian winter has been that most, if not all, Aborigines depend greatly on their dogs for warmth. It may be that we should seriously consider the "blanket function" of the dingo when explaining why Aborigines kept the animals.

widespread and apparently uncritical assumption that tame dingoes were productive hunters, as efficient as their wild relatives,
and I suspect that some observers tended to confuse exoticism
with utility.

Early writers also point to the great affection that the Aborigines lavished on their dogs, the extent to which the animals were
treated as pets. Thus Lumholtz says of the dingo in northern
Queensland that "its master never strikes, but merely threatens
it. He caresses it like a child, eats the fleas off it, and then kisses
it on the snout" (1889, p. 179). Smyth asserts that the Aborigines
"are very kind to their dogs, and indeed nothing more offends a
black man than to speak harshly to his dogs. . . . If anyone gave
a black man's dog a blow, he would incur bitter enmity" (1878,
1, 147). Other observers, such as Beveridge (1883, p. 58), Chewings (1936, p. 12), Curr (1886, *2*, 47), Berndt and Berndt (1945,
p. 66), Horne and Aiston (1924, p. 32), Kreft (1862–1865, p.
370), Mitchell (1839, *2*, 347), and Petrie (1904, p. 61), speak in
similar vein of the kindness that the Aborigines show their dogs,
a kindness that I have also seen displayed among all the Aboriginal groups with whom I have resided. I am inclined to regard this
phenomenon as an instructive example of what Downs calls the
"European" as distinct from the "Asian" attitude toward dogs
(1960, p. 45).

Nevertheless, as a number of the writers point out, together
with these displays of affection by Aborigines there generally goes
a casual indifference to the material welfare of the dogs—a neglect
that seems at times to verge on the irrational. For instance, in
Central Australia I have often observed that, no matter how many
dogs a man owns (and nowadays there may be more than twenty
dogs to a family), he flatly refuses to destroy or otherwise dispose
of any that are crippled, deformed, or diseased (see also Spencer
and Gillen, 1898, p. 18; Horne and Aiston, 1924, p. 31). Instead
they are left to starve to death slowly as they compete unsuccessfully with stronger dogs for limited food supplies. Indeed, the
failure of these owners to feed their dogs adequately has impressed
me forcibly, as it has other observers such as Chewings, Horne and
Aiston, Petrie, and Smyth. Curr remarks that "the dog, notwith-

standing its services and their [the Aborigines'] affection for it, fares very badly, receiving nothing but the bones. Hence the dog is always in very low condition, and consequently peculiarly subject to the diseases that affect the canine race" (1886, *2*, 47).[8] Mitchell goes so far as to say that the dingoes "are always miserably thin, so that we knew a native's dog from a wild one, by the starved appearance of the former" (1839, *2*, 347). Consideration of this aspect of the association between Aborigines and dingoes seems to me important. Whereas it might be argued that hungry dingoes would probably be better hunters, I suggest that this need not be to their owners' advantage. Not only would the hungry dingoes be more likely to consume the game before the hunters got to it, they would also be ready to return permanently to the bush in search of better food supplies.

In contrast to this view of the perennially hungry dingo in the camp, however, Lumholtz (1889, pp. 178–179) and Basedow (1925, pp. 118–119) assert that Aborigines as a rule fed their dogs well. As Lumholtz is referring particularly to people who lived in northern Queensland at the junction of savanna and rain forest, where game was relatively plentiful by Australian standards, his statement should not be generalized too widely. Basedow, who is commenting mainly on inland Aborigines, goes on, however, to argue the case at some length. First, he denies that the many dingoes (and, later, mongrels) in the camps served any useful purpose other than to warn of the approach of strangers (and it is true that in this respect dogs are both useful and effective). Moreover, he says, "a native just holds the unruly mob around him for company's sake; he prefers to rely on his own skill and instinct when hunting, and rarely allows his dogs to go with him; in fact, there seems to be little inclination on the part of the dogs to accompany the chase with the master." Basedow actually attributes such deplorable characteristics of the camp dogs to "the unreasonable amount of petting and pampering" their owners give them. Thus, whereas many observers imply that the continuing hunting efficiency of the dingoes was the reason both

---

[8] Mathew (1889, p. 92) comments on the frequency with which Aborigines were infected with a disgusting kind of purulent mange by their dingoes.

for taming them and then for caring for them, Basedow argues that their taming makes them useless as hunting dogs.

Although Basedow appears to have overstated his case for the inefficiency of tame dingoes, it may well be that in general they were less effective as hunting aids than people (including the Aborigines) now suppose them to have been. Thus, Beveridge says of the dingoes he saw in native camps in southwestern New South Wales between 1845 and 1868 that "though not speedy, they are useful in following wounded animals" (1883, p. 58), which suggests that the dogs possessed only limited utility. On the whole, Mitchell's comment may have been valid: "In the interior we saw few natives who were not followed by some of these animals, although they did not appear to be of much use to them" (1839, 2, 347). Alternatively (or in addition), there may have been significant differences among tribes or from region to region in the efficiency of the training and use of dingoes, or in the kinds, numbers, and habits of the animals available for hunting. On Lumholtz' evidence, for instance, the Aborigines of northern Queensland not only seem to have been noticeably proficient in using dingoes—more so than, say, the dwellers of the plains—but they also had access in the rain forests to game, such as tree-climbing kangaroos, that dogs could hunt easily. Also instructive in this regard is Mitchell's account (1839, 2, 295) of the relative difficulties involved in running down emus and kangaroos with dogs.

My experience with the Walbiri inclines me toward the views of Basedow and Mitchell in this matter. For instance, during the twelve months at Hooker Creek in 1953–1954, men employing so-called "hunting dogs" were able in this way to secure only three kangaroos and about six large goannas.[9] According to Walbiri men there and elsewhere, the manner of rearing, training, and using such dogs today differs little from the traditional treatment of dingoes in the camp. If this assertion is true, then I cannot be-

[9] Goanna (the word is a corruption of iguana) is the name given to any of a number of species of the *Varanus* lizard, which are widespread through inland Australia. The smallest species are at least two feet in length; the largest (the pirinti or *Varanus giganteus*) attains a length of seven to eight feet and is a dangerous opponent for a dog. All goannas have excellent flesh that resembles fowl and is highly prized by Aborigines.

lieve that, in this tribe at any rate, tamed or camp-reared dingoes were particularly effective in hunting or that they were much more than pets in the past.

Furthermore, Walbiri men spoke of the way in which they often relied on wild dingoes as being more effective in running down large game, both in the days when tame dingoes were common in the camps and in the recent past when mongrels had replaced them. That is to say, the men described a frequently recurring situation which closely resembles that hypothesized by Downs for the hunters and wild dogs of mesolithic Europe. A group of Walbiri men out hunting picked up the relatively fresh tracks of a dingo (or pair of dingoes) which in turn was trailing a kangaroo. If necessary they followed the dingo for the whole day, endeavoring to overtake it just as it was pulling down the exhausted quarry. Without harming the dingo, the men despatched the kangaroo with spears or boomerangs and gutted the carcass then and there preparatory to carrying it back to the camp. According to some men, it was common for some scraps of offal to be left for the dingo to eat. (The late W. Braitling of Mount Doreen Cattle Station, a careful observer who spent some thirty years among the Walbiri, also told me he had witnessed such behavior.)

This kind of behavior, as well as that exhibited by desert Aborigines in sparing dams when hunting dingoes, seems to indicate some notion of conservation on the part of the hunters—a recognition of the advantages to be gained by not consuming the whole of a given set of resources or commodities at one time. It is interesting that definite evidence of this also exists in the contemporary practice of "dogging," that is, the taking of dingo scalps. This phrase needs elaboration.

As I mentioned earlier, the depredations of dingoes have made them a serious pest to pastoralists, for a grown dog can kill dozens of sheep or calves in a night. Consequently, in regions such as the western plains of Queensland and New South Wales where dingoes abound, settlers early undertook strenuous, and sometimes combined, campaigns of trapping, poisoning, and shooting to exterminate the animals (see, for instance, Duncan-Kemp, 1933, p. 41; Finlayson, 1952, p. 115; Lumholtz, 1889, p. 38; Macintosh,

1956, *passim*). Indeed, if, as often happened, a cunning dingo became known as a great killer of stock, local graziers contributed
a relatively large sum of prize money to go to the man who destroyed the beast. This practice, which persists today, attracted
many skilled trappers and riflemen to the area.

By the early 1900's, measures to keep down the numbers of dingoes had become so extensive and so expensive that the state governments had to act, both individually and jointly. One kind of
scheme, for instance, has involved the building of thousands of
miles of stout wire-netting fences to close off the known breeding
grounds of dingoes in the interior. The cost of erecting and maintaining these fences has been tremendous. A parallel measure has
been the institution of payments for dingo scalps handed in to
authorized agents (such as policemen) of the state governments.
Thus, South Australia began paying scalp bonuses in 1913, Central Australia (now the Northern Territory) and Western Australia in 1924. The amounts ranged from seven shillings and six-
pence to two pounds a scalp, and by 1935 nearly £350,000 (then
worth about $1,000,000) had been paid out for some half million
scalps (Finlayson, 1952, p. 115). Such payments are still made; in
the Northern Territory, for instance, a scalp is now worth one
pound.

From the first a number of Aborigines in regular contact with
Europeans, as well as indigent European bushmen, gladly took up
"dogging" as a congenial, albeit precarious, way of making a living. Before long, in areas of South and Central Australia, the
dingo scalp became an informal but standard item of currency, as
the beaver pelt had done in the Hudson's Bay region of Canada.
Indeed, in the more remote parts of Australia, transactions in
terms of scalps still take place; for instance, an Aborigine can
tender a scalp to the storekeeper on a Northern Territory cattle
run in return for a pound's worth of supplies. There is the guarantee that eventually at some police station or other the scalp can
be redeemed for cash.

The Walbiri, who began to have frequent and sustained dealings with Europeans from about 1932 onward, also engaged sporadically in hunting dingoes for scalps, and they were still doing

so when I worked among them. In particular, at places such as Yuendumu and Mount Doreen where dingoes are common, the older men go dogging in the late winter months (July-August). For several days at a time they search the hills for the caves and overhangs in which the bitches shelter with their young. The men catch and kill the pups, whose scalps are worth as much as those of adult dogs, but they spare the bitches to breed again. Similarly, they rarely attempt on these expeditions to pursue the grown males.

Here, then, is an Aboriginal system of "harvesting" dingoes annually, with all that this idea implies of conservation. So successful is it that, at the times I was at Yuendumu, fewer than one hundred hunters could secure five hundred to seven hundred scalps in the short season, that is, from £500 to £700. Finlayson (1952, p. 116) mentions an analogous practice among the Pidjandjara to the south of the Walbiri, and Horne and Aiston (1924, p. 57) among the Dieri and Wonkonguru near Lake Eyre.

DISCUSSION

The kinds of evidence I have indicated here concerning the conservational practices of Aborigines, their pursuit of wild dingoes in the hunt, and their keeping young dingoes in the camp touch on the general problem of the extent to which Aborigines really "domesticated" dingoes or merely exploited them. In particular, two questions need to be asked: Did the dingoes brought from the bush into the camps stay there? Did they breed there?

Data bearing directly on these questions are few, largely because the speed with which European dogs of all breeds have replaced dingoes in the camps has prevented the making of systematic observations. The process of substitution began soon after the first European settlement in New South Wales in 1788, and the wide and rapid spread of dogs (see, for instance, Basedow, 1925, p. 118; Berndt and Berndt, 1945, p. 66; Lumholtz, 1889, p. 178; Smyth, 1878, *1*, 147; Spencer and Gillen, 1898, p. 18) appears to have been due to some extent to the deliberate policy of early explorers and officials of making placatory gifts of dogs to

Aborigines (see, for instance, Mitchell, 1839, *1*, 233, 241). Equally important, however, has been the eagerness of the Aborigines themselves to acquire European dogs, even the oddest mongrels, partly as a kind of status marker and partly in the belief that they would excel the tame dingo as a hunting aid. This attitude still persists, for instance among the Walbiri; and its prevalence may be another reason for doubting the claims that have been made for the efficiency and indispensability of the tame dingo in the chase. At any rate, so widespread are European dogs today that tame dingoes are still to be found only among one or two Aboriginal tribes, such as the isolated Pintubi of western Central Australia.

What evidence there is suggests that, as a rule, dingoes brought from the bush returned to it sooner or later. In the first place, general observations of dingoes' behavior (such as those of Macintosh) point to the independence of the animal, its apparent indifference to human endeavors to hold its interest or affection. Secondly, the very generality and persistence of the practice of taking dingo pups alive suggest that, for whatever reasons, the numbers in the camps had constantly to be replenished. Thirdly, the fact that in some tribes dingoes were lamed indicates that they were likely to desert their owners. Fourthly, Lumholtz (1889, p. 179), a keen observer, noted that in northern Queensland at least the dingo often ran away, "especially in the pairing season, and at such times it never returns." Also to be considered in this connection is the likelihood that camp dingoes were much worse fed than were wild dingoes and therefore tempted to leave in search of food. Given, then, a tendency for tame dingoes to abscond, a tendency over which the Aborigines seem to have had very little control, it is unlikely that they were really reliable hunting aids.

When we turn to the question whether or not dingoes bred in the camps, we are on shaky ground, for there is a great dearth of directly relevant evidence. However, the long-term, experimental observations by Macintosh of dingoes reared at the University of Sydney indicate that the breeding habits of the animals are considerably affected when they are under restraint, and the change is generally in the direction of a lower breeding rate. On this basis it seems to me reasonable to assume that, if dingoes did breed while living in Aborigines' camps, they would not do so at a rate high enough to counterbalance the constant loss of tame dingoes through death or running away.

In short, the Aboriginal situation does not appear to have been one of "domestication" of dingoes, in the sense of a complete and regular reproduction of the species through more or less controlled and selective breeding in the company of man. Instead, the relationship seems merely to have been one of intermittent exploitation of a pool of wild dingoes to replenish the smaller group in the camp. In these circumstances there could have been only a limited degree of truly selective breeding, although the Aboriginal practice of destroying weak or deformed pups in the bush may have had some effect. Nevertheless, the association between Aborigines and dingoes must have been one of "quasi domestication," that is, the repeated training of randomly acquired individuals in successive generations, not the domestication of the whole species.

SUMMARY

In conclusion, I recapitulate three points that have emerged from this brief survey.

1. Downs' hypothesis that a relationship of mutual exploitation developed between hunters and wild dogs in mesolithic Europe becomes plausible in the light of evidence that such a relationship has existed in some parts of Australia between Aborigines and wild dingoes until quite recently. This kind of association continued sporadically even after the introduction of European dogs into the camps. But, although such a symbiosis may have been a necessary precursor to the domestication of the dog, there is no evidence from Aboriginal Australia to indicate that it was a sufficient cause of domestication.

2. Although Australian Aborigines in some regions at least went beyond the maintenance of a mutually exploitative relationship with dingoes, in that they captured dingo pups to rear, this in itself was no more than "quasi domestication" of the animal. That

is to say, man here was simply tapping the supply of wild dingoes to replace losses occurring among those kept in the camps.

3. The available evidence, limited and uneven as it is, suggests that over wide areas of Australia the tame dingo was by no means an effective hunting dog and that it contributed relatively little to the Aborigines' larder. It seems that only in ecologically specialized regions where particular kinds of game were abundant (as in the tropical rain forest) was the tame dingo a significant economic adjunct to the family hunting unit.

ACKNOWLEDGMENTS. This is a revised version of a paper read before Section F at the 35th Congress of the Australian and New Zealand Association for the Advancement of Science in Brisbane, 1961. Some of the data derive from anthropological field work carried out in Central Australia under the auspices of the Research Committee, University of Sydney. I am grateful to Mr. David Moore for his valuable bibliographical aid and to Dr. Anthony Leeds for his criticism of the penultimate draft of the paper.

REFERENCES

BASEDOW, H. 1925. *The Australian Aboriginal.* F. W. Preece, Adelaide, Australia.

BERNDT, R. M., and C. H. BERNDT. 1945. *A Preliminary Report of Field-Work in the Ooldea Region.* . . . Oceania Reprint, Sydney, Australia.

BEVERIDGE, P. 1883. On the Aborigines inhabiting the great lacustrine and riverine depression. . . . *J. Trans. Roy. Soc. New South Wales, 17,* 19–74.

CALVERT, A. F. 1901. *The Exploration of Australia.* 2 vols. G. Philip, London.

CHEWINGS, C. 1936. *Back in the Stone Age.* Angus and Robertson, Sydney, Australia.

CURR, E. M. 1886. *The Australian Race.* 4 vols. Trubner Co., London.

DOWNS, J. F. 1960. Domestication; An examination of the changing social relationships between man and animals. *Kroeber Anthropol. Soc. Papers, 22,* 18–67.

DUNCAN-KEMP, A. M. 1933. *Our Sandhill Country; Man and Native in Southwestern Queensland.* Angus and Robertson, Sydney, Australia.

ETHERIDGE, R. 1916. The warrigal or dingo, introduced or indigenous? *Mem. Geol. Surv. New South Wales, Ethnol. Ser.*, *2*, 43–54.

FINLAYSON, H. H. 1935, reprinted 1952. *The Red Centre; Man and Beast in the Heart of Australia.* Angus and Robertson, Sydney, Australia.

HASSELL, A. Y. n.d. (about 1861–1862). My dusky friends; Sketches of the south eastern natives of Western Australia . . . . Manuscript, Mitchell Library, Sydney, Australia.

HELMS, R. 1896. Scientific results of the Elder Exploration Expedition. Pt. III. *Trans. Roy. Soc. South Australia, 16,* 238–332.

HORNE, G., and G. AISTON. 1924. *Savage Life in Central Australia.* Macmillan and Co., London.

IRVINE, F. R. 1958. Wild and emergency foods of Australian and Tasmanian Aborigines. *Oceania, 28,* 115–142.

KREFT, G. 1862–1865. On the manners and customs of the Aborigines of the lower Murray and Darling. *Trans. Phil. Soc. New South Wales,* 357–374.

LUMHOLTZ, C. 1889. *Among Cannibals.* J. Murray, London.

LUOMALA, K. 1960. The native dog in the Polynesian system of values. In *Culture in History* (S. Diamond, editor), pp. 190–240. Columbia University Press, New York, N. Y.

MACINTOSH, N. W. G. 1956. Trail of the dingo. *The Etruscan, 5* (4), 8–12.

MACINTOSH, N. W. G. 1961. Personal communications.

MATHEW, J. 1889. The Australian Aborigines. *J. Roy. Soc. New South Wales, 23,* 335–449.

MEGGITT, M. J. 1958. Notes on the vegetable foods of the Walbiri of Central Australia. *Oceania, 28,* 143–145.

MEGGITT, M. J. 1962. *Desert People.* Angus and Robertson, Sydney, Australia.

MITCHELL, T. L. 1839. *Three Expeditions into the Interior of Eastern Australia.* 2 vols. T. and W. Boone, London.

PETRIE, C. C. 1904. *Tom Petrie's Reminiscences of Early Queensland.* Barker, Brisbane, Australia.

ROTH, W. E. 1901. *Food: Its Search, Capture and Preparation.* North Queensland Ethnogr. Bull. 3. Brisbane, Australia.

SMYTH, R. B. 1878. *The Aborigines of Victoria.* 2 vols. J. Ferres, Melbourne, Australia.

SPENCER, B. 1896. *Report of the Horn Expedition to Central Australia. Mammalia.* Macmillan and Co., London.

SPENCER, B., and F. J. GILLEN. 1898. *The Native Tribes of Central Australia.* Macmillan and Co., London.

SPENCER, B., and F. J. GILLEN. 1904. *The Northern Tribes of Central Australia.* Macmillan and Co., London.

STIRLING, E. C. 1896. *Report of the Horn Expedition to Central Australia. Anthropology.* Macmillan and Co., London.

SWEENEY, G. 1947. Food supplies of a desert tribe. *Oceania, 17,* 289–299.

TINDALE, N. B. 1959. Ecology of primitive aboriginal man in Australia. In *Biogeography and Ecology in Australia* (A. Keast *et al.,* editors), pp. 36–51. W. Junk, The Hague.

TROUGHTON, E. 1951. *Furred Animals of Australia.* Angus and Robertson, Sydney, Australia.

WILHELMI, G. 1860. Manners and customs of the Australian natives, in particular of the Port Lincoln district. *Trans. Roy. Soc. Victoria, 5,* 164–204.

WOOD JONES, F. 1925. *The Mammals of South Australia.* 3 vols. Government Printer, Adelaide, Australia.

A Re-examination of Hunting, Trapping, and Territoriality among the Northeastern Algonkian Indians

ROLF KNIGHT

Department of Anthropology, Columbia University, New York, New York

DISCUSSIONS on the nature of and explanations for family hunting territories among the northeastern Algonkian have been a staple of Canadian ethnology for almost half a century. The term "family hunting territory system" refers to a situation in which a band area is divided more or less rigidly, depending upon the specific band and the particular account, into distinct and permanent tracts for more or less exclusive use by hunting groups of two to four related nuclear families. This situation differs from that usually found in hunting societies, in which unrestricted access to unimproved band resources is generally open to all band members.

There are essentially two contending explanations of the so-called Algonkian family hunting territory system. One, presented by Speck, the "discoverer" of this phenomenon, holds that the system represents an aboriginal adaptive adjustment to the strategic resources of subarctic taiga. Given the supposed conservability of beaver, in an area where beaver were a major subsistence item, harvest on a sustained-yield basis would be advantageous in damping the fluctuations inherent in subarctic hunting. Family hunting territories are said to provide the "private" control necessary for the development and maintenance of beaver conservation (Speck, 1915, 1923, 1931; Speck and Eisely, 1939).

27

The other, currently dominant, position is enunciated by Leacock (1954). She questions Speck's hypothesis, noting that family territoriality varies (in the eastern subarctic woodlands) within one biotic zone; that, indeed, its strength decreases outward from the center of the earliest and most intensive trade (*ibid.*, p. 6). She holds that caribou and not beaver were the major food animals of the area. A shift from cooperative caribou hunting to individualized fur trapping and dependence upon trade foods allowed family self-sufficiency, while competition for fur resources fostered the development of family territoriality. Throughout, Leacock's thesis is that the rigidity and exclusiveness of family territories is directly proportional to the degree of dependence upon the fur trade. In sum, she says: "Algonkian family territoriality adds a new dimension to the knowledge of land-holding patterns among hunting peoples, although it may be finally agreed that its significance lies more in the sphere of acculturation than in that of primitive economics proper" (1954, p. 1).[1]

Though current positions disagree on when and why the family hunting territory system was established, they do agree that such private control would exist in the Labrador taiga among Indian groups that had been engaged in the fur trade for a long time. The situation in the East James Bay area is important in the consideration of this theory, in that over 250 years of contact with and involvement in a trapping-trading-hunting economy did not lead to the indigenous development of restricted hunting or trapping tracts.[2] Beaver conservation was neither present nor feasible formerly, and private control of tracts was of little significance

---

[1] The core of Leacock's explanation is contained in the following: "[Aboriginally] Owing to the uncertainty of the hunt, several families were necessarily dependent upon each other, thus providing a kind of subsistence insurance or greater security than individual families could achieve. With production for trade, however, the individual's most important ties, economically speaking, were transferred from *within* the band to *without*, and his objective relation to other band members changed from the cooperative to the competitive. With storable, transportable, and individually acquired supplies—principally flour and lard—as staple foods, the individual family becomes self-sufficient, and larger group living is not only superfluous in the struggle for existence but a positive hindrance to the personal acquisition of furs" (1954, p. 7).

[2] Rupert House was established in 1668 as Fort Charles, and has been in almost continuous operation ever since.

until beaver-trapping territories, beaver conservation, and beaver allotment quotas were introduced in the 1930's under the aegis of the Hudson's Bay Company and the government (J. A. Anderson, 1961; J. W. Anderson, 1961; Denmark, 1948).

It is my belief that until some stable and significant amount of income other than that from trapping and hunting was available to the band, long-run minimum conditions did not allow subarctic hunter-trappers to compartmentalize general band areas into permanently delineated tracts given over to the exclusive use of particular families, and still survive. Nearly all discussions dealing with Algonkian family hunting territories fail to separate mechanisms for establishing traits from those for maintaining them over the long run. They fail to deal adequately with the long-run minimum conditions which, rather than periodic booms or even average conditions, set the limits for the maximal development and distribution of social forms.

A satisfactory understanding of fundamental patterns of resource use and control would seem to require a fundamental analysis of relevant ecological principles in local context. I can hardly do better than quote Hallowell on this point:

Instead of concentrating upon cultural descriptions, the facts of geographical distribution and problems of historical depth and continuity, the major question becomes in effect: What are the *actual* determinants or controlling factors involved? Once this question has been broached, the level of inquiry is shifted from the plane of description and chronological reconstruction to that of process and structural dynamics of human adjustment. It involves a more detailed examination of all the conditions under which a given human population makes its fundamental ecological adjustments in a specific locale. Within this frame of reference however, we are forced to take new data into account, data of a *non cultural* nature. For we can hardly pursue an ecological hypothesis without giving due weight to relevant demographic facts, as well as those pertaining to the character, incidence and fluctuations of fauna or other pertinent information. Perhaps in this case, as well as in others, our very devotion to cultural description and historical explanation, on the implicit, if not explicit, assumption that culture is a phenomenon sui generis, has blinded us to the rele-

vance of some of the very data that are needed if the actual dynamics
of the hunting-territory system is to be fully understood or explained
(1949, p. 36).

Unfortunately, the application of this prescription has been
rarely begun and never fully carried out. I shall indicate an
initial attempt in this direction. Much of the material presented
here was gathered in the field at Rupert House, East James Bay,
and Nemiscau, east-central Quebec, during the summers of 1961
and 1962. It seems generally applicable to the eastern Canadian
subarctic.

I shall first describe the fluctuating nature of human and faunal
demography in the eastern subarctic, which, along with historical
accounts of the actual ecological adjustments, seems to invalidate
Speck's descriptions and hypotheses. Next, a reconsideration of
faunal resource use and the requirements of contemporary technology suggests that fur trapping is not so different from hunting, and indicates why some basic cooperative organization is still
operative. This adds theoretical underpinning to the fact that
family territoriality was not established at Rupert House even
after a long history of trade. Finally, an alternative understanding
is offered for those *changes* indicated by Leacock. The replacement of caribou by moose and of muskets by rifles seems to have
made larger hunting units and extensive separate hunts nonadvan-
tageous. It seems to have improved the opportunities for and
returns from trapping—quite apart from any hypothetical acculturative shift to "individualized," barter economy.

The East James Bay Region and Its Inhabitants

The area east of James Bay and the central and southern regions of the Labrador peninsula constitute a northern taiga inter-
laced with extensive tracts of muskeg and stunted tamarack.
Moose, woodland caribou, and bear are the larger game animals;
weasel, fox, otter, mink, and especially beaver are the main fur-
bearing animals. Rabbits and fowl—ducks, geese, and various
grouselike birds—are important subsidiary sources of food for hu-

man and animal predators. Rather harsh climatic conditions throughout the subarctic have produced relatively simple plant and animal communities which are noted for their fluctuating character (Kimble and Good, 1955, p. 117). Interdependent mouse, rabbit, grouse, and fox cycles occur (Elton, 1942). Such cycles occur in different areas at different times and with different demographic peaks and depressions. Though other subarctic species do not follow *clear-cut* demographic cycles, the game density of "family territory" sized tracts of land (approximately 400 to 450 square miles) varies considerably from tract to tract at any one time, and on any one tract over time.[3] Over a period of five or more years, a relatively rich tract may become depleted of most fur bearers. Its carrying capacity for certain types of game may be temporarily altered; one of the not infrequent brush fires may destroy half the caribou and beaver potential of a particular tract, or overgrazing of prime moss and lichen ranges may make the area temporarily undesirable to caribou. On other occasions, game density itself is altered; certain animal diseases may take a particularly heavy toll in some areas, woodland caribou herds may just not enter some areas in certain years. Probably most important, unplanned or unavoidable overhunting and overtrapping can easily break a tenuous stability which takes years to re-establish.

The thesis of aboriginal family hunting territories among the northeast Algonkian is based on the assumption that the proper organization of resources could mitigate hunting insecurity

[3] The size of "family territories," and the character of the game and its density, are of course crucial variables which present differing bases for local social organization. Rogers (1963, p. 57) lists 14 eastern Algonkian bands with average family hunting territory size ranging from 93 to approximately 2000 square miles. There is considerable variation *within* bands as well; Rupert House trapping territories in 1961 ranged from approximately 40 to over 700 square miles. Since the size and composition of trapping-hunting groups and the density of game per square mile vary, in estimating the significance of data it is often important to adjust figures for persons per square mile, hunters per square mile, hunters per game unit, and the like. It is also necessary to take into account the faunal profile of different tracts. For instance, the coastal zones around Rupert House are easily reached and are particularly rich in fowl and small subsistence game, which are more easily taken by older men or trapping-hunting groups deficient in labor power. On the other hand, the coastal zones are poor in all the important fur animals and large game, whose capture demands greater effort and stamina. In 1961 there was a heavy concentration of incapacitated trapping-hunting groups along the Rupert House coastal zones.

through exploiting beaver on a sustained-yield basis. Beaver are said to be amenable to a planned harvest because they are non-migratory and because their numbers can be effectively estimated. Their lodges are highly visible, accessible, and relatively permanent. Adult beaver are almost always found in mated pairs; inhabited beaver lodges contain an adult pair and the last brood of kits (usually two or three) and possibly a pair of yearlings. A trapper, once he was familiar with a particular area, would presumably know how many beaver lodges there were, where they were, and, roughly, how many beaver there were. Speck and Eisely (1939) claimed that only one subsection of a family territory was trapped each year, allowing the remaining beaver to multiply, or, alternatively, that not all beaver were taken from any one lodge.

The older trappers of Rupert House, on the other hand, claim that formerly, when *they* trapped, they tried to clean the area out. They say that their marginal income and day-to-day food requirements demanded that they take all they could get. They add that there was no point in trying to conserve animals, that if they did not trap a lodge there was no assurance that they would return to the area or that the beaver would still be there if they did.

There was universal agreement among my informants that formerly only very few hunting groups held even tenuous rights to particular tracts, and that even those that did could usually be prevailed upon to accept additional hunter-trappers in distress. Otherwise, "You could hunt and trap where you wanted and nobody could say anything." This statement is borne out by numerous trapping histories. Different trapping groups worked the same area over a period of years. Some families had trapped virtually throughout the band area, and even outside it, during the course of their trapping life. Hunting-trapping groups occasionally started out with their winter destination undecided. Other groups which could not reach their planned destinations began trapping wherever freeze-up had caught them; still other groups trapped a certain area in early fall and then decided to move to another area and perhaps coalesce with another hunting group. All these mainly pragmatic adjustments would of course be impossible under a system of restricted tract holding. The creation of beaver territories is *the* demarcation point in recent history to all local Indians.[4]

Government–Hudson's Bay Company conservation techniques in operation during my stay were based on clearly mapped beaver territories which are "exclusively" assigned to various families. A beaver quota, set so as to allow trapping only the natural increase and determined by a tally of inhabited beaver lodges per territory, is assigned each territory. Since tags are issued to the amount of the quota, and since only tagged beaver pelts can be sold, no financial gain can be had by overtrapping one's quota (although the meat can be eaten and the pelt sold to someone who did not manage to trap his quota). This tightly regulated conservation system, *after extensive restocking,* showed considerable success for well over a decade (Kerr, 1950). But under continued trapping it has begun to collapse. At present, about a third of the Rupert House families cannot be assigned a quota because of lack of beaver. Quota differentials of from 6 to 90 beaver per territory have developed, and the over-all number of beaver remaining seems to be falling. Personal histories show that continual, administratively directed readjustment of trappers to nominally exclusive beaver territories has been necessary almost from the inception of this system.

Given no other income, no welfare payments, and only the minimal credit that was formerly available from the Hudson's Bay Company, any hunting-trapping group that was forced to remain on a particular "hunting territory" sized tract would probably starve to death, at one time or another, within a generation. Even the best hunters and trappers, even when working familiar

[4] After giving the Hudson's Bay Company position that beaver conservation and private hunting territories were traditional among the northeastern Algonkian, D. E. Denmark, director of the Hudson's Bay Company beaver preserves, says: "In the operation of large conservation schemes, it is essential that everyone who has any influence over the natives should lend their support. We have been very fortunate in James Bay in having the full co-operation of the Federal and Provincial Governments, the Royal Canadian Mounted Police, the Indian Affairs Branch and the Anglican and Roman Catholic Churches. Their help has been invaluable. Further success in beaver conservation depends on their continued support, on the efforts of the post managers and on the co-operation of the natives" (1948, p. 43).

territory, have a season or a year when illness, some accident, bad luck in hunting, or any of a number of other factors makes it difficult or impossible for them to sustain their families, and then they must move in with some other group. Personal histories and parish records indicate that in the past, cases of starvation occurred most frequently in the early spring, when breakup restricted and immobilized hunting groups for three to four weeks. Indeed, immobilization is clearly recognized by local people as the major factor in cases of starvation.

There is considerable change in relative family size from generation to generation. One man has four sons, each with a large family of his own, another has an infertile daughter. In the recent past, tuberculosis, pneumonia, measles, and starvation have virtually eliminated whole families. If the allegedly permanent nature of territories were maintained, numerous tracts would exist with very few hunters to work them, whereas other tracts would have a relative overpopulation of hunters, even if an equal man/land ratio had initially been set up. Not only would a system of strictly compartmentalized, private hunting-trapping territories be disastrous in the long run for nearly all groups, but it also would result in a less efficient exploitation of the total area's resources. With the close survival margin that existed even at the best of times, failure to adjust quickly to the frequent fluctuations would be most unadaptive. It appears that even if beaver could have been maintained in a stable beaver/territory ratio, men could not.

Leacock (1954, p. 7) maintains that involvement with a developed trapping-trade situation creates family self-sufficiency and subsistence security. Indeed, it is this self-sufficiency and security, the ability to get credit, to have a source of stored cash foods, that fosters the alleged individualization of nuclear family trapping units and the development of private trapping tracts. Trade allegedly removes the necessity of having "a sort of hunting insurance" through interfamily and intergroup cooperation and sharing. Because Leacock views acculturative conditions, in this case fur trade, as generically different from natural ones, in this case hunting, she gets herself into the position of considering fur animals as providing only fur, and game animals as providing only food. In fact, virtually all animals killed are also eaten, regardless of any other uses they are put to, or of the prime reason for their capture.

Even with a very substantial increase in the use of cash foods (to the point where they are the dominant trade item), the importance and amount of country food consumed remains high, in trapping as in hunting.[5] Fur animals, especially beaver, provide considerable quantities of meat, particularly the fats so nutritionally desirable in subarctic winters. If the beaver catch is good, these animals will provide the main food of the winter camp (from November to March). Large game, small mammals (such as rabbits and porcupine), fowl, and fish provide alternative, additional, and seasonally supplemental foods of continuing importance, especially for fur-poor families.

The ongoing requirement for native food obtained by trapping or hunting raises a question about the alleged development of family self-sufficiency in subsistence pursuits. Many of the same labor requirements apply to both trapping and hunting. Moreover, both are carried out intermittently by the same group. The average hunting-trapping group at Rupert House today still consists of more than a nuclear family. The size of these groups falls within set limits. The desirability of having a number of hunter-trappers operate out of one camp, to increase the probability of sustained kills and to protect the group from starvation when

---

[5] It is important to note not only the total amount but also the faunal composition of game eaten. The list below constitutes a *minimal* estimate, since a number of families, to my knowledge, under-reported their kill. Furthermore, I have not included fish, another basic food source. The weights of utilizable meat are calculated from weights per animal estimated by Rogers (1963, p. 30).

Birds, game, and fur animals taken, Rupert House band, September 10, 1960, to May 10, 1961:

Large game: 43 moose (17,200 lb utilizable meat); 26 caribou (3250 lb); 1 bear (210 lb). *Total,* 20,660 lb utilizable meat.

Fur animals: 750 beaver (26,250 lb utilizable meat; Rogers estimates 55 lb meat per beaver, but 35 lb seems a more accurate average); 900 muskrat (1800 lb); 380 mink (130 lb); 53 otter (530 lb); 55 marten (55 lb); 30 lynx (150 lb); 45 fox (135 lb). *Total,* 29,050 lb utilizable meat.

Birds and small game: 1960 geese (9800 lb utilizable meat); 4400 grouse, ptarmigan, and partridge (2200 lb); 3000 rabbits (4500 lb). *Total,* 16,500 lb utilizable meat.

Total amount of country food taken (not including fish): 66,210 lb.

accident or illness immobilizes one hunter, is balanced by the limited number of people who can be sustained in one camp because of the low game density and the restricted effective radius of hunting-trapping. Consumption patterns are intimately connected with production organization. Since a crucial proportion of the food comes from animals taken on the trap line, either hunted or trapped, and since it is not feasible to transport this food to the post, it is essential that a large percentage of the population be spread over the hunting-trapping groups in order that they may receive this food. Only persons who now have sufficient government welfare support remain on the post.

A common attitude is that with acculturation, almost anything goes. Leacock holds that as Indian groups became more integrated into the fur trade, they became less limited by and more independent of the environment. But if we look at a trapping-trade situation from a trapper's-eye view, we see that not only do the various animal populations continue to fluctuate, but a whole host of new factors, fluctuating and only partly predictable, enter. Prices of pelts change from year to year and possibly between the time the trapper leaves the post and the time when he returns with the pelts. The availability of credit varies. The acceptable condition of pelts changes. Posts open, expand, decline, and close, requiring changes in routes or relocation of trapping areas. Transport routes and costs change, changing the price of commodities at different posts. Though the development of the fur trade did undoubtedly offer new opportunities and goods which allowed a much more effective utilization of the environment, a potentially higher standard of living, it did not necessarily create a stabilization of income and a subsistence security base against economic fluctuations.

CHANGES IN ECOLOGICAL AND SOCIAL RELATIONS

The question then arises, How are we to understand the changes in economic and social organization that have been documented by Leacock and other ethnographers of this area? Why did Leacock's Montagnais-Naskapi hunters shift to greater reliance upon trapping and to smaller production-consumption groups? Instead of invoking the powers of acculturative processes, we should ask if and why greater involvement with mixed hunting-trapping was more advantageous to the Montagnais-Naskapi than hunting large game. If we look closely at changes in the demography and character of the large game animals upon which these recent hunters were dependent, and add to this a functional consideration of changes in technology, an answer somewhat different from Leacock's suggests itself.

Conditions over much of the Labrador peninsula produce the rich, luxurious carpets of lichen and moss that are the subsistence base of formerly extensive herds of woodland caribou (Banfield and Tener, 1958, p. 567). Throughout the mid and late nineteenth century, and reaching a peak in the early 1900's, extensive forest fires swept the entire area, particularly the Rupert River basin. "Low wrote in 1896 that at least one half of the forest area of the interior has been totally destroyed by fire within the past twenty-five or thirty years" (Elton, 1942, p. 300). This had great importance for the fortunes and composition of the large game in the region.

Though fires repeatedly destroy forest and lichen-moss growth about equally, the rate of regeneration of these two plant forms is quite different. Lichen and moss carpets are a climax growth and require around thirty years of undisturbed growth to regenerate (Banfield and Tener, 1958, p. 569). Taiga woodland, on the other hand, although it may take as long a time as moss to reach climax character, begins initial regeneration within a year or two with a profusion of weeds, willows, and brush.

The same fires that rendered large tracts unfit for use by caribou, at the same time opened extensive new niches for moose. Moose are a subclimax animal par excellence. They cannot do well in dense woods or on tundra or open plains; they are animals of the margins, dependent upon brushy fields and secondary forest. The main diet of moose is shrub foliage and grassy weeds, although there is considerable seasonal variation (Peterson, 1955). Furthermore, whereas caribou require much larger uninterrupted ranges because of their herd character, the solitary nature of moose demography can well fit into a patchwork of small suitable ranges.

In the past fifty years, moose populations have expanded throughout the area, and where moose once were a rarity they now far surpass woodland caribou as the predominant large game animal. Rogers (1963, pp. 33, 41) similarly reports that in the Mistassini area, about 150 miles east of Rupert House, although moose entered the area only thirty to fifty years ago they now far outnumber caribou. Caribou and moose are different in behavior and demography, and such differences must be reckoned with in hunting. The pattern of game replacement has relevance for the activity and organization of the dependent Indian groups.

Caribou are herd animals, whereas moose are solitary. Caribou behavior is much more predictable than that of moose (Banfield, personal communication). Caribou can be driven, whereas moose cannot; caribou constantly group up, even when attacked by man. Local hunters claim that if a lead animal can be brought down, the rest of the herd will often mill about for a minute or two until a new leader is established, and that even after a number of animals have been shot the remainder may run but a short distance and group up again. Moose, on the other hand, usually travel alone for most of the year (although females will often be accompanied by their calf or yearling). Three or four moose yarding together under winter conditions will be a maximum concentration. Furthermore, moose are extremely erratic. They are easily excited and when disturbed will rapidly leave the vicinity, frequently moving beyond the radius that the hunter can effectively cover. In addition, the manner in which moose escape and the routes they take are comparatively unpredictable—and therefore relatively successful. Driving moose is virtually impossible (Peterson, 1955).

Moose, it would seem, not only are better suited than caribou to the recently extended subclimax biome created by forest fires, but also are a generally more effective species in an environment containing armed hunters. With the advent of modern rifles, human predation has become the overriding factor in game animal survival (Banfield, 1957; Banfield and Tener, 1958).

The importance of this species replacement to hunting and so-

cial arrangements can be fully understood only if the local technology is known. We must realize that rifles were introduced to
the area only in 1903 and that poor-quality muskets were still the
predominant firearm on the James Bay coast and at Mistassini as
late as 1918 (J. W. Anderson, 1961; Rogers, 1963, p. 40*n*). Such
muskets had a very limited range, were rather inaccurate, and
could not be fired rapidly. With muskets, and given the character
of caribou, the most effective way to make a substantial kill was to
drive a herd into an ambuscade. This technique, to be effective,
required at least four or five hunters, preferably more. The decline of the caribou population and the spread of high-powered
repeating rifles made it less necessary and less profitable to collect
a large number of hunters for extended caribou hunts. There
were fewer caribou to be had, and a man and his son alone might
well kill a number with modern rifles—if they should find them.

Local trappers told me that woodland caribou, in bands of
twenty to thirty animals, are more easily detected than moose and
can be driven, but their manner of "stationing" guard animals
and the greater distance they move each day while feeding make
caribou much more difficult and tedious to stalk and track than
moose. On the other hand, tracking and stalking is pre-eminently
the method called for in hunting moose. Apart from the fact that
they cannot be driven, moose, when not disturbed, travel comparatively short distances each day while feeding, making it more
feasible to follow old moose spoor than caribou spoor. Furthermore, moose respond to calls during the mating season, whereas
caribou do not. Since only one or two moose will be encountered
at one time, even with muskets no advantage accrues from mobiliz-
ing more than one or two men to hunt them. Indeed, in view of
the high-strung personality of moose, a larger body of hunters
might well be a disadvantage.

The replacement of muskets by high-powered rifles and the
replacement of woodland caribou herds by solitary moose have independently and in conjunction allowed and fostered the development of smaller hunting-production units. One of the basic principles of subarctic hunting is to spread the human population as
widely and evenly over the land as possible (given animal, tech-

nological, and aid requirements), so as to maximize man-animal contacts. Division into smaller hunting groups more closely approximates this principle, since, given the same over-all population, it results in more hunting groups.

Finally, whereas caribou are more likely to be found in muskeg and older forest, moose frequent stream and lake margins—exactly the location of the bulk of the fur animals. Beaver, mink, and otter, the most important fur animals, live either in or on the margins of streams and ponds. Moose hunting is carried on parallel to and in conjunction with trapping without the necessity of any important displacement or modification in either.

It would certainly be surprising if these hard-pressed people were to maintain basic organizational and behavioral forms adapted to species and tools that were no longer of great importance, and fail to exploit new, apparent ecological opportunities. The desire to improve material standards of living seems sufficiently universal to allow us to dispense with explanations primarily based upon the possible strengthening of acquisitive values by newly introduced barter or money economies. The present analysis holds that closer consideration of faunal and technological factors gives a fuller and clearer explanation of changing territoriality and social organization among the northeastern Algonkian than do mere intimations that barter and money economies are inherently divisive of formerly more communal societies.

CONCLUSIONS

In sum: Among the northeastern Algonkian the generally low subsistence margin in conjunction with fluctuations in localized faunal and human demography required frequent and smooth readjustments of personnel over the band area. This made private control and restricted use of strategic resources unfeasible and unadaptive. The practice of beaver conservation in former times seems empirically and theoretically doubtful. Neither the *potential* conservability of beaver nor the development of the fur trade seems a sufficient reason for the development of family territoriality. It is my belief that integration in and dependence upon a trade economy per se does not lead to or even allow the maintenance of private control and restricted use of strategic resources. Leacock herself mentions individuals who established full-fledged private hunting-trapping tracts, sometimes under the influence of Europeans, many generations ago. But, not only did this pattern not become general for their band, but even such tracts generally seem to have disappeared in later surveys of the area. The requisites for establishment are different from those for maintenance, and what may be feasible for a longer or shorter period for some individuals is not necessarily feasible for the bulk of a population.

Instead of the degree of integration in a trade economy, it is rather the creation of a regular and reliable survival security, which this integration may produce, that is important as the requisite for family territoriality. It seems clear that such long-run survival security was not forthcoming throughout the 250-year trading-trapping history of Rupert House, and *most* other trading posts. This explains the failure of family territoriality to develop. It could not be maintained.

Current theories are inadequate. The explanation of indigenously developed family hunting-trapping territories, under trade and pre-trade conditions, will have to take into consideration other principles and factors, or other analyses of ones already presented. In any case, no explanation which disregards the material conditions of life, or which treats these in a cavalier fashion, can be expected to give a satisfactory answer.

REFERENCES

ANDERSON, J. A. 1961. *Angel of Hudson's Bay; The True Story of Maude Watt.* Ryerson Press, Toronto, Canada.

ANDERSON, J. W. 1961. *Fur Trader's Story.* Ryerson Press, Toronto, Canada.

BANFIELD, A. W. F. 1957. Plight of the barren ground caribou. *Oryx, J. Fauna Preservation Soc., 4* (1) , 5–20.

BANFIELD, A. W. F., and J. S. TENER. 1958. A preliminary study of the Ungava caribou. *J. Mammal., 39* (4) , 560–573.

DENMARK, D. E. 1948. James Bay beaver conservation. *The Beaver,* Outfit 279, Sept., 38–43.

ELTON, C. E. 1942. *Voles, Mice and Lemmings; Problems in Population Dynamics.* Clarendon Press, Oxford, England.

HALLOWELL, A. I. 1949. The size of Algonkian hunting territories; A function of ecological adjustment. *Am. Anthropologist, 51,* 35–45.

KERR, A. J. 1950. Subsistence and social organization in a fur trade community. Rupert House 1947. MS report in Library of Department of Citizenship and Immigration, Ottawa, Canada.

KIMBLE, G. H., and D. GOOD. 1955. *Geography of the Northlands.* Am. Geograph. Soc., Spec. Publ. 32. New York, N. Y.

LEACOCK, E. 1954. *The Montagnais Hunting Territory and the Fur Trade.* Am. Anthropol. Assoc., Mem. 78, Vol. 56, No. 5, Pt. 2.

PETERSON, R. 1955. *North American Moose.* University of Toronto Press, Toronto, Canada.

ROGERS, E. 1963. *The Hunting Group–Hunting Territory Complex among the Mistassini Indians.* Nat. Mus. Canada, Bull. 195. Ottawa, Canada.

SPECK, F. 1915. The family hunting band as the basis of Algonkian social organization. *Am. Anthropologist, 17,* 289–405.

SPECK, F. 1923. Mistassini hunting territories in the Labrador peninsula. *Am. Anthropologist, 25,* 452–471.

SPECK, F. 1931. Montagnais-Naskapi bands and early Eskimo distributions in the Labrador peninsula. *Am. Anthropologist, 33,* 557–600.

SPECK, F., and L. C. EISELY. 1939. The significance of the hunting territory systems of the Algonkian in social theory. *Am. Anthropologist, 41,* 269–280.

The Virginia Deer and Intertribal Buffer Zones in the Upper Mississippi Valley

HAROLD HICKERSON

Department of Anthropology, State University of New York at Buffalo, Buffalo, New York

A COMMON FEATURE of intertribal relations in the Plains and Woodlands of North America was the "debatable" or buffer zone.[1] The buffer zone comprised territory on the frontiers between tribes which, except for communal drives, was normally unoccupied. Such lands could not be entered in safety except by war parties or large hunting parties prepared at a moment's notice for war. Activities requiring residence in lodges by small groups were virtually impossible in such zones.

On the Plains, bison hunting by large communal parties was carried on in the contested sectors of the upper reaches of the Arkansas and Platte-Republican rivers, perhaps also in the intertribal debatable region of the Sweet Grass Hills in northern Montana, and in other places where the bison congregated (Grinnell, 1956; Roe, 1951, pp. 541 ff.; DS-BSR, 1878, pp. 63–64). Mobility through horse transport and an economy supporting large groups

---

[1] Additional research would disclose buffer regions in other areas as well. The Southeast and California might be especially fruitful for such research. It should be pointed out that L. H. Morgan proposed the universality of buffer zones between tribes (1877, p. 114), bringing to F. Engels' mind a parallel to the forest or "desert" buffers of the ancient world (1902, p. 110). As Morgan perhaps sensed, there are distinctions between the Greco-Roman, German, Slavic, and Welsh buffers (marches), among others, and the type of "debatable" zone discussed here. This comparison is outside the scope of this paper, and is reserved for discussion at some future time.

in temporary summer hunting and ceremonial encampments permitted intensive use of debatable sectors, but only, in the last
analysis, by force of hand.

In the Woodlands, where there was a lack of rapid transport,
and where the game supply was far less abundant and less migratory than on the Plains, the debatable zone was more stable and
much more difficult for hunters to enter. Among the Chippewa
and Santee (eastern) Sioux of Wisconsin and Minnesota, enemies
who faced each other across an extensive buffer zone, there was
a clear demarcation between village life and hunting-ground life.
Horticulture, the wild rice harvest, maple sugar production, fishing—pursuits requiring stable residence—were carried on at villages sequestered from enemies. Hunting of hoofed game, especially the Virginia deer, was carried on away from the villages by
bands of hunters drawn from the village personnel. Such hunting
inevitably carried the bandsmen toward the buffer zone, where
the game existed in greatest quantity.

In the buffer zone the hunting bands, made up of about 15 to
20 responsible men[2] (leaders of households consisting normally of
one or two nuclear families), were also warrior bands. During
the era of the fur trade such bands could not long remain in the
buffer hunting grounds; they were constantly subject to attack
from vigilant enemies. Besides, trapping for peltry, which involved much of their time and energy, required setting trap lines
by hunters working as individuals or in pairs. This was impossible in the buffer. The trappers would be cut off, or their traps
broken.

Furred game, chiefly the muskrat among the prairie-dwelling
Sioux, beaver and marten among the woods-dwelling Chippewa,
were trapped in safe areas and not in the buffer. Only during
times of truce could furred game be trapped in the buffer zone.
Such truces were rare before the third decade of the nineteenth

[2] Most of my information is for the Chippewa (see Hickerson, 1962, chaps. 2, 3,
for this and the following). The size of the eastern Sioux hunting band was certainly not larger. Such bands, whose entire personnel comprised perhaps 75 to 100
persons, were maximal in terms of winter resources and means to exploit them.
Several such bands would constitute a village; the village functioned as an organism
among the Chippewa and Sioux chiefly from late spring to early fall.

century, when the establishment of Indian agencies and occasional
effective interference in Indian affairs by fur traders resulted in
some regulation of warfare. With certain notable exceptions, however, temporary cessations of warfare did not lead to a concentration of Indian activity in the buffer zone. As long as economic
relations and ecological conditions remained fairly constant, as
they did throughout the pre-reservation historical period, such
a zone could not be occupied for more than a few days by one
group to the exclusion (and at the expense) of the other.

Of extraordinary durability and stability was the buffer zone,
the strip of debatable land, lying between the Chippewa and Sioux
in western Wisconsin and central Minnesota. This zone was in
existence from about 1780 to the 1850's—from the time of Chippewa settlement of the interior lakes of those two states to the
time of the confinement of the Indians to reservations. There is
considerable information on this zone,[3] and also enough material
on the natural history of the region to afford a glimpse of the in-
terplay of historical and ecological factors underlying intertribal
warfare and the development of the buffer.

It is my purpose to show that this buffer zone took its character and its shape from the distribution of the Virginia deer in the
mixed forest and park-land regions of Wisconsin and Minnesota.
The struggles of the Chippewa and Sioux over game resources,
of which the deer was the most important for food, centered in
the buffer. We shall see that warfare between members of the two
tribes had the effect of preventing competing hunters from occupying the best game regions intensively enough to deplete the
supply. We shall see further that in the one instance in which
a lengthy truce was maintained between certain Chippewa and
Sioux, the buffer, in effect a protective zone for the deer, was
destroyed, and famine ensued.

I shall first indicate the reliance of the Chippewa and Sioux on
the deer for food, and the effect of undisturbed hunting during

[3] For a detailed description of this zone, see Hickerson, 1962, chap. 2. The buffer
is represented on the accompanying map. The main sources for this delimitation
are: MPHC, *11*, 485–487; Cruikshank, 1923, *1*, 390; Williams, 1953, pp. 326–327, 452;
Keating, 1825, *2*, 9; ASP-MA, *5*, 335–336; Schoolcraft, 1834, pp. 268–269. These are
only a few of many sources on the contested area.

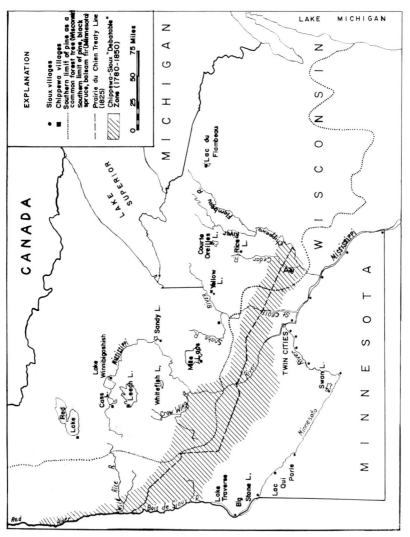

INTERTRIBAL BUFFER ZONES AND BOUNDARIES IN T HE PERSPECTIVE OF VEGETAL ZONES IN WISCONSIN
AND MINNESOTA

a period of truce on the subsistence economy of both peoples. In the second half of the paper I discuss the effect of the distribution and habits of the deer in its natural habitat on intertribal warfare, and the relation of deer habitat to war zones.

It is relevant at this juncture to review very briefly the history of Indian occupancy of this region. In 1679 the Chippewa of Lake Superior and the Sioux who lived in interior Wisconsin and Minnesota established an alliance based on the fur trade. Chippewa brought French commodities to the Sioux in exchange for peltry and rights to hunt in their territory (see Hickerson, 1962, chaps. 2, 6). This alliance was broken in 1736, and thenceforth the Chippewa and Sioux were at war. Over a period of forty years Chippewa from the shores of Lake Superior drove the Sioux out of the wooded parts of the two northern states, establishing their villages at some of the larger lakes formerly occupied by their enemies.

By the 1780's Chippewa occupation of the forested parts of the two states was complete, but they continued to combat the Sioux, who now occupied contiguous prairie regions on the upper Mississippi and Minnesota rivers (see map for major village locations). This later struggle, a war of attrition following a war of conquest, was for dominion over transition forest and prairie edge regions in western Wisconsin and central Minnesota. It was never resolved.

The contested zone, as the map shows, extended without break from the Chippewa River in west central Wisconsin to the valley of the Red River of the North in western Minnesota.

THE RELIANCE OF CHIPPEWA AND SIOUX ON THE VIRGINIA DEER

The Chippewa and Sioux exploited a variety of wild and domestic products. Wild rice and maple sugar were more used by the Chippewa, but the eastern Sioux also harvested wild rice in the lower Minnesota and St. Croix River regions. The eastern Sioux cultivated maize to a greater extent than the Chippewa, but this pursuit was not entirely lacking in the interior Chippewa villages. Both peoples hunted furred game for the trade; the Sioux, who lived near marshy tracts, specialized in muskrat trapping, whereas the Chippewa chiefly trapped beaver and marten. Both peoples hunted hoofed game for subsistence, but also for the trade in deerskins. The Sioux had greater access to the bison, but, lacking horses, the Santee divisions were never chiefly reliant on the bison hunt, as were their congeners to the west. Indeed, bison were never numerous in the upper Mississippi Valley, and by 1830 they were gone in the whole region east of the Red River.

Unlike the Sioux, who were always but desultory users of fish, the Chippewa, originally a Great Lakes people, had also been great fish eaters. But the Chippewa peoples who migrated south from Lake Superior in the eighteenth century came to emphasize hunting at the expense of fishing, which in the smaller interior lakes was neither as dependable nor as rewarding as at the great whitefish and sturgeon fisheries of the Great Lakes.[4]

Let us look at a few sources on the preoccupation of Sioux and Chippewa with the Virginia, or white-tailed, deer. In 1788–1789 a trader, Jean Baptiste Perrault, built a post on Red Cedar River near its junction with the Chippewa, right in the buffer zone. There he carried on a good trade with Menominee from eastern Wisconsin.[5] In midwinter a small contingent of Chippewa arrived at his post from the north to trade beaver pelts, and much to Perrault's consternation a larger group of Sioux arrived next day. Despite protestations of peace a fight broke out, but not before the Sioux leader, Little Crow, had addressed the Chippewa:

My brothers, we have taken the liberty of approaching your lands for awhile. You know that the deer seeks the thick woods for The winter, and that upon it depends the life of our women and children. We hope therefore that you will bear with us for a Couple of months

[4] For example, Chippewa from Leech Lake, Minnesota, were already in their winter hunting grounds during the height of the fall fishery (Boutwell, 1832–1837; Hickerson, 1962, chap. 5). As late as 1820, Chippewa still living on Lake Superior were virtually year-round fishermen (Hickerson, 1962, p. 81).

[5] Neutral Menominee frequently accompanied traders into areas contested by Chippewa and Sioux, forming perhaps a native equivalent of a buffer state (Hickerson, 1962, chap. 2). Their occupancy of these neutral zones was not spontaneous; it was arranged through negotiations with the belligerents.

On the upper waters of that branch of your river, and we will retire as soon as we have acquired provisions for our spring (MPHC, *37*, 545–548).

The Chippewa agreed, but ordered the Sioux to depart as soon as they made their catch. Here, then, the reliance of the Sioux on the deer hunt for winter and spring provisions is indicated. A reading of the journals of their agent, Lawrence Taliaferro, shows that this reliance never diminished, and perhaps even increased as the bison entirely left the Mississippi region. Among dozens of deer references in Taliaferro, we find the following. In 1836, during a period of starvation, Taliaferro noted that the Sioux had not killed a single deer during their summer hunt. This was during a period of truce with the Chippewa, and Sioux blamed the Chippewa for killing off the game in the buffer zone (*10*, July 20, 24–26, August 10, 1836). In July 1838, at the end of a period of truce and just before a major outbreak of war, a Sioux chief complained to Taliaferro that the Chippewa

have swept off all our game on the Mississippi & the small streams— —coming & going from this Post— —once they never were to be found below Crow Island [mouth of Crow Wing River] when we were at War— —but since your Fort was established here & peace was started our lands have suffered to such an extent that we cannot see a Deer or a Bear— —in all our days journey (*12*, July 9, 1838; brackets mine).[6]

Without deer, the Sioux economy was in dire straits. It is also clear that the Chippewa, who did not ordinarily have as much access to the bison as the Sioux did,[7] were reliant for a great part of *their* subsistence on the Virginia deer. There is extensive evidence for this in traders' journals for the first decade of the nineteenth

[6] There are other references to the reliance of the Sioux on deer and the risks they incurred in hunting them (for instance, Thomas G. Anderson in WHC, *9*, 159, 183 ff.). A very interesting account of a Sioux deer hunt in the contested zone is that of Pond (1893, pp. 67–69). Their reliance on deer is quite clear in this account.

[7] Before the disappearance of the bison east of the Red River, the Chippewa in Minnesota did hunt bison on occasion under conditions of great risk in the debatable grounds of the upper Mississippi (see, for instance, Tyrrell, 1916, p. 281; Williams, 1953, p. 183). The Chippewa in Wisconsin and extreme eastern Minnesota never had access to the bison.

century, those of Michel Curot (WHC, *20,* 396 ff.) , François V.
Malhiot (WHC, *19,* 163 ff.) , and Thomas Connor (Gates, 1933,
pp. 245 ff.) . These journals show that traders and Indians in the
St. Croix and Chippewa River valleys placed great reliance during
the furred-game trapping season on deer meat for provisions.
Aside from individual hunting, deer were hunted communally by
bands of Chippewa ranging toward the buffer region (Hickerson,
1962, chap. 3) .

A trader, George H. Monk, for 1807, noted with respect to the
large Chippewa village at Sandy Lake in Aitkin County, Minnesota, that

deer abound on the frontiers, say about white fish lake. . . . Thence
downward the deer is a constant inhabitant of the banks of the Mississippi (MH, *5,* 35–36) .

Whitefish Lake is not far north of the entrance of the Crow
Wing, at the north end of the contested zone on the Mississippi.
But read what another trader, William Johnston, says about the
Sandy Lake region in 1833:

Sandy Lake is considered as the central trading post, of the Fond du
Lac department, from which clerks separate for the Upper and lower
Mississippi; and occupied by the principle trader. It is only for the
above cause that it is occupied, and the clerks having always to
rendezvous at this place before proceeding to the Lake. As for the
Indian population, which was numerous, they say; formerly; it has
lately dwindled away to only a few lodges; which was caused by the
encrease of the red Deer, at places south of this (MPHC, *37,* 173–174) .

The Chippewa, as well as the Sioux, were always chasing the
Virginia (red) deer into the contested zones, the "frontiers." Let
us look at another statement by Schoolcraft, the Chippewa agent,
who traveled along the Red Cedar River, a branch of the Chippewa in western Wisconsin, in 1831:

At [Rice Lake] at the distance of perhaps sixty miles from its head,
I found the last fixed village of Chippewas on this stream, although
the hunting camps, and other signs of temporary occupation, were
more numerous below than on any other part of the stream. This may
be attributed to the abundance of the Virginia deer in that vicinity,

many of which we saw, and of the elk and moose, whose tracks were fresh and numerous in the sands of the shore (1834, pp. 268–269; brackets mine).[8]

The Virginia deer, and not its larger cervine relatives, would be most sought, if only because it was more easily hunted and transported. The Indians in such dangerous regions did not normally take their women with them and did not set up their lodges. It is senseless killing numbers of elk in places where the lodges cannot be moved a short distance to the elk, but the elk must be moved a great distance to the lodges. The smaller deer were undoubtedly the chief target of the hunters along the Red Cedar.

The explorer-trader David Thompson, who traveled through Minnesota and along the south shore of Lake Superior in 1798, described at length the poverty of the Chippewa who continued to live in the vicinity of Lake Superior. They could not kill enough deer even to supply leather for their clothing (Tyrrell, 1916, pp. 286, 298). Even in the Mississippi headwaters region Thompson found deer and beaver very scarce and the Chippewa in a starving condition, having to rely on wild rice, wild fowl, and maple sugar. But that was during a year of bitter warfare, and although Chippewa from Sandy Lake were trying to hunt bison south of the Crow Wing junction, it was with the greatest trepidation that they were entering the frontier sectors (*ibid.*, pp. 263–264, 281–282).

We perceive from Thompson's negative statements on the distribution and availability of deer the importance of deer hunting. Without Virginia deer the Lake Superior Chippewa had to tide over the winter with fish they had dried or frozen in the fall, with the occasional moose they could kill, and perhaps with a small supply of wild rice they had been able to cache if the harvest was good.

But their congeners to the south, more numerous than the lake

---

[8] A. W. Schorger writes that Schoolcraft's reference to moose in Barron and Dunn counties represents the "southernmost point recorded for the moose in the western part of the state" (1956, p. 1). There could not have been many in that region, which is not moose habitat. The elk, a grazer which loves meadows and prairie openings, found a good habitat there (Schorger, 1942, pp. 32–34; 1956, pp. 1–10).

shore Chippewa,[9] with only occasional access to the larger deer and bison, were usually willing to risk life and limb to follow the deer in regions where the enemy, just as reliant on deer as they, was willing to fight them at every opportunity. It was chiefly their utilization of deer meat, supplemented by the meat of other large and small game, which enabled them to sustain populations much larger than those on the lake shore, where the primary dependence was on fish, often on fish alone.

This reliance, and its relation to the buffer zone, is illustrated by data on truces which opened the buffer to hunting, or, rather, rendered the buffer zone an innocuous hunting ground. In another paper I have discussed in detail, using Taliaferro's journals covering the period 1826 to 1839, and data from the Schoolcraft expeditions to Wisconsin and Minnesota of 1831 and 1832, relations between the Sioux and Chippewa in the valley of the St. Croix River and in the Mississippi Valley itself above the Twin Cities (Hickerson, 1962, chap. 2; see Taliaferro, 1821–1839, vols. 3–13; Schoolcraft, 1834, pp. 265 ff., for primary data).

The Indians of these regions lived close to the United States agency at the junction of the Mississippi and Minnesota rivers. With the support of the agent and at the urging of civil chiefs on both sides following a general peace and boundary treaty at Prairie du Chien in 1825, they remained at peace for thirteen years. Frequent visits to the agency, exchanges of commodities (Chippewa traded birchbark canoes and maple sugar to Sioux for guns, traps, and blankets), and dances, extensive councils at the agency, parleys, and ball games in the hunting grounds marked this era. Throughout there were numerous reports of Sioux and Chippewa hunting in proximity on both sides of the Prairie du Chien boundary line. Still there were hostile outbreaks on several occasions, and in 1831 war broke out instigated by a Sioux war chief, Medicine Bottle. Only the patience of the Chippewa on that occa-

---

[9] Hickerson, 1962, chap. 2. The number of Chippewa who lived on the frontier facing the Sioux was about 4000. They lived in seven large villages ranging from about 300 to 1000 (Leech Lake), and a number of smaller villages (see Schoolcraft, 1834, pp. 221–224). The Sioux who fought the Chippewa were slightly more numerous, perhaps 5000 to 6000 in all. Their main villages were in about the same population range (see Keating, 1825, *1*, 396) as those of the Chippewa.

sion prevented a full-scale outbreak, and the incident was dropped for the moment.

Reports of famine affecting both Sioux and Chippewa came in, starting in about 1828, three years after the truce began, and reaching a climax first in 1831 and then again in 1835–1838. Accompanying such reports were complaints lodged on frequent occasions by the Sioux that Chippewa hunters were crossing the Prairie du Chien line and destroying the game. A typical complaint was that lodged by the Sioux chief Little Crow in July 1838, which I cited above. The Chippewa complained as bitterly to their agent, Schoolcraft, of Sioux incursions, and were described by the Sioux agent as being in deplorable condition:

It would move the feelings of a *Deist* or of the Devil himself much less a Christian Man to look on the *garb* & conditions of most of the Chippeways of the *St. Croix—Snake,* and *Rum Rivers* (Taliaferro, *9,* July 6, 1835).

In the summer of 1839 after warlike incidents in 1838, the Sioux, in retaliation for a Chippewa attack in another quarter, in one day killed over a hundred Chippewa from Mille Lacs Lake and the St. Croix River who were returning to their villages after a visit to the agency. After this, portions of the St. Croix and Mississippi again became buffer zones as they had been before 1826, and warfare continued until the reservation period in the mid 1850's.

In other sectors no such lengthy truces occurred, but occasionally at the instigation of traders and/or civil chiefs a year's truce would be arranged (involving exchanges of presents by the belligerents in the hunting grounds) to permit undisturbed hunting (see Hickerson, 1962, chap. 2). No correlation between such momentary truces and abundance of game can be seen in such sectors, because of lack of detailed source data on the one hand, and insufficient time span on the other. Where the lengthy truce did obtain, as we have seen, the deer soon ran short and hostilities began again as a response to famine, resulting in the restoration of the buffer zone. It remains for us now to demonstrate specifically that the buffer zone was indeed deer habitat.

THE HABITAT AND DISTRIBUTION OF THE VIRGINIA DEER

There is an extensive literature on the habitat, distribution, and habits of the Virginia deer in Wisconsin and Minnesota. It is emphasized by biologists in both states that the deer is not a creature of the closed forest, but rather of open forests where there is a great variety of browse. Thus, an area of "oak openings and small prairies" is excellent deer habitat (Swift, 1946, p. 7). Deer thrive in brushy areas, and plants such as mountain maple, red osier dogwood, and the willows are favored foods (Erickson and Burcalow, 1954, p. 8; Krefting and Erickson, 1956, p. 397; Stenlund and Gunvalson, 1957).

Deer do not thrive in mature coniferous or broad-leaf forests, where there is little understory browse because of the heavy canopy, and where there is little "edge." Deer also shun boggy areas and grassy areas without tree cover (Fredine, 1940, p. 41; Benson, 1954; Stenlund, 1955, p. 41; 1956, p. 35; Dahlberg and Guettinger, 1956, p. 13; Christensen, 1959, pp. 230–231). In Wisconsin and Minnesota distribution of deer may be viewed in the light of data on the vegetation of the two states before the logging era which began at the time the Sioux and Chippewa were confined to reservations, in the mid nineteenth century.

First, western Wisconsin was divided basically into two major plant communities, a northern conifer-hardwood forest and a southern hardwood forest. The mixed northern forest was made up chiefly of the sugar maple and the yellow birch, and hemlock and pine among the coniferous varieties (Finley, n.d., map; Curtis, 1959, *passim*). The southern hardwood forest was more mixed, with large tracts of oak and oak openings and extensive brush lands. Maple and basswood, of course, were common trees. Conifers were scarce.

The geographer R. W. Finley, whose depiction of forest areas is followed on our map, and the botanist J. T. Curtis show the division between the northern and southern forest to be a staggered line crossing the central part of Wisconsin from east to west. Below the line, pine is no longer a common forest tree.

What of deer distribution in terms of plant communities? The conservationist E. Swift writes that southern Wisconsin, with its tremendous forest "edge," was ideal habitat for deer. In the north, where there were stands of mature pine, hemlocks, and the gigantic northern hardwoods, conditions "were not conducive to sustaining many deer" (Swift, 1946, pp. 7–8, 23, 60). These northern forests covered the entire area of Chippewa village habitation (*ibid.*, p. 17; Curtis, 1959, pp. 533–537; Hickerson, 1962, chap. 2).

The biologist E. M. Christensen points out that much of northern Wisconsin's forests were monotypic mature stands with little understory, supporting few deer. He cites early authors to show that there was generally poor range in the north (1959, pp. 230–232). A. W. Schorger also cites early authors exhaustively to show that northern Wisconsin had few deer before the logging which transformed the virgin forests into ideal habitat (second-growth deciduous trees and shrubs). According to Schorger, there were limited open areas along the St. Croix River, a center of Chippewa village habitation, with fair deer populations. Again, Schorger cites a statement by Lieutenant J. Allen, who accompanied Schoolcraft on his expedition of 1832, that the Chippewa of Lac du Flambeau, a prominent village well within the pine timber (Vilas County, near the Michigan line), killed plenty of deer. Schorger surmises, however, that these Chippewa had to descend the Flambeau River to its junction with the Chippewa in extreme southern Rusk County, very near the southern forest line, to hunt the deer (1953, pp. 198–203).[10]

Finally, in their definitive study of the history of the Virginia deer in Wisconsin, B. L. Dahlberg and R. C. Guettinger (1956) present a map of deer distribution under conditions of the original vegetation cover. In the south, where optimum conditions prevailed, they estimate the population at 20 to 50 deer per square mile. In the northeast, where there were open swampy areas providing "edge," they estimate 10 to 15 deer per square mile. In the northwest, where there was the heaviest unbroken virgin timber and thus the least "edge," there were less than 10 deer per

[10] The Flambeau Chippewa were always in bitter enmity with the Sioux, never relaxing hostilities, even when other Chippewa were at peace (Hickerson, 1962, chap. 2).

square mile.[11] It was in the northwest and the western part of the
northeastern area, where the deer population was the smallest,
that the Chippewa who were at war with the Sioux, and contested
the buffer area with them, lived. All authorities indicate, then,
that the deer population in Wisconsin was much heavier in the
south than in the north woods. A glance at our map shows that
the contested zone in Wisconsin coincided with the break in vegetation zones and deer density.

In Minnesota the picture was even clearer. There the northern
forest was more decidedly coniferous. Norway and white pine
tracts were even greater in extent, and deer range was poorer, than
in northern Wisconsin. Parts of northern Minnesota not in dense
woodland comprised great bogs, unsuitable for habitation by the
Virginia deer. As in Wisconsin, the Chippewa villages were located entirely within the northern forest, which comprised the
northern one-third of the state.

The southwestern third of Minnesota, occupied by the Sioux,
was prairie. Between the prairie and the northern forest was a
belt of mixed hardwood forest and park land running from southeast to northwest, about 40 to 50 miles wide in the western part
of the state, somewhat wider (with the addition of the "big woods"
in the extreme southeast) to the east (Borchert, 1959, p. 24; Stenlund and Gunvalson, 1957). On our map we use as the terminal
line of the coniferous forest the "Southwestern Limit of the Pines,
Black Spruce and Balsam Fir" in Folwell (1921, _1_, 10).

As for the distribution of deer, according to G. Fredine, a
conservationist:

The white-tailed deer was originally restricted in range to the hardwood forests and prairie lands of the southern portion of the state. . . .
Up to about the year 1860 deer were not common in the coniferous

---

[11] Dahlberg and Guettinger predicate deer density on vegetation zones: "Original
deer numbers cannot be estimated except in relative degrees of density based on
present-day knowledge of maximum and minimum density for similar habitat. We
can only speculate on the probable density of deer for the various areas of the
state" (1956, p. 14). The lines drawn by these authors fit the original forest cover
map of the Wisconsin Geological Survey of 1882 (reproduced by Swift, 1946, p. 15,
to indicate deer areas). This map is very close to the Finley map. The latter is
more authoritative for original forest cover.

forests of the north central and northeastern portions of Minnesota. Under the big timber that existed in this area, there was very little undergrowth to serve as food and cover for deer (1940, p. 41; see also Benson, 1954).

M. H. Stenlund in his study of the timber wolf in the Superior National Forest of northeastern Minnesota found that deer, upon which the wolves largely subsist, were relatively abundant in cut-over regions, whereas in the uncut areas which resemble the original northern forest

Deer populations are low . . . despite the fact that they are not hunted and wolf populations are lower than in neighboring cutover areas. . . . Rocks, jack pine, and mature hardwoods which make up the habitat in these wilderness areas are not conducive to large deer production (1955, p. 41; see also Gunvalson *et al.*, 1952, p. 121).

The transition forest-park region was the great habitat for deer in the early nineteenth century, superior to the open prairie because of its greater variety of browse and good winter shelter (Stenlund and Gunvalson, 1957; Erickson and Burcalow, 1954, p. 8; Krefting and Erickson, 1956, p. 397).

In Wisconsin and Minnesota, then, there were few deer in the regions inhabited by Chippewa. Although there is no explicit material on deer density in the prairie regions of Minnesota inhabited by the Sioux, the openness of the terrain, more suitable for grazing than for browsing animals, would have precluded an intensive occupancy by deer. No war zone developed in the prairies immediately south of the Minnesota River, even though there was in early times an abundance of game of every kind common in that latitude. The advance of the Chippewa to the park region in the eighteenth century represented their optimum extension. Beyond that the openness of the country, affording as little shelter for humans as for animals, and their inability to secure permanent occupancy of the buffer, prohibited further advances by the Chippewa.[12]

---

[12] By the middle of the nineteenth century, it is true, the Chippewa had made small advances in the Otter Tail Lake district of western Minnesota (Hickerson, 1962, chap. 2), but this did not seriously affect the ecological balance.

The retreat of the Sioux to the Minnesota River in the eighteenth century, and increasing trade in deerskins and other peltry
during the same period, led to depletion of game resources near
at hand, namely in the prairies. This was especially true in the
last years of the French regime and the early years of the British
regime (see Nute, 1951; Gates, 1933, pp. 11 ff.; Kellogg, 1935, pp.
104 ff.) . Thus, even if deer had originally been more numerous
in the prairie than in the closed forest, undisturbed occupancy
of such a region, far from the war zones, by Indians would have
resulted in their depletion through hunting. By the turn of the
nineteenth century the Sioux were relying on the buffer zone and
the country peripheral to it for their supply of hoofed game, as
we have seen above.

The data I have introduced from the writings of naturalists,
most of whom are conservation experts, dovetail with the reports
of early fur traders and officials, who indicated that deer were
scarce in regions of heavy human concentration and abundant in
contested regions, the unpopulated buffers. Ideal deer habitat, as
we have seen in the reports of the biologists, was precisely the
zone described by the early authors as contested.

The northern forest was not entirely without deer. But there
are indications that because of certain habits of the Virginia deer
(in combination with factors peculiar to the balance of Indian
economy during the fur trade era) , the deer quickly became extinct in regions readily accessible to Indian hunters. The habit of
the deer most conducive to its own depletion in certain locales
is yarding. Wisconsin and Minnesota biologists agree that the winter range of deer in years of average snow cover and cold is but
10 per cent of the summer range (Dahlberg and Guettinger, 1956,
p. 145; Fredine, 1940, p. 49; Swift, 1946, p. 57) . The deer enter
the yards at the time when the snow has become so deep as to
inhibit movement and make shelter necessary. These yards may
be in the hardwood, but more often in the north they are in white
cedar groves (Dahlberg and Guettinger, 1956, pp. 61, 145–146) .

Deer tend to enter the same yards winter after winter along
definite trails (*ibid.*, pp. 57, 60, 62; Stenlund, 1956, p. 34) . In the
yards the range of the deer is small, amounting to daily movement

of about one-quarter mile (Dahlberg and Guettinger, 1956, p. 61). It is easy to see how deer in accessible regions were destroyed, especially in the interior, where the demands of the fur trade made incessant hunting a necessity for survival (*ibid.*, pp. 16–18). Schorger remarks that the "prevalence of coniferous trees and the deep snow . . . rendered the deer an easy prey to wolves and Indians" (1953, p. 197).

Christensen supplies source data to show that the yarding areas were well known to whites and Indians (1959, pp. 232–233). Dahlberg and Guettinger cite the Michigan naturalist I. H. Bartlett to the effect that Indians could catch deer on the migration routes by the fence surround method (1956, p. 56). Although the consensus is very strong against extensive deer migrations, it would seem to have been quite feasible for Chippewa and Sioux to surround the deer on their way in and out of the winter yards, besides doing some very efficient hunting on snowshoes of relatively immobile deer *in* the yards.

We see, then, how concentration of deer during winter and early spring months when they were most hunted[13] would lead to their depletion in all but the contested regions where hunters did not have ready access to them. Of primary importance in this ecological configuration was the eroding influence of the fur trade on game populations. I shall not dwell on this here, except to say that emphasis on fishing and storing of fish for winter use (Chippewa) and on the wild rice harvest with extensive caches (Sioux) in the pre-trade economy tended to militate against wholesale destruction of game for peltry or provisions.[14] Hunting with firearms at the expense of the time-honored pursuits was a concomitant of trade. The Indians needed vast amounts of game to support themselves and the traders who flocked greedy, hungry, and unprovided into the heart of the Indian country.

[13] Hickerson, 1962, chap. 3. The Sioux party mentioned by Perrault (above) asked the Chippewa for permission to hunt deer from January to March. This was precisely the time they were most likely to be tightly yarded (Dahlberg and Guettinger, 1956, p. 148).

[14] The Sioux in the seventeenth century occupied the parts of Minnesota and Wisconsin occupied by the Chippewa in the nineteenth, and also the prairies of the Minnesota River. The Chippewa were confined to the region about northern Lake Huron and eastern Lake Superior.

SUMMARY AND DISCUSSION

To recapitulate: The buffer, or debatable (contested), zone was widespread among historical North American Indians. One kind of buffer zone was a strip of territory in which nonmigratory game was abundant owing to favorable conditions in the ecology and lack of intensive exploitation. In western Wisconsin and central Minnesota there was a buffer lying between Chippewa on the north and Sioux on the south, affording an abundance of game, but difficult of entry by hunters from both sides because of the constant danger from enemies.

This contested region, which extended from the Chippewa River on the southeast to the Red River on the northwest, had the appearance of a refuge for the Virginia deer and other game upon which the Chippewa and Sioux placed great reliance for subsistence and trade. As long as the buffer region provided a deterrent to heavy hunting on the part of both tribes, the supply of deer within it, the natural habitat, remained high. This supply provided a source of food for hunters on the periphery of the debatable zone and for those who were willing to enter the zone for short periods at great risk (see ASP-MA, 5, 335).

Unfortunately, we cannot estimate the number of deer in the buffer zone and the region marginal to it. We do not know either the rate of use of deer meat by the Chippewa or Sioux, or precisely what proportion of deer meat there was in their diet. Unquestionably, there was great seasonal variation. Thus, wild rice during and after the harvest (September-October) and before the first fast snows of winter would be used to the exclusion of other foods, except for the wild fowl which, stuffed with rice, were easily taken in the rice ponds. In winter and spring, aside from rice caches, deer meat was the staple. When the supply of meat failed during these seasons, the Chippewa and Sioux were in danger of starving. In spring also a supply was laid in for summer. This was more necessary for the Sioux, who did not fish as much as the Chippewa, and who did not normally manufacture maple sugar, a spring staple for the Chippewa. We may only generalize by saying that the deer hunts were critical in supplying food for part of the year, and that the buffer zone provided a reservoir for this food. The maintenance of the buffer, that is, the warfare which kept a large portion of the best deer habitat a buffer, was a function of the subsistence requirements of the Chippewa and Sioux. During times of extended truce, even in very limited regions like the St. Croix River valley, when hunting was carried on in the buffer, the supply of deer meat became depleted and the war was revived as a response to famine.

Naturally, not only the deer ranged in the buffer zone. It is true that the beaver also thrived in parts of the contested region, but chiefly as a result of the absence of trappers. The beaver, according to the naturalist A. B. Erickson, was widely and sparsely distributed in Minnesota in early times, occupying but a small part of its range except in local areas favorable for the production of aspen. Even if aspen was nowhere dominant in the northern coniferous forest (Erickson, 1939, pp. 195–196), neither was it dominant in broad regions in the transition forest. Although the beaver were perhaps more densely distributed in their natural state in the transition forest and tribal frontier area of Minnesota (but not in the tribal frontier region of Wisconsin), they still would not be the focus of intertribal competition for exploitation. Nowhere were beaver trapped where there was not other game to sustain the trappers. There is every indication that beaver were usually caught in areas safe for trapping, in sufficient numbers to provide the Chippewa with trade necessities. As for the Sioux, their furred game was mainly the muskrat, caught chiefly in the open marshy areas to the south of the contested zone (Berryman, 1955, p. 18).

Furred-game trapping demanded at most times the dispersal of the trappers and the maintenance of the traps along set lines. But hunters could easily be cut off in their isolation, and the traps readily broken. Trapping, except under conditions of truce, was not carried on in the contested zones; those zones, then, did not develop their character because of competition over furred game.

The moose and the bison were not creatures of the transition forest. Although bison were to be found until about 1830 in the contested region along the Mississippi itself, at no time were they the prime target of the horseless Chippewa hunters for any but the briefest time during the summer. By and large, the bison was not as much an inhabitant of the prairie south of the Minnesota River as the moose was of the bog and forest regions of extreme northern Minnesota.

To conclude: Warfare was a function of competition over game and was waged chiefly in the areas where prime game was most abundant. Throughout the period of the existence of such contested, or buffer, areas (1780 to 1850), the Virginia deer, of all game animals the most important for the Chippewa and Sioux, because of its habitat requirements and its habit of yarding in the winter was scarce in regions open to undisturbed hunting. The effect of warfare, then, was the regulation and preservation of a supply of deer in and near the buffer zone for the use of Indians hunting in bands, often at great risk of their lives. Such warfare, except in the one local region in which the Indian agency was a disturbing factor in the regulation of Indian relations, was chronic, and even during times of temporary truce was endemic.

The contested areas took their character and shape from the distribution and habits of the Virginia deer. Subtract any species besides the deer, including even the beaver, from such areas, and the war zone—warfare itself—would hardly have been altered. Subtract the deer, leaving the other fauna, and the configuration would have been entirely different.

REFERENCES

ASP-MA. 1832–1861. *American State Papers, Military Affairs*. 7 vols. Washington, D. C.

BENSON, R. I. 1954. Whitetails moving south. *Conservation Volunteer, 17*, Sept.-Oct.

BERRYMAN, J. H. 1955. Are furbearers worth saving? *Conservation Volunteer, 18*, 18–23.

BORCHERT, J. R. 1959. *Minnesota's Changing Geography*. University of Minnesota Press, Minneapolis, Minn.

BOUTWELL, W. T. 1832–1837. Journals. MSS Dept., Minnesota Historical Society, St. Paul, Minn.

CHRISTENSEN, E. M. 1959. A historical view of the ranges of the white-tailed deer in northern Wisconsin forests. *Am. Midland Naturalist, 61*, 230–238.

CRUIKSHANK, E. A., editor. 1923–1925. *The Correspondence of Lieut. Governor John Graves Simcoe, with Allied Documents Relating to His Administration of the Government of Upper Canada.* 3 vols. Ontario Historical Society, Toronto, Canada.

CURTIS, J. T. 1959. *The Vegetation of Wisconsin; An Ordination of Plant Communities.* University of Wisconsin Press, Madison, Wis.

DAHLBERG, B. L., and R. C. GUETTINGER. 1956. *The White-Tailed Deer in Wisconsin.* Wisconsin Conservation Dept., Game Management Div., Tech. Wildlife Bull. 14. Madison, Wis.

DS-BSR. 1878. *Reports upon the Survey of the Boundary between the Territory of the United States and the Possessions of Great Britain from the Lake of the Woods to the Summit of the Rocky Mountains, Authorized by an Act of Congress Approved March 19, 1872. Archibald Campbell, Commissioner, Captain W. J. Twining, Corps of Engineers, Brevet Major U. S. A., Chief Astronomer.* U. S. Dept. of State, Boundary Survey Reports. Washington, D. C.

ENGELS, F. 1902. *Origin of the Family, Private Property and the State.* Charles H. Kerr and Co., Chicago, Ill.

ERICKSON, A. B. 1939. Beaver populations in Pine County, Minnesota. *J. Mammal., 20,* 195–201.

ERICKSON, A. B., and D. W. BURCALOW. 1954. The St. Croix Park deer herd. *Conservation Volunteer, 17,* 6–17.

FINLEY, R. W. n.d. Generalized vegetation map of Wisconsin. (After R. W. Finley map in library of Dept. of Geography, University of Wisconsin.) Madison, Wis.

FOLWELL, W. W. 1921. *A History of Minnesota.* 4 vols. Minnesota Historical Society, St. Paul, Minn.

FREDINE, G. 1940. Deer inventory studies in Minnesota. *Proc. Minnesota Acad. Sci., 8,* 41–49.

GATES, C. M., editor. 1933. *Five Fur Traders of the Northwest, Being the Narrative of Peter Pond and the Diaries of John Macdonnell, Archibald N. McLeod, Hugh Faries, and Thomas Connor.* University of Minnesota Press, Minneapolis, Minn.

GRINNELL, G. B. 1956. *The Fighting Cheyennes.* University of Oklahoma Press, Norman, Oklahoma.

GUNVALSON, V. E., A. B. ERICKSON, and D. W. BURCALOW. 1952. Hunting season statistics as an index to range conditions and deer population fluctuations in Minnesota. *J. Wildlife Management, 16,* 121–131.

HICKERSON, H. 1962. *The Southwestern Chippewa; An Ethnohistorical Study.* Am. Anthropol. Assoc. Mem. 92.

KEATING, W. H. 1825. *Narrative of an Expedition to the Source of St. Peter's River, Lake Winnepeek, Lake of the Woods, &c. Performed in the Year 1823, by Order of the Hon. J. C. Calhoun, Secretary of War, under the Command of Stephen H. Long, U. S. T. E.* 2 vols. G. B. Whittaker, London.

KELLOGG, L. P., editor. 1917. *Early Narratives of the Northwest, 1634–1699.* Charles Scribner's Sons, New York, N. Y.

KELLOGG, L. P. 1935. *The British Régime in Wisconsin and the Northwest.* State Historical Society of Wisconsin, Madison, Wis.

KREFTING, L. W., and A. B. ERICKSON. 1956. Results of special deer hunts of the Mud Lake Natural Wildlife Refuge, Minnesota. *J. Wildlife Management, 20,* 297–302.

MH. 1915– . *Minnesota History.* 38 vols. Minnesota Historical Society, St. Paul, Minn.

MORGAN, L. H. 1877. *Ancient Society.* Charles H. Kerr, Chicago, Ill.

MPHC. 1877–1929. *Historical Collections of the Michigan Pioneer and Historical Society.* 40 vols. Lansing, Mich.

NUTE, G. L. 1951. Marin versus La Verendrye. In MH, *32,* 226–238.

POND, S. W., JR. 1893. *Two Volunteer Missionaries among the Dakotas, or the Story of the Labors of Samuel W. and Gideon H. Pond.* Congregational Sunday-School and Publishing Society, Boston, Mass., and Chicago, Ill.

ROE, F. G. 1951. *The North American Buffalo; A Critical Study of the Species in Its Wild State.* University of Toronto Press, Toronto, Canada.

SCHOOLCRAFT, H. R. 1834. *Discovery of the Sources of the Mississippi, or Narrative of an Expedition through the Upper Mississippi to Itasca Lake, the Actual Source of This River; Embracing an Exploratory Trip through the St. Croix and Burntwood (or Broule) Rivers; in 1832.* Harper and Bros., New York, N. Y.

SCHORGER, A. W. 1942. Extinct and endangered mammals and birds of the upper Great Lakes region. *Trans. Wisconsin Acad. Sci., Arts and Letters, 34,* 23–44.

SCHORGER, A. W. 1953. The white-tailed deer in early Wisconsin. *Trans. Wisconsin Acad. Sci., Arts and Letters, 42,* 197–247.

SCHORGER, A. W. 1956. The moose in early Wisconsin. *Trans. Wisconsin Acad. Sci., Arts and Letters, 45,* 1–10.

STENLUND, M. H. 1955. *A Field Study of the Timber Wolf (Canis lupus) on the Superior National Forest, Minnesota.* Minnesota Dept. Conservation, Bur. Wildlife Development, Tech. Bull. 4. St. Paul, Minn.

STENLUND, M. H. 1956. How to produce deer. *Conservation Volunteer, 19,* 33–36.

STENLUND, M. H., and V. E. GUNVALSON. 1957. Grass, brush, trees—deer range. *Conservation Volunteer, 20,* May-June.

SWIFT, E. 1946. *A History of Wisconsin Deer.* Wisconsin Conservation Dept., Publ. 323. Madison, Wis.

TALIAFERRO, L. 1821–1839. Journals. 13 vols., 2 letterbooks. MSS Dept., Minnesota Historical Society, St. Paul, Minn.

TYRRELL, J. B., editor. 1916. *David Thompson's Narrative of His Explorations in Western America 1784–1812.* Champlain Society, Toronto, Canada.

WHC. 1855–1931. *Collections of the State Historical Society of Wisconsin.* 31 vols. Madison, Wis.

WILLIAMS, M. L., editor. 1953. *Narrative Journal of Travels through the Northwestern Regions of the United States Extending from Detroit through the Great Chain of American Lakes to the Sources of the Mississippi River in the Year 1820, Henry R. Schoolcraft.* Michigan State College Press, East Lansing, Mich.

Southern Athabaskan Herding Patterns and Contrasting Social Institutions

PETER KUNSTADTER

*Department of Sociology and Anthropology, Princeton University,
Princeton, New Jersey*

THIS PAPER deals with two related questions. Over thirty years ago Reichard stated the first of these: "Why did the Navajo take to the life of the shepherd whereas the Apache did not?" (1928, p. 157).[1] This question has not yet been satisfactorily answered, but we are able to bring a bit more evidence to bear than was Reichard. Secondly, we shall have some things to say about the effects of livestock on the cultures involved. In this paper we shall limit our discussion primarily to the residents of the Mescalero Apache reservation and their ancestors, as contrasted with the Navahos. We shall consider only the past hundred or hundred and twenty years, because this is the period during which livestock have come to be of major importance to these people.

We shall first examine the data to see if, in fact, the problems exist, that is, whether there are any differences with respect to the use of livestock among these groups, and whether the groups differ in any respect which might be the result of differences in use of

---

[1] Reichard's answer was that the Apaches held more strongly than did the Navahos to a common tradition of destruction of property at the death of the owner, thereby precluding the accumulation of large herds. This suggestion seems empirically inaccurate, and logically begs the question of why the difference exists.

livestock. Next we shall consider a series of variables—cultural, historical, and ecological—and try to relate them to patterns of livestock use. In examining the Southern Athabaskans, the southwestern Apaches and Navahos, we are making use of Eggan's suggested method of controlled comparison, that is, we are limiting our comparisons to groups which share many features, in order to isolate significant differences with reference to our particular problem (Eggan, 1954).

INTERGROUP DIFFERENCES

One question which arises immediately concerns the facts of the case: was Reichard correct in assuming that the Navahos have adopted the "life of the shepherd" while the Apaches have not? In other words, to what extent does the problem really exist? or how much of a difference are we really trying to explain? We can use several types of information in trying to answer this question: economic reliance on livestock, diversification of economy related to livestock, patterns of herding, internal or external exchanges of livestock, relations of livestock to annual rounds of activity, and influences on religion and belief systems.

It is difficult to get quantitative estimates of the degree of reliance on livestock for income or for foodstuffs. During the early 1950's the Mescalero Apaches derived as much as 35 per cent of their total personal income from the sale of cattle (Kunstadter et al., 1956, 3, 87; Kunstadter, 1961). In the same years, the proportion of Navaho income from livestock, primarily sheep, was only about 12 per cent at the most (Kunstadter et al., 1956, 2, 169; Navajo Yearbook). These figures require some explanation. In the first place, Navaho reliance on sheep as a major economic resource has been declining since it reached a high point, probably in the 1920's. Secondly, although the Mescaleros eat practically none of their livestock, Navaho families are known to rely heavily on mutton, when available, as a favored foodstuff. Some Navaho residence groups may slaughter sheep as often as twenty times per year, which would imply hidden (nonmonetary) increase in reliance on sheep to as much as 20 per cent of the total. Likewise it should be pointed out that cattle prices in the early 1950's were abnormally high, and the figure given for the Mescaleros probably represents a maximum for income from cattle.

The Navahos depend heavily on their own sheep for meat, and to a certain extent on their goats for milk. On the other hand, the Apaches are much more likely to purchase their meat from the store, for reasons we shall discuss later. Also, the Mescaleros make virtually no use of secondary products of livestock, such as hides or milk, whereas the Navahos make extensive use of wool in making rugs. The absence of such activity among the Mescaleros cannot be explained on the basis of ignorance of the necessary techniques. Leatherwork, which traditionally was practiced with buckskin, remains only as a minor art, except in costumes for the female puberty rites, where buckskin, not cowhide, is still used. Navahos were actually imported to teach the Mescaleros rug weaving, but the innovation was not successful (RCIA, 1897, p. 193). Both groups slaughter animals on ceremonial occasions, but among the Apaches the cattle are likely to belong to the tribe, whereas Navaho ceremonial sheep are almost always individually owned.[2]

The patterns of herding among the two groups are quite different. Among the Navahos, sheep are herded by individuals or family units, with the owner or his relatives maintaining close control over his own stock. The unit of operation is the family herd. Among the Apaches, on the other hand, cattle are run by a cattle growers' association. The individual owner often has no direct control over his livestock, which are mixed in with a larger herd, and usually located at a great distance from the owner's residence. By contrast with the Navaho, the Apache stock owner cannot butcher an animal whenever he wants to. He must apply to the association for permission to slaughter, and he must wait until one of the cowboys happens across a steer with the proper brand. Likewise, the individual cannot sell his cattle whenever he wants, but must wait for the annual or semiannual auction, at which time outside bidders come onto the reservation to purchase the

---

[2] Is the presence of readily slaughtered foodstuff one explanation for the far greater development of public ceremonialism among the Navaho as contrasted with the Apaches?

cattle. Among the Apaches, livestock are individually owned, but not individually controlled.

The annual round of activity is little influenced by livestock among the Apaches. A few extra cowboy jobs may be available during roundup or sale times, but these jobs are temporary, and are not a major source of income. By contrast, among the Navahos, lambing and shearing times are periods of great activity, during which other occupations, for instance off-reservation wage work, are delayed or suspended. As will be explained later, neither group makes any extensive movement of place of residence in connection with the requirements of the livestock for feed, water, or shelter.

The influence of livestock on religion is remarkably slight in all Athabaskan groups. We have mentioned that meat is considered to be appropriate ceremonial food, but it seems to have no special import beyond this. Among the Apaches one class of shamans specialized in the treatment of diseases which are associated with horses, for example, injuries caused by falls from or kicks by horses, and this power may have been extended with reference to other domesticated animals (Opler, 1941, p. 206). Although these shamans were supposed to have the power to be successful with livestock, there is no indication that they practiced magic for the increase of their own or other people's animals. Among the Navahos there is practically no ceremonial mention of domesticated animals, although agriculture forms an important and well integrated part of their ritual life.

In summary, the evidence points to the somewhat curious conclusion that although livestock are more important monetarily to the Apaches, they play a much more significant part in the life of the Navahos, and apparently have done so for the past eighty years or so. How can this difference be explained?

We can discuss three kinds of variables in relation to the observed differences in herding: patterns of cultural and social organization prior to the reservation period; history of contact with other societies; and differences in local ecology or environment. As we have mentioned, the selection of our cases controls as many variables as possible: differences in pre-reservation culture, historical contacts, and ecology are small.

PRE-RESERVATION CULTURE AND SOCIAL ORGANIZATION

We shall consider the following dimensions of variability in comparing pre-reservation Apache and Navaho cultures: economy, types of functional social groupings, and belief systems.

Economy

With respect to the economy, it seems clear that the Navahos were more agricultural than the Apaches, while the Apaches were more dependent on hunting, especially buffalo hunting, and the gathering of wild vegetal foods (cf., e.g., Hill, 1938; Opler, 1941). This point should not be stressed too strongly, since the Apaches were to a certain extent agricultural, and the Navahos did hunt and gather to supplement their agricultural food production. Both groups also relied to a certain extent on raids on Spanish and Indian communities to supplement their economies, and also engaged in trade with these groups; both took captives as slaves; and both could have learned agricultural and herding techniques from Pueblo or Spanish sources, either through trade or through capture.

Before the reservation period, the greater reliance by the Apaches on hunting and gathering was apparently reflected in considerably more mobility than was found among the Navahos; for example, the Apaches were more or less continually on the move in their food quest, making trips onto the Great Plains for buffalo, into the desert for mescal roots, and into the mountains for such things as wild potatoes. Usually the Apaches "holed up" in approximately the same mountain location each winter. By contrast, the Navahos were apparently less nomadic, as indicated by their use of more permanent dwellings—hogans (mud-covered frame structures) as compared with the Apache wickiup (brush shelter) or tepee. The Navahos moved less frequently, perhaps only twice a year, between the lower elevations where their agricultural fields were located in the summer, and the higher elevations where wood was more readily available for fuel in the winter.

Social Groupings

We can also detect some differences in the social groupings of Navahos and Apaches, although there are many over-all similarities (cf. Opler, 1936b; Carr *et al.*, 1939). In general the groupings of the Navahos seem to have been more permanent and better defined than were those of the Apaches. Apache groupings were as follows: At the lowest level were the nuclear families, rarely polygynous, usually found grouped into matrilineally extended (matrilocal) families, or "encampments." The encampment was composed of several nuclear families which tended to camp and move together, and among which there was cooperation in economic production, distribution, and consumption. This was not a property-holding group, nor did it have formal political unity or leadership. Encampments were apparently subject to fission and fusion for reasons of economy or personality. "Bands" were named groupings which tended to be territorially distinct, which tended to be endogamous, and within which membership was supposed to be inherited and permanent. However, intermarriage between bands occasionally took place, and encampments from one band sometimes visited, stayed with, and cooperated economically with groups from other bands. Bands were not property-holding groups, except in the sense that they controlled access to useful wild products within a given area, and, at least just before the reservation period, may have controlled access to valuable irrigable agricultural lands. Bands did not have unified political leadership, and bands might also be subject to fission and fusion.

"Tribes" may not have been recognized as such by the pre-reservation Apaches. "Tribes" consisted of several bands, speaking a common dialect, and sharing minor cultural features, such as shoe or dress styles. Like the bands, they were supposed to be territorially distinct (Opler, 1955), but the historical record indicates that members of different tribes occasionally visited with and cooperated economically with members of other tribes. Likewise, although there was never supposed to be fighting within a single tribe, in fact feuds occurred within a single band of a tribe, and members of different tribes sometimes cooperated in warfare. In any case, tribes had neither political unity nor centralized political leadership, and did not exercise anything but the vaguest control over economic resources.

The Eastern Apaches (Jicarilla, Mescalero, Chiricahua) did not have clans, but the Western Apaches (San Carlos, White Mountain, etc.) did (Goodwin, 1935, 1942).

At the present time the Apache band does not exist, except in the memories of older persons; it is definitely not a functional unit. The typical residence pattern is now one of neolocal, nuclear families, although some extended groupings are found. These usually consist of matrilineally linked relatives, and they only rarely cooperate for economic production. Most of the population today is concentrated around the agency town of Mescalero, and movement of the population is toward this center. However, there are some small farming "communities," located in small cultivable valleys, which are still inhabited.

The modern tribe among the Apaches is a federally chartered corporation, organized under the Indian Reorganization Act (IRA). The elected governing body, known as the "Business Committee," derives historically from attempts by the Mescaleros to gain control over reservation resources, such as timber, which were not being used by tribal members, but which were salable to the rest of the world. The Business Committee was a more or less informal group of leaders until it was granted legal status under the IRA. Today the Business Committee functions primarily in the area of economic dealings with the rest of the world. Its functions of maintaining order within the reservation are not universally respected.

The basic functional units of Navaho society are as follows: the household, the residence group, the residential lineage (or "outfit"), the band (or community?), the clan, linked clans, and the tribe. With minor exceptions, these pre-reservation social groupings have persisted during the reservation period. The Navaho household is usually composed of a nuclear family, although another relative may be included in the group. The household is sometimes polygynous, sororal polygyny being the preferred type. Marriage is usually matrilocal, and the "residence groups" often represent the results of matrilocal marriages (i.e., they are matrilineal extended families). The residence groups cooperate economically in production, distribution, and consumption, and ordinarily act as a unit in managing the individually owned livestock. Land use rights belong to the individual using the land, but residence units will usually be cultivating adjacent fields. Thus, although the residence group is not strictly a property-*owning* group, it does seem to be a property-*managing* unit. At the next level of organization is the residential lineage, or "outfit." This level may not in fact be a distinct one in all parts of the reservation (Adams, 1958; Hill, 1938, p. 28; Kimball and Provinse, 1942; Kluckhohn and Leighton, 1951, pp. 59, 62–63). Whereas the "residence group" usually consists of several hogans, all within hailing distance of one another, the "outfit" is a larger group, which has grown up around a single large sheep-owning family. The outfits have sometimes been referred to as land use communities, since they cooperate in the land use of as much as 12,000 to 80,000 acres, with members coming together during times of extensive labor, for example, in plowing, sheep dipping, lambing, and shearing. Large outfits are apparently a recent (reservation period) development, relating to the concentration of a large number of livestock in the hands of a family with too few individuals to manage them adequately. The outfits are not necessarily geographically contiguous units.

Kluckhohn and Leighton mention the "band" as a significant non-kin social group (1951, pp. 68–69) and suggest that modern communities, or settlements, are the successors of this level of organization. Today these communities are frequently centered around a trading post (Adams, 1958). This unit is not definitely bounded geographically, but is defined more in relation to services which are located with the trading post, such as schools. It is not ordinarily a property-owning or cooperating group, though it may act as a political unit in electing a representative to the tribal council. Although such a community might have a respected spokesman (who would not ordinarily be the elected representative) , this person could lead only by consensus.

"Clans" are named, exogamous matrilineal descent groups which tend to be localized in the sense that a high proportion of any one clan may be concentrated in a single area of the reservation, though it is not restricted to that area.[3] Clans are linked, or associated with other clans, into phratries (unnamed) , which are exogamous. Although the literature clearly indicates that clans were exogamous units, other attributes of the clan are not clear. Thus, although clans were not completely localized, and did not share or own common property (e.g., they had neither a clan meeting house nor clan ceremonies) , nor have clan officers, nevertheless they are supposed to have functioned (or still function) in the payment of the blood price (Reichard, 1928; Haile, 1954, pp. 5–9) .[4]

The Navaho "tribe" did not exist aboriginally as a political unit, but represented a group sharing a common language, culture, and territory. As with the Apaches, the Navaho tribal council was created in the 1920's to handle previously unallocated communal resources, primarily oil (Haile, 1954, p. 2) . The tribal government was supported and molded by the Indian Reorganization Act, in spite of the fact that the group never officially accepted a Federal charter. The tribe today attempts rather unsuccessfully to control individuals' use of communal property, especially grazing land.

As compared with the Mescalero Apache concrete social groupings, Navaho society seems to have had more levels of groupings, and at least some of these groupings appear to have been more solidary with respect to the handling of economic goods and the rendering of economic services. These solidary groups also appear to have persisted more successfully, and in some cases expanded among the Navaho during the reservation period.

[3] This is exactly what one would expect, given matrilineal descent, clan exogamy, matrilocal residence, and an expanding, semimobile population.

[4] This must be an error in interpretation. It is probable that matrilineally related persons in a given locality were responsible for the blood price for one of their number, and since they were matrilineally related they shared a common clan; but their obligation was probably not merely by virtue of their *clan* membership.

Kinship terminologies of the Southern Athabaskans apparently reflect the greater solidarity of the matrilineal descent group among the Navahos, who have an Iroquois terminology system, as compared with the Chiricahua and Mescalero, who have matri-Hawaiian systems (Opler, 1936*b*; Murdock, 1949, pp. 334, 341; Bellah, 1952).

Belief Systems

The belief systems of the Navahos and Apaches seem in general to have been rather similar. The general range of religious beliefs of the Athabaskans was similar, for example, with respect to the general nature of the spirit world, causation of diseases, witchcraft, fear of and avoidance of the dead, and so forth. Attitudes with respect to property seem to have varied somewhat, although this aspect of the belief system has not been as well studied in Apache groups as among the Navahos. Among the Navahos it is clear that ownership of productive resources tended to be a personal thing, although the residence group had a claim on the property of any of its members, especially during times of scarcity and need. Conscious attempts were made among the Navahos to start a child's herd by giving him several sheep, which, with their increases thenceforth, would be considered as definitely belonging to the child, whether or not he actually tended them himself. This pattern does not seem to have existed, or at least was not as definitely established, among the Apaches. For the Apaches, ownership seems to have been established more exclusively by *use*. In the early days livestock were not frequently kept for their increase, but instead might be merely impounded for later slaughter, in which case the ownership resided with the captor (e.g., Opler, 1941, p. 327).

There are no entirely clear rules of inheritance of property among the Navahos, a situation which occasionally leads to disputes (Kluckhohn and Leighton, 1951, pp. 59–62; Haile, 1954, p. 51). Livestock have usually been distributed to the children before the death of a parent—the wife does not usually share in the husband's estate; there is a matrilineal bias in the distribution of the estate of an individual who dies without a (verbal) will, which probably results from the fact that the property is more likely to be administered by matrilineal relatives, since women retain their sheep in their own herds, and men frequently are required to leave their sheep with their parents' herd when they move away at marriage. Some property, for example jewelry, a horse, the dwelling, may be destroyed or abandoned at the death of the owner, but there is no wholesale slaughter of livestock, nor abandonment of productive property, such as agricultural fields.

The traditional Apache pattern of inheritance is not adequately described in the literature. At present, inheritance tends to be bilateral, but inheritance of livestock is frequently the subject of litigation in the tribal court. The problem cannot be easily resolved by the individual actions of the potential heirs, since they do not ordinarily have physical control over the livestock, which are run by a cattle growers' association. The traditional pattern of destruction of property at death is illustrated by Opler's quotation from a Chiricahua informant:

They kill the horse that has carried the dead person's possessions [to the grave]. . . . If a man has several horses sometimes they kill them all; sometimes only his favorite horse or horses, the ones he actually used all the time. . . . They don't kill all the horses of a family though. All the horses of a family are not thought of as belonging to one person, even to the man who is the head of that family. If a family has five or six horses, one is considered the property of a child, another of the wife, and so on. A man might not be considered to possess more than one or two horses of his own. These are his favorites and the ones he always used, and they are killed at his death (Opler, 1941, p. 474) .[5]

At present there is no destruction of livestock at the death of the owner. The house where the deceased person lived may be abandoned temporarily, but is usually reoccupied by the survivors, sometimes with some external modification such as repainting, so the survivors "will not be reminded of the dead person."

[5] This quotation indicates the inaccuracy of Reichard's contention that stock raising was prevented among the Apaches by strict adherence to the rule of property destruction. Livestock were destroyed, but not all the livestock of a given family were destroyed at the death of the head of the household.

HISTORICAL FACTORS

Under historical factors we shall consider gross population movements involved in the conquest situation and the establishment of the present reservations. We shall also consider external intervention in Southern Athabaskan livestock practices.

The history of contact with other societies appears to be generally comparable among the Mescalero, Chiricahua, and Jicarilla Apaches and the Navahos.[6] All these groups had extensive raiding and trading contacts with Pueblo Indians before the American conquest (which began in the 1840's and was not completed until the 1880's), although the Navahos had more permanent contact and intermarriage with them than did the Apache groups. Likewise, trading and raiding experience with the Spanish appears to have been roughly similar. With the coming of the Americans into the Southwest in the mid nineteenth century, all the Apache groups were subdued by military force; the Eastern Apaches were displaced, at least temporarily, the Mescaleros being removed from their location around the present Alamogordo, New Mexico, to the Bosque Redondo reservation on the Pecos River. They were temporarily joined there by the Navahos who had been forced to take "the long march" from northwestern New Mexico and northeastern Arizona. Eventually both these groups were allowed to return to permanent reservations within their traditional ranges. The Chiricahuas were moved several times to various reservations in Arizona and New Mexico, and finally were taken to Florida in 1886, thence to Alabama, and thence to Oklahoma; after 1913 they were again relocated, half of them remaining in Oklahoma, and the remainder joining the Mescaleros in New Mexico. They were under close military supervision as prisoners of war between 1886 and 1913. In the early 1880's the Jicarillas were removed from their traditional New Mexico location, and were placed on the Mescalero reservation for several years before being sent back to a reservation close to their original range. The effects of the conquest period included military conquest and mili-

---

[6] The Western Apaches were more isolated and did not suffer as much physical displacement from their original habitats.

tary subjugation; movement of the populations from their traditional locations to temporary reservations; return of the populations to a reduced portion of their traditional range.[7]

The effects of the enforced movements of the Athabaskan populations were clearly felt in their livestock herds. The animals were
usually taken away from the Indians when they were moved, and
destruction of the herds was one of the specific aims of the conquest. It seems clear that this affected the Apache groups more
than it did the Navahos, since control over the Navahos was never
as complete as it was over some of the smaller Apache groups.
Apparently some of the Navahos were able to hide out in the
mountains and hidden valleys, retaining their livestock, while
their relatives were taken to Bosque Redondo. With the Apaches
the roundup of people and livestock was much more complete.

After the conquest and subjugation of the Southern Athabaskans, it was general government policy to issue livestock and encourage herding and farming. Among the Navahos these issues
of livestock were supplementing a going concern, whereas the
Apaches were starting over from scratch. It is also clear from the
literature that the Navahos (Hill, 1938) and the Jicarilla Apaches
(Opler, 1936a) were much more agricultural during the early his-
toric period than were, for example, the Mescaleros or the Chiricahuas (Kunstadter, 1961). The first years after the permanent
reservations were established were very difficult ones economically.
It is not surprising then that the Navahos, and possibly also the
Jicarilla Apaches, were able to retain some of their livestock, by
being able to subsist on their agricultural produce. The rest of
the Apaches frequently consumed the stock which were issued to
them, rather than allow the stock to live and increase. Thus the
mixed economy of agriculture and stock herding, which acts to
reduce the efficiency of herding among the contemporary Navahos,
may have been of great survival value during the particularly hard
times of the early reservation period (see below).

We should not neglect to mention the conditions which ob-

---

[7] The amount of land in the reservations was such that there were about 1000
acres per capita as of 1900. Population increase since that time has greatly reduced
the per capita amount of land.

tained before the time when the reservations were established.
The Indian settlements were subject to raids by other Indians or
by the Spanish, in which livestock were one of the favorite types
of booty. The Navaho herding pattern, which returned the livestock home every night, and which did not involve movements of
more than a mile or two during the daytime, was probably advantageous in protecting the herds against loss, before the pacifica-
tion of the region.

Ecological Factors in Athabaskan Herding Patterns

The differences in natural resources which were available to
Athabaskans for herding were relatively minor. All the Athabaskans' reservations cover wide ranges of ecological variation, with
respect to altitude and its concomitant rainfall and ground cover,
and with respect to available surface water (Castetter, 1956). In
terms of actual settlements, the permanent camping places of the
Apaches seem to have been at a slightly higher, wetter, and colder
elevation than those of the Navahos. The Navahos tended to settle
in lower, wider valleys, where water was available for agriculture,
and where the growing season was sufficiently long to grow corn.
If anything, this difference in location should have favored stock
raising among the Apaches, because of the greater availability of
grazing land.

We have already indicated that the extent to which the Navahos
have integrated sheep into their economy is much greater than
that to which livestock have become a part of the lives of Apach-
ean groups. We should mention that the Navahos have actually
been criticized because their way of life is *not* optimally adapted
to herding (e.g., Adams, 1958). The Navaho reservation has been
subject to considerable local overgrazing, whereas the reservation
as a whole may actually be understocked.[8] Erosion has been intensified by repeated passage of large numbers of sheep over the

---

[8] See, e.g., *The Navaho Yearbook,* 1955, pp. 190–191. The figures indicate that the
Navaho range is carrying about 10 per cent less than the optimal number of livestock; some areas are as much as 46 per cent over optimal carrying capacity, while
others are as much as 29 per cent under capacity.

same paths. Apparently at least two patterns of herding exist. In one, found in the western part of the reservation, the sheep are moved out to graze every morning, and may be returned at mid-day and then taken out again in the afternoon. They are rarely taken more than a mile or two from the permanent residence, which has been located with reference to agricultural fields, not grazing lands. Little effort is made to move the sheep to higher pastures in the summer, when grass is plentiful in the mountains. No deliberate effort is made to raise feed for the stock (Adams, 1958).

Hill gives a different description, indicating greater movement of sheep, but clearly states that herding patterns are influenced by agricultural practices:

The introduction of sheep among the Navaho created some additional monthly activities [besides those related to agriculture]. In former times when the rams were allowed to remain all year with the flocks, the lambing season came in February. Later, when the rams were separated, the lambs came in May. During this period the flocks required constant attention. May was also the time for shearing and preparing the wool for the market.

In June and July it was customary for those who owned sheep to drive their flocks to the mountains in order to escape the heat of the valleys. However, only one or two members of the family normally accompanied the flocks;[9] the rest remained at the fields. In August the sheep were brought back *so that the herders could assist with the harvest.*

. . . It is seldom necessary to take the sheep more than ten or fifteen miles in search of water, pasturage, or to escape temperature extremes. These movements can therefore hardly be classed as nomadic, as the distance travelled is not significant and the permanent household is not disrupted (Hill, 1938, p. 18; emphasis added).

Such annual migration as there is may be considered backward with respect to the ideal for livestock; annual movements of the household are determined by need for firewood.

---

[9] Under these circumstances it would definitely be advantageous to have a large cooperating group, from which one or two individuals might be selected to herd, while the remainder tended the crops.

Concerning the movements made for summer farming and winter fuel, if they are made at all the distance travelled is usually negligible. Formerly, before the removal of the timber from the lower altitudes, these moves were not made; the people staying all year around at their fields. In more recent times, since wagons have been introduced, wood is hauled to the summer residence which is then occupied all winter (*ibid*).

Recently some Navahos have begun to farm at higher altitudes, usually growing introduced European crops, such as wheat. This development, which might aid in the movement of sheep to higher elevations in the summertime, may not actually be very widespread (Hill, 1938, p. 20).

Mescalero herding practices also show a lack of adaptation to ecological conditions. The number of cattle is perhaps only 40 per cent of the optimum carrying capacity (Kunstadter, 1961, p. 207). Cattle are not moved regularly to the most favorable locations; no effort is made to feed them in the winter, government-drilled wells have not been maintained, and new ones have not been drilled to increase the amount of available range. In sum, it is evident that neither the Navahos nor the Apaches have achieved an optimum relation between their livestock and their environment.

CONCLUSIONS

What can we now say about the reasons for differences in herding patterns, and the effects of livestock on the way of life of the peoples involved?

At the time when livestock became important in the lives of the Southern Athabaskans, the Navahos had larger functional social groupings and had more levels of them. These groupings, which undoubtedly were related to the greater Navaho dependence on agriculture, had beneficial effects with respect to herding, and in turn seem to have been reinforced or supported by herding: (1) There was a larger locally available supply of unskilled "free" labor (women and children) for the minimal ordinary tasks of herding. (2) There were larger cooperating groups for periods of intensive labor (lambing and shearing). (3) There was probably some mutual protection against raiders by virtue of the large group size.

Cooperation in these larger groups was assured by making sure that every individual, children included, had a personal, defined stake in the herd; to this end, the children were assigned a few sheep with which to start their holdings.

The choice of sheep as contrasted with cattle may have been a particularly fortunate one for the Navahos. This is somewhat paradoxical, since cattle would seem to be better adapted to the southwestern environment than sheep. It is often the case that although grass is available, surface water sources are widely dispersed; and cattle are able to go greater distances for water than are sheep. In addition, under most circumstances cattle will survive without close supervision, in a more or less wild state, whereas sheep need much more protection and apparently are unable to survive or reproduce successfully in the wild.

There appear to be some advantages with sheep, however, given the Navahos' existing type of technology: (1) Their wool and hides are more usable, given native technology. (2) The meat comes in "small packages" which can be consumed by a family without undue spoilage, and less suprafamilial distribution of the single animal is necessary or desirable than would be the case with a larger animal, such as a steer. (3) Conversely, the smallness of capital investment in a *single* sheep allows widespread cooperation and sharing of meat (for ceremonial occasions), with moderate expenditure, as compared with the expenditure necessary with cattle. Where cattle are herded in subsistence economies, they are only rarely killed for meat. More frequent exchanges (or "prestations") are possible with sheep than with cattle, for a given amount of animal protein.[10]

Why didn't the Apaches raise sheep? The Mescalero Apaches were encouraged to do so several times, and issues of sheep were made to heads of household in the 1890's, and again in the

---

[10] If this is an illustration of a general principle, there is probably a minimum size of significant animal exchanges; e.g., the giving of guinea pigs probably would not have the same effect as the exchange of sheep.

1920's.[11] For a time some Apache sheepherders were quite successful, but the occupation was not a favored one. There was some
direct intervention in sheepherding in the period from 1910 to
1920, when unsuccessful sheepherders were forced by the Indian
agent to turn over their sheep to the more successful herders, in
exchange for a share in the profits. Likewise, there were policy
changes which favored the raising of cattle or horses, rather than
sheep and goats, and at times the Apaches were encouraged to
turn in their sheep in exchange for cattle. The fact that the reservation was relatively small probably helped in the agent's attempt
to maintain control over the type of stock which were herded.
The reasons for the shift in policy are not entirely clear, although
in part it may have been due to pressure from cattlemen in the
surrounding areas who were prejudiced against sheep.

In addition, the Apaches did not like to herd sheep. Some of
them hired "Mexicans" to do this work for them. The Indians
complained that it was very difficult to control the sheep, especially when they got into the underbrush on the sides of the
steeper mountain canyons. The Indians also complained about
the bitter cold of the winter, and the amount of personal attention
that the sheep required.

Another factor probably related to lack of success in herding
was the Apache settlement pattern during the reservation period,
which saw the dwellings bunched up more closely than they had
been in pre-reservation times, and much more closely than in the
usual Navaho sheep-raising settlement.

Ownership of cattle has apparently had very little effect on
Apache social structure. Since the Apaches do not have direct control of their individually owned cattle, modifications of dwelling
arrangements or inheritance patterns have no effect on the cattle.
Likewise, the pattern of cattle herding is not related to any conceivable form of kinship cooperation, and cattle have remained
peripheral to the social structure in spite of their economic importance.

---

[11] Sheep were issued at the rate of 10 per capita in 1897 (RCIA, 1897, p. 193) ; 10
sheep or 20 goats were issued per capita in 1924 (RIRA, 1924, p. 14). See Kunstadter,
1961, pp. 100–104, 194–196, for further details.

REFERENCES

ADAMS, W. Y. 1958. Shonto: A study of the role of the trader in a modern Navaho community. Doctoral dissertation, University of Arizona.

BELLAH, R. N. 1952. *Apache Kinship Systems.* Harvard University Press, Cambridge, Mass.

CARR, M., K. SPENCER, and D. WOOLLEY. 1939. Navaho clans and marriage at Pueblo Alto. *Am. Anthropologist, 41,* 245–257.

CASTETTER, E. F. 1956. The vegetation of New Mexico. The University of New Mexico Third Annual Research Lecture. *New Mexico Quart., 26* (3) , 257–288.

EGGAN, F. 1954. Social anthropology and the method of controlled comparisons. *Am. Anthropologist, 56,* 743–763.

GOODWIN, G. 1935. The social divisions and economic life of the Western Apache. *Am. Anthropologist, 37,* 55–64.

GOODWIN, G. 1942. *The Social Organization of the Western Apache.* University of Chicago Press, Chicago, Ill.

HAILE, B. 1954. *Property Concepts of the Navaho Indians.* Catholic University of America Anthropol. Ser. No. 17. Catholic University of America Press, Washington, D. C.

HILL, W. W. 1938. *The Agricultural and Hunting Methods of the Navaho Indians.* Yale University Publ. Anthropol. No. 18. Yale University Press, New Haven, Conn.

KIMBALL, S. T., and J. H. PROVINSE. 1942. Navaho social organization in land use planning. *Appl. Anthropol., 1* (4) , 18–25.

KLUCKHOHN, C., and D. LEIGHTON. 1951. *The Navaho.* Harvard University Press, Cambridge, Mass.

KUNSTADTER, P. 1961. *Culture Change, Social Structure, and Health Behavior; A Quantitative Study of Clinic Use among the Apaches of the Mescalero Reservation.* University Microfilms, Ann Arbor, Mich.

KUNSTADTER, P., W. H. KELLY, and R. A. HACKENBERG. 1956. *Social and Economic Resources Available for Indian Health Purposes in Five Southwestern States.* University of Arizona, Bureau of Ethnic Research, Tucson, Ariz.

MURDOCK, G. P. 1949. *Social Structure.* The Macmillan Co., New York, N. Y.

The Navaho Yearbook of Planning in Action (compiled by R. W. Young) . Navaho Agency, Window Rock, Ariz.

OPLER, M. E. 1936a. A summary of Jicarilla Apache culture. *Am. Anthropologist, 38,* 202–223.

OPLER, M. E. 1936b. The kinship systems of the southern Athabaskan-speaking tribes. *Am. Anthropologist, 38,* 620–633.

OPLER, M. E. 1941. *An Apache Life-Way.* University of Chicago Press, Chicago, Ill.

OPLER, M. E. 1955. An outline of Chiricahua Apache social organization. In *Social Anthropology of North American Indian Tribes* (F. Eggan, editor), enlarged edition, pp. 172–239. University of Chicago Press, Chicago, Ill.

RCIA. *Annual Report of the Commissioner of Indian Affairs.* Government Printing Office, Washington, D. C.

REICHARD, G. A. 1928. *Social Life of the Navaho Indians.* Columbia University Contr. Anthropol., vol. 7. Columbia University Press, New York, N. Y.

RIRA. *Annual Report of the Indian Rights Association.* Philadelphia, Pa.

Reindeer Herding and Chukchi Social Institutions

ANTHONY LEEDS

Department of Anthropology, The University of Texas, Austin, Texas

IN THIS WORK, I shall attempt rather to outline a model of what I conceive to be the ecological situation among the Chukchi than to give full documentation. I shall assume for the purposes of this paper that the family—a man, his wife, and his children—comprise a minimal, permanent operative social unit, at least in the absence of the institutions of the state.

The Chukchi, as of the time, about 1900, when Waldemar Bogoras (-Tan) was last in that area, were found between 155° east and 170° west longitudes, that is, between the Chukchi River and the Bering Strait, and between 63° and 70° north latitudes.[1] Their taking possession of this area resulted from a steady expansion of the Chukchi to the west and south in the past three centuries, since originally they were found only in a very small part of the tract in the northeast. The expansion is assertedly related to the increase in the size of reindeer herds (Bogoras,[2] p. 15), their fundamental source of subsistence, throughout the area, though Bogoras (*ibid.*, p. 732) also attributes the spread to continued vigor and war successes of the Chukchi under conditions in which neighboring tribes were being weakened by Russian acculturation. The evidence, however, is not conclusive that the absolute number of

---

[1] I have been unable to get any detailed map of the area whatsoever. The accompanying maps are based on several in Bogoras (1904–1909), e.g. p. 17 and insert map at end of part I (1904); on the map in Hammond's *Atlas;* on *Karta Narodov* (1956); and finally on the "Ethnographic Map of Siberia" reproduced in Levin and Potapov (1956).

[2] Unless otherwise indicated, "Bogoras" refers to Bogoras, 1904–1909.

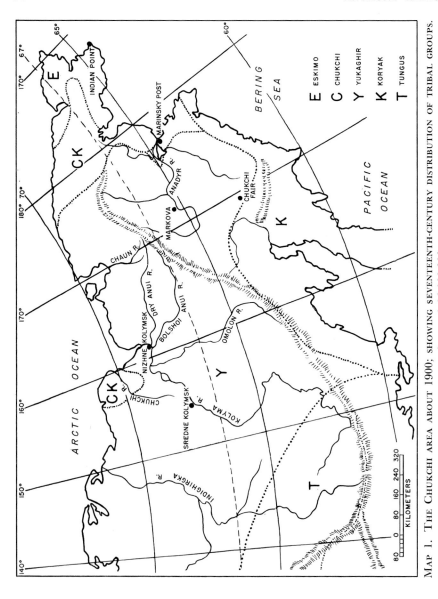

MAP 1. THE CHUKCHI AREA ABOUT 1900; SHOWING SEVENTEENTH-CENTURY DISTRIBUTION OF TRIBAL GROUPS.
SCALE, 1:16,000,000

Sources: Bogoras, 1904–1909, page 17 and end plate, part 1; Hammond *Atlas*; Dolgikh, 1960

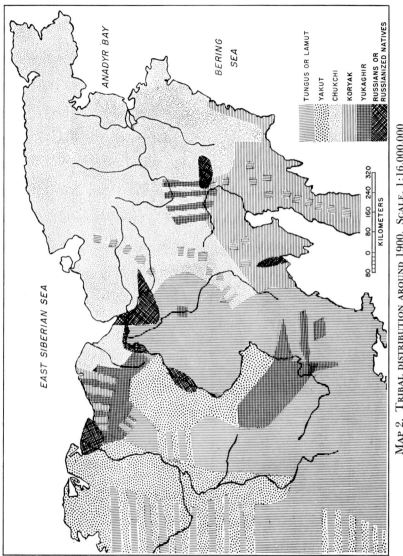

MAP 2. TRIBAL DISTRIBUTION AROUND 1900. SCALE, 1:16,000,000

Sources: Bogoras, 1904–1909, end plate, part 1; Levin and Potapov, 1956, "Ethnographic Map of Siberia"; *Karta Narodov*, 1956

reindeer in the area as a whole grew greatly, although there appear to have been at least some increases, possibly periodic (see
below). The Chukchi expansion from the early nineteenth century on occurred at the expense of the Lamut and others who were
driven back while their herds were captured. The Chukchi also
took over what had been a no man's land between them and the
Koryak, with whom they had been more or less continuously at
war (*ibid.,* p. 15). Still others intermingled and assimilated with
Koryak groups (*ibid.,* p. 16). Thus, it seems clear that the Chukchi increased their reindeer holdings immensely, regardless of
whether the absolute total increase was large or small.

It should be noted in this connection that the rather ambiguous
human population figures for past periods do not indicate an increase among the Chukchi corresponding to the increase in their
reindeer holdings. Rather, they appear to have spread out more,
to have been more securely supplied with reindeer, less dependent
upon emergency resources from the sea—with whose littoral habitat
a symbiotic relation was maintained[3]—and finally better adapted
to conditions of reindeer herding. The conditions will be made
clear in what follows, and their relationships with various Chukchi social institutions discussed.

We may turn first to the relationship between environmental
factors and herd size. Bogoras discusses herd sizes at some length.
It can clearly be inferred from his data and from the corresponding, though semifictionalized, data in Odulok (1934) that, within
relatively narrow ranges, maximum and minimum feasible herd
sizes can be delimited with a relatively wide range of optimal herd
sizes falling between the maxima and minima. The variations of
all these ranges depend upon both synchronic and diachronic
ecosystemic variations in climate, topography, pasture, and pests
affecting the reindeer.

---

[3] The Maritime and Reindeer Chukchi have usually been considered separate
subdivisions of the same tribe. I shall undertake to show in a later paper that this
is not the case. Sea resources provided an emergency stabilizer in the relationship
between man, reindeer food, and environment under stress conditions. Though a
part of the Chukchi stayed permanently on the coast, there was, nevertheless, a continual oscillation of the population, in the areas near the sea, between reindeer and
sea resources, depending primarily on the variations in size of the reindeer herds.

Minimum Limits of Herd Size

Let us first consider the range of minimal limits of herd size. Given the family as minimal social unit (see Bogoras, p. 569, who specifically asserts that the married couple is the basic socio-economic unit), the minimal herd size is determined by the amount of food, here mainly reindeer meat and products, that such a family consumes in a year, and by the number of animals, especially does, needed to supply that amount continuously through the years. That is, a herd may be considered as consisting of a nonconsumable part serving to maintain or increase the herd, and a consumable part whose use reduces the herd. If the consumable part becomes too small over any length of time, the nonconsumable part is endangered by the hunger of the owners. If the latter part is reduced by inclement weather, disease, animal or human predators, or dispersion, then the entire herd is endangered, and with it, of course, the very lives of the family.

As a rule, the Chukchi can use reindeer only for meat, since, given the limited food supply available to reindeer in the tundra, the consequently reduced amount of does' milk must be left for the fawns (Bogoras, pp. 71, 78, 84). Milking the does endangers the lives of the fawns, so reindeer milk provides only an occasional treat. The use of reindeer for meat, of course, means slaughtering them, except for an occasional tidbit of antler skin cut off with a knife.

In consequence, a minimal continuing reindeer herd consists of (a) a permanent segment of breeding does; (b) several stud bucks; (c) a number of gelded beasts used for transporting the household effects by sledge as the herd moves from pasture to pasture, and also sometimes used for hunting; (d) a sufficient number of other animals, mainly bucks, to slaughter for food throughout the year; (e) a few "fattened" barren does and "fattened bucks," the latter ranging from a very few up to a number equal to that of the does (Bogoras, p. 79). Some of the "fattened bucks" appear to be geldings, not studs; their role in the herd dynamics and hence in the ecological picture is not clear, since Bogoras remarks that the Chukchi herder will kill a pregnant doe before killing a "fattened buck," and, further, that herds without "fattened large bucks" and fattened barren does look poor—all signs of wealth are gone (*ibid.*).[4] Most herds consist of at least 50 per cent does, but the percentage may be much higher, especially in larger herds. Bogoras (*ibid.*) gives as average proportions the following figures: to every 100 (breeding?) does, about 12 stud bucks, 10 to 15 sledge deer, 60 to 70 half-grown fawns (about half of which, presumably, are females), and a few "fattened bucks."

The literature does not give estimates as to the size of such minimal herds, but the internal evidence (in both Bogoras and Odulok) suggests that the range of minimum herd numbers may be between something like 70 and 100 animals for a small family. With the proportions given above, assuming 50 per cent does and no "fattened bucks," a herd of 100 would consist of 50 does, about 7 breeding bucks, 8 sledge geldings, and 35 fawns. Some of the fawns must replace does and bucks that die, run away, or are barren. In other words, there are perhaps 30 animals *a year* in a herd of this size available for the family to consume. Any undue inclemency of weather, disease, man, or animal with respect to such a herd is likely to reduce it suddenly and catastrophically below a point where it can maintain either the family or itself. Such a case is graphically described in Odulok.

Bogoras (p. 612) mentions, in passing, single men who possess herds numbering in the twenties, a number corresponding roughly

---

[4] I would offer the following hypotheses. From what precedes and follows in the text, I would suppose that the proportion of "fattened bucks" increases as total herd size increases. Herd size is, by definition, a measure of wealth, so that "fattened bucks" are, by the same token, symbols of wealth, successful herdsmanship, power, prestige, and the rights, advantages, influences, and authority pertaining thereto. At the same time, I would hypothesize that the killing of a pregnant doe would occur with greater frequency the larger the herd. As will be pointed out in discussing maximum herd limits, various means of maintaining those limits exist, and I suspect killing pregnant does may be another since it kills both the reproducing female and the unborn young (this does not apply, be it noted, to a *nonpregnant* doe, which is, as it were, kept in store for a year). This interpretation is consistent with the probably high proportion of does in larger herds. Fatness in these animals may be regarded as concentrated storage of food resources, especially against the dangerous lean season before the spring pasturing and refattening begins. However, "where the signs of wealth are gone," no preferential treatment can be given, of course, to "fattened bucks," so the "normal" killing of male animals and preserving of females would be expected.

to the minimum of seventy for a small family. He indicates that such herd-camp units have a low viability; the single men tend to join together. Bogoras repeatedly points to the essential importance of the couple or nuclear family as the minimal viable unit (pp. 537, 569–570).

In connection with the threat of herd reduction by catastrophe, it is important to observe that the herd of semidomesticated, or, better, half-tamed, animals is supplemented as food resource by wild reindeer, ordinarily "hunted" or captured by using the "tame" animals as decoys (note parallels with dingo dogs discussed in Meggitt's paper in this volume). It is most important to note that the greater the mass of the herd of "tame" deer, the easier is the capture of wild animals, while the smaller the mass, the more difficult is their acquisition, since the "tame" animals are just as likely to join the wild ones as vice versa. In fact, there is some tendency to repopulate the wild reindeer from "tame" stock, especially under stress conditions (see Bogoras, p. 82).[5] In short, the ability to utilize wild deer decreases with decreasing herd size and therefore converges at a minimum limit with minimum herd size.

Other sources of food are, at best, of tertiary importance. Most of the tundra and fluvial forest flora, except for a few seasonal berries, mushrooms, and so on, are not available regularly or at all as food supplies for human populations. Hunting supplies a more significant share of food, apparently, but, given Chukchi hunting technology, seems to be sporadic and unreliable. Furthermore, effective hunting of some of the more mobile larger animals such as wolves and foxes involves the use of sledge reindeer for running them down, hence, at least for a certain level of hunting productivity, is dependent on the existence of a minimal herd in the first place.

Several factors exist which may reduce the nonconsumable, maintenance segment of the herd below the level adequate for the viability of the minimum family-maintaining herd. Unless there

[5] A similar situation has been noted for pigs in Melanesia, in Vayda, Leeds, and Smith (1961).

is the minimal labor division of the minimum family, a husband and wife, there is, in general, no herd. Conversely, without a minimal herd there is no family (see Odulok, 1934: the family disintegrates as the herd is reduced); the minimal group necessary for socio-cultural continuity becomes nonviable. That even husband-wife units are inadequate as labor units is suggested by Bogoras' comment (p. 41) that a measles-cold epidemic in 1900 severely reduced the population of children, with the result that many herds were scattered, and also by Bogoras' innumerable references to the important herding work of children.

Reduction of herd size may occur for several reasons. Among the factors, Bogoras lists a number of insect plagues (p. 80) and what are probably virus diseases, which, in severe epidemics, may decimate or entirely eliminate a herd in a matter of days or weeks. The likelihood that the herd will be reduced beyond the point where it can regenerate is greater where the herd is smaller. Bogoras (p. 73) mentions a hoof disease epidemic in the Omolon area in 1901 which greatly reduced herds. In a bad summer, one-third to one-half of the herds may die of this disease (*ibid.*, p. 80). Bogoras (p. 81) also speaks of a "scab disease" which is rarer, but more contagious. A disease of midwinter, it causes the reindeer to die of cold and exhaustion. The disease may rage for several years, disappear, break out again. The herder kills off diseased animals, trying to avert further disaster by sacrificing to the spirit of disease. Bogoras cites a case where 3000 animals caught the disease in three days and were slaughtered (*ibid.*).

A second source of herd reduction consists of animals of prey: wolves, wolverines, and black bears, who follow the herds and prey at night. Wolves may kill several score of reindeer in a night. Human predators may be included here. Theft of animals (see Bogoras, pp. 624 ff.) and capture of stray animals both occur.

A third source of herd reduction is loss of animals, often during snowstorms, when the herdsman must stay in his house while the reindeer wander afield. Fog is the most dangerous cause of dispersion and loss (Bogoras, p. 82), especially if insects are present, since they make the animals restless. Beasts of prey may also cause loss of reindeer by dispersing them (*ibid.*, p. 81). Lost or dispersed animals may be appropriated by other herdsmen who find them or may simply return to the wild state.

It may be recalled that Chukchi reindeer are only half tamed. Though they differ slightly in appearance and morphology from the wild reindeer, they appear to have no specific traits dependent on their association with man. They interbreed freely with the wild deer, an event considered highly desirable by Chukchi herders.

That they are so poorly domesticated is the fourth source of herd reduction, namely, a permanent tendency for the tame deer to join the wild deer in the neighborhood. If the herdsman is not alert or not present at the moment of meeting between wild and tame deer, he may lose reindeer. An escaped tame reindeer is more wary than the wild animal (Bogoras, p. 82). If the herdsman is alert, he may capture wild reindeer; these are usually used for slaughter. The Call of the Wild appears to be proportionately greater for small herds than for large, and the effect much more drastic. Thus, if 10 deer from a herd of 70 are lost, the herd is reduced by 14 per cent; whereas, if 10 out of 5000 are lost, only 0.2 per cent are gone. Even with a 14 per cent loss from 5000, there is little danger to the survival of the herdsman and his camp, whereas a 14 per cent loss from a herd of 70 may be fatal to the family camp group.

A fifth source of the reduction of herds is the reduction of their food resources because of factors to be discussed below.

Certain other disadvantages of small herd size deserve mention. Small herds have few sledge beasts. Unlike their analogues in large herds, these beasts must do all the work, since there are no replacement animals. The result is that sledge reindeer in poor herds wear out quickly (Bogoras, p. 95) and the herder is pressed to find new ones among his already limited resources, or is threatened with worse danger because he is immobilized both from using his pasture resources to best advantage and from hunting.

Again, in a small herd, several days may be needed to round up the sledge beasts (ibid.), in contrast to large herds, where it is only a matter of hours. This situation results from the greater tendency of animals in small herds to return to the wild. A delay of days in moving the herd may drastically endanger both herd and camp.

Bogoras (p. 576) mentions that reindeer in old and established herds develop a strong attachment to one another which tends to hold them together. Since the turnover rate in small herds is necessarily much greater than in large herds, and the incidence of running wild is higher, establishment of attachments among the herd animals is less possible. Consequently, herd instability is reinforced, whereas in large herds stability is strengthened.

Maximum Limits of Herd Size

We turn now to the maximum limits. The largest herds among the Chukchi range between 3000 and 5000 animals. Such herds are found in ecologically more favored areas, that is, in areas in which greater concentrations of foodstuffs suitable for reindeer are found.

Variation in food supply is governed in the tundra by a number of factors which I shall not consider in detail here. These include temperature, absolute and mean; presence of large bodies of water to modify temperatures (see Table I); length of summer; frequency and severity of tempests in winter; mists; protection from cold winds; amount of snow cover as insulation for plant life in winter (see Berg, 1937, p. 6), although too much may prevent reindeer from getting to the foods at all; degree and level of permanent ground frost; drainage; evaporation; altitude (in some parts of the tundra, winter temperatures are higher at higher altitudes; *ibid.*, p. 5); and soil types.

In a very generalized way, one may say that the river valleys are somewhat warmer in this subarctic region, somewhat moister, and better drained, and hence have lower permanent frost levels (Berg, 1937, p. 16) than the interfluves. Consequently, most of the river valleys support a certain amount of forest growth and other plant life sheltered by it, though these forests become progressively shrubbier and finally disappear, even in the river valleys, near the northern limits of the Chukchi lands.

Along the arctic shore, in many areas, in summertime, is found

TABLE I. Temperature ranges in the Chukchi area
(Adapted from Bogoras' data, 1904–1909, p. 24)

	Kolyma area[a]		Anadyr area[d]	
	Nizhne-Kolymsk[b]	Sredne-Kolymsk[c]	Marinsky Post[e]	Markova[f]
Winter	−27.00°F	−31.00°F	− 1.84°F	− 8.32°F
Spring	+ 8.49	+ 5.72	+ 7.88	+ 8.24
Summer	+50.67	+52.16	+48.20	+54.68
Fall	+ 5.61	+ 9.32	+24.08	+18.34
Annual average	+ 9.50	+ 9.14	+19.58	+18.34
Absolute maximum	−	+84.92	+68.36	+79.88
Absolute minimum	−	−58.72	−44.86	−52.6

[a] The Kolyma River freezes about mid October, and thaws in early June.

[b] Near the mouth of the Kolyma, about 50 miles from the coast.

[c] About 200 miles from the coast. It will be noted that the range is greater and the annual average lower than for Nizhne-Kolymsk.

[d] The Anadyr estuary freezes about mid October and thaws in mid June.

[e] At the mouth of the Anadyr.

[f] About 500 miles from Marinsky Post, due west.

a fairly luxuriant growth of mosses, lichens, and grasses, and occasional other types of plants, except where it is sandy (Bogoras, p. 24). In the interfluves—cold, wind-swept areas with little precipitation—are found only reindeer "moss" (actually a kind of lichen, *Cladonia rangiferina*; Berg, 1937, p. 13), mosses and other lichens, and, in later summer, mushrooms. Bogoras (p. 76) gives an extensive inventory of kinds of mosses and comments on their locations.[6]

Summer temperatures are somewhat higher inland and also westward, and southward where the larger rivers or their tributaries—the Indighirka, the Kolyma, the Omolon, the Bolshoi Anui,

[6] Bogoras' list of mosses (p. 76) follows. The names are translated from the Chukchi. (*a*) Genuine, white, or large moss (*Cetraria islandica*). This is the most common. (*b*) Small or fine moss or small moss with tender fibers; black or light green. (*c*) Bald or ground-bones moss; light green, small, round rolls of fibers. Scarce, especially on the tundra. (*d*) Glacier moss; like genuine moss, but dark brown. Good fodder but very localized. (*e*) Wolf's moss; black like rough tangled horsehair, or like wolf's hair. Poorer fodder. (*f*) Earlike moss (*Cetraria arctica*); light green, in large flaps. Sprouts chiefly on burnt ground; good fodder but scarce. (*g*) Pricking moss; light green and dark brown. Grows only on burnt ground; good fodder but scarce.

and parts of the Anadyr—are generally found. Consequently, the total floral biomass is greater in these areas and the food supply for reindeer is concomitantly greater. The correlation between floral biomass and herd size as given in Bogoras' rough census (pp. 26–27) is almost embarrassingly neat.

In passing, I should like to make brief reference to two significant facts. First, there is evidence that mean temperatures in the tundra have risen over a considerable time, at least since well back into the nineteenth century (see Berg, 1937, pp. 7–8, speaking of the western tundra; Bogoras, *passim*).[7] Such temperature increases imply increased evaporation, longer frost-free seasons, and so on, all conditions favorable to an increase of the floral biomass, hence of the number of reindeer which can be supported. I have already mentioned the reported increase of reindeer throughout the area during the past century, inconclusive as the evidence is.

The second fact is that, although the population increase of the Chukchi appears to have been relatively small in the past two or three centuries, perhaps a matter of a 50 per cent growth, the Chukchi have spread into a territory at least eight or ten times as great as their original one three centuries ago. This was accomplished primarily by means of warfare against the Koryak (see Bogoras, p. 72), the Yukaghir, the Lamut, the Chuvantzy, and other groups to the west, southwest, south, and southeast, especially for, and by, appropriation of their reindeer herds.[8] Herd capture is undoubtedly less laborious and time-consuming than breeding an equivalent number of reindeer over a period of years, under Chukchi conditions.[9] Bogoras (p. 73) remarks that to build an independent herd (size not specified) takes about twenty-five

[7] Berg (1937) mentions that in postglacial times the tundra was considerably warmer than today and that consequently the tundra, over millennia, has been encroaching on the forest. One result, in wide areas adjacent to the forest belt, is a mixed forest and tundra vegetation, because in the latter some smaller and hardier forest plants persist (*ibid.*, p. 16). Thus, the rise in temperature mentioned in the text is a recent upward fluctuation in the larger cooling trend.

[8] "The continuous warfare on the Koryak border was carried on by the Chukchee chiefly for the purpose of carrying away herds of reindeer" (Bogoras, p. 72). The Koryak are reported as formerly having had very large herds.

[9] The principle operating here—that warfare constitutes, as it were, a labor-saving ecological device—is suggested by Vayda (1961a) with respect to swiddening, a different kind of ecological system.

years. Warfare also enabled the Chukchi herdsmen to acquire workers to care for herds, a point to be discussed below.

This warfare and expansion of Chukchi reindeer herders appears to have had several important consequences: the spacing out of herds over larger parts of the potentially available territory, with the possible concomitant increase in total numbers; the relative isolation of major groups of herds in different watersheds or other partially separated areas, probably decreasing the effects of epidemics on these herds as compared with the more concentrated ones of Chukchi two or three hundred years ago; facilitation of the capture of wild reindeer; and, finally, a more stable man–animal–food supply relationship.

Obviously, the absolute amount of food available for reindeer governs the maximum number of reindeer which can be supported on any given area of land. This absolute amount varies from area to area according to the local conditions in regard to the factors listed above, and from time to time, depending on seasonal cycles, annual mean temperature variation, unexpected climatic events, and so on. Neither statistical nor cartographic data are available to show, for any given area, how many acres of reindeer pasture exist, on the average, nor how many reindeer can be supported per acre.

Whatever the maximum amount of food available, however, the nature of the food resources is such as to necessitate certain behavioral and technical adaptations. As remarked above, the main foods are mosses, lichens, and, in the summer, grasses and leaves. The growth rate of the mosses and lichens is about 1 to 2 millimeters per year in the arctic tundra, and 2 to 3 in the typical tundra (Berg, 1937, p. 13). If grazed lightly, the winter pastures may be used for three or four years, but then must be fallowed for five or six years (Bogoras, p. 77).[10] Light grazing is a matter of a few hours to a day or two. With a longer period of grazing, the growth rate of the flora is so impaired that pasture recovery may require twenty years or so. If the pastures are trampled by reindeer for prolonged periods—that is, for more than a few hours or

___

[10] One may note the interesting parallel, here, with swiddening; see Conklin, 1957; Leeds, 1961; Vayda, 1961a; and many others.

a day—either the plants themselves are caused to wither and die
or the snow on top of the plants is so hardened as to seal them off,
with the same effect, and pasture recovery may involve a score of
years (*ibid.*). Consequently, herds must move constantly over a
vast area. A given camp's range of wandering, chiefly along some
river with its neighboring lands (Bogoras, p. 25), extends approximately 100 to 150 miles over nearly the same territory year after
year. Camps may not trespass on the territories occupied by other
camps in a given season (*ibid.*).

The summer pasturage is less easily exhausted than the winter,
especially on the arctic shore between the Kolyma River and
Chaun Bay, where in Bogoras' time it had been used for fifty years
and was still thriving, sprouting again each spring, especially near
the shore (Bogoras, p. 77). The area was sometimes so crowded
in summer that one could even see the tents of others in the
distance!

Contributing to the necessity for herd movement are the insect
plagues, which become markedly more severe and dangerous in
summer, especially in the forested areas. The herds move away
from the insects in general, and specifically away from the forested
river valleys out onto the windier open moss pastures of the tundra in the spring, returning to the edges of the wooded areas only
in the late fall. The numerous mountain ridges and the rivers
themselves constitute natural physical and vegetational boundaries
to pasture areas. Therefore, the movements of herds are, as indicated above, patterned along known territories through an annual migratory cycle usually with a stably continuous human
group, characterized, however, by instability of its personnel (see
below, p. 103).

The necessity for constant movement increases with herd size.
Bogoras (p. 95), speaking of camps, says that the lightest camps
can move 25 miles in a day; large ones, generally 10 to 15, except
in the fall, when they can go only 3 to 5 miles a day. In other
words, the greater the herd, the more difficult it is for the herders
to meet the need for increased herd movement by moving the
reindeer mass, a job which is done on foot since no riding animals
which can be used for herding are available. Consequently, the

tendency to wear out pastures increases as the herd size increases, and the susceptibility to insect plagues and epidemic diseases becomes concomitantly greater. The case of 3000 animals slaughtered in three days in a herd totally infected with scab disease was mentioned above. In short, herd size is limited by the increasing immobility of the herd, because of pressure on the food supply in any given locality and because of danger from insects and diseases.

Another factor setting upper limits to herd size is unexpected climatic variation, especially unusually prolonged cold and snow or other extremes of weather which may reduce the total available food supply below average levels. Such an event occurred in the winter of 1901, after thirty years of herd increases (since about 1870), when as much as half of many herds died from unavailability of food (Bogoras, p. 27). Reindeer either die or leave the herd, thus equilibrating the herd at a smaller size in accord with the reduced food supply. Unusually hot summers tend to foster the hoof disease mentioned above. The effects of such extremes of natural factors are proportionately greater in the larger herds.

A subsidiary and indirect contribution to herd size limitation is made by the use of fire to create a smudge to protect the animals from insects. Fire destroys lichens and mosses, and, if widespread, ruins pastures for many years.

In sum, we find a situation in which human survival is fostered by maintaining herd size relatively stable and within defined limits, a situation dependent on the nature of the animals themselves, on the natural conditions, and on the biological and cultural needs of the human population. These needs must be met by trying to keep herd sizes well above the defined minimum, and below the maximum, range limits and by avoiding rapid and drastic variations of herd size. The latter effort is especially necessary for the possessors of small herds, who are constantly in relatively greater danger of unexpected food reduction, famine, or starvation.

Given these environmental, animal, and human exigencies, we should expect to find socio-cultural institutions rather than only "natural" means operating to maintain optimal herd sizes and avoid herd size variations toward the extreme lower and upper range limits. Further, since the larger herds require more labor, and since labor requirements vary with long- and short-term variations in herd numbers, we should expect to find social institutions adapted to these conditions also. Again the neatness of fit of such institutions, which are indeed to be found among the Chukchi, as I shall show, is almost embarrassing. In a very general sort of way, we might describe them as institutions directed at maintaining optimal herd size. Furthermore, not only should we expect to find such social and technical institutions, but we should expect to find concomitant ideological reinforcements for them as well. It is almost superfluous to say that Chukchi culture is, of course, rife with them. I shall refer, here, only to a few institutions and ideological aspects. They will suffice, however, to show what sort of cultural mechanisms—cultural equilibrating mechanisms, if you will—operate in this ecosystem.

Means for Increasing the Size of Small Herds

What ways are open to a "poor" Chukchi herdsman to increase his herd, that is, to move away from the minimum range limits to an optimal range, by manipulating the environmental, technical, and social factors controlling the limits? An optimal range of herd size, though it might fluctuate within certain parameters with seasonal, annual, and other natural variations, would be characterized by herds sufficiently large, relative to a human population of a given size, to be able to produce enough males for slaughter throughout the year, to maintain a supply of breeding males, to compensate for sterile females as well as to maintain the female breeding proportion, and to maintain a supply of sledge animals. It is necessary to produce all these, while at the same time averting the threat of any catastrophe's occurring to the group, by virtue of either the loss of reindeer or the sterility of does, which would endanger the minimal food supply or the minimal reproduction necessary to keep the herd population stable or growing through time. A herd of optimal size and composition is one whose reproductive capacity remains virtually unaffected by the slaughter of animals within it for food, but at the same time does not, under various kinds of circumstances, exert undue pressure on the herd's food supply.

Herd Aggregation

One socio-technical institution available to poor men for increasing herd size is that of aggregating several small herds (Bogoras, pp. 82–83, 612), especially in the spring breeding season and the subsequent optimal grazing season, the summer (see above), when pastures can be more intensively used if herds are larger. Herd aggregation functions to move the size of the herd away from the minimum range limit and hence from the danger of catastrophes leading to starvation; to create better breeding conditions; to increase the possibilities of wild deer capture; to improve protection against predators and loss; to create better herd management conditions; and so on.

Aggregation of herds also secures a more adequate and varied labor supply of young and old men and women as well as children, because it involves the aggregation of camps. The composition of poor men's camps generally ranges from a nuclear family, through a nuclear family with a sibling of one of the spouses, to the more common grouping of two or three nuclear families, or about ten to fifteen persons (Bogoras, p. 612). The group described by Odulok (1934) consisted of one family with five or six persons, later joined by another smaller one, still later split apart entirely into individuals or couples attaching themselves to the camp. Such camps are almost always made up of close relatives where people are poor enough so that it is not necessary to keep herds apart, nor is it requisite to keep them together (Bogoras, p. 612). Where a man's herd is small, his sons will not divide it. Occasionally larger groupings of five to eight more distantly related families may temporarily join "in order to form a herd of decent size," then disperse again (*ibid.*). Camps, families, and family groups are quite unstable in composition over time (*ibid.*, pp. 537, 541, 542, 549, 556, 612, 667; see also Czaplicka, 1914, p. 28).

The aggregate camp may also be set up in winter if herds or the labor supply to care for them are depleted. Even the increased security of such a herd may not be proof against severe adverse circumstances, as the case described by Odulok (1934), which is fully confirmed as factual by Bogoras' more general statements, shows. The case is also interesting because it underlines the explicit awareness among the Chukchi of the labor needs for herding, and their assessment of the labor supply available in any given camp. The Chukchi measure this supply against the labor needs and determine a policy of action accordingly.

The data are insufficient to demonstrate conclusively whether a man, deciding to join his herd with that of another, confronts a series of possible other camps whose labor supply he assesses as prelude to choosing among them, but this appears to be the case, since there are always what Bogoras (p. 627) calls the neighboring camps. These, though widely dispersed in the tundra, are the only groups in frequent contact. A group of neighboring camps is a kind of pool from which disaster help may be drawn and which carries out the annual migration as an aggregate in order always to be in each other's neighborhood (Bogoras, p. 628). Choice appears also to be governed by the expectation of positive response and mutual assistance, in particular from close relatives, and also, of course, from distantly related friends, but not from possible competitors or hostile persons, especially rich, "strong" men. In this connection, it is important to note that, except among the poorest herdsmen, the group of neighboring camps usually consists of patrilaterally related household groups (Bogoras, pp. 537–542, especially p. 538; Murdock, 1957, p. 679, however, says the Chukchi have bilateral descent; see footnote 15).

Aggregating herds and camps is accomplished by agreement and by contractual arrangements in which adults create a new nuclear family unit by committing their respective infants and prospective heirs to marriage. The contract described by Odulok (1934) remained in effect at a later date when the minimum limit of herd size was passed and the joint camp disintegrated. The parties in this case were a man poorer in reindeer and richer in labor and a man poorer in labor and richer in reindeer.

The choices involved in herd aggregation require, on one hand, that the herder have information about conditions in accessible camps, and, on the other, that he be able to communicate his decisions so as to consummate the choice. Though the dissemination of information is, as such, not discussed by Bogoras, yet there are numerous agencies in Chukchi society by which communication is achieved.

One agent of information dissemination is what Bogoras (pp. 625–627) calls the "idle wanderers," men who, living almost outside camp and family ties, wander aimlessly from place to place subsisting on handouts. Plainly, they may serve as a fount of gossip as they go from place to place.

The numerous occasions when people meet comprise a second means of relaying information. Such occasions occur throughout the year, although tending to cluster about certain major ceremonials, festivities, and fairs (fairs: Bogoras, pp. 12, 49, 54, 65–66, 612, 700, etc.; gatherings: pp. 554, 662; festivities—races, and the like: pp. 77, 264–267, 628, etc.; ceremonies: pp. 372–378, 531–536, etc.). These events also serve as occasions for distributing resources or redistributing goods, a point returned to below.

Exceedingly important in disseminating information are trade and travel by Chukchi, Koryak, Eskimo, and Russians (Bogoras, pp. 12, 44, 48, 54, 55, 65–66, 545, 636, 686 ff., etc.). Sometimes a whole family will pack their sledges and move slowly from camp to camp, traveling east to west and back, attending fairs at either end (ibid., pp. 65–66). It is of interest to note the speed with which travel, hence also information dispersion, may be effected. Bogoras states that trips of 200 miles in two days can be accomplished (p. 95) and that, with dog teams, up to 500 miles in ten days can be covered (p. 113). He says that one winter he traveled 4000 to 5000 miles (ibid.).

Bogoras, in discussing "paupers," remarks that they must, like the "idle wanderers," move about in search of support from neighbors, distant relatives, or masters of camps in various places (p. 624). He speaks, too, of wandering hunters, who, being without herds of their own, move about hunting wild reindeer (p. 549). In connection with a murder case, Bogoras describes the pursuit of the murderer, some years later, by the then grown sons of the victim. They traveled a great distance from camp to camp, seeking information about the criminal (p. 666). One may assume that they also carried information from camp to camp. Again, a man in search of a wife may travel to various camps to look over the situation (*ibid.*, p. 583), even perhaps working for a possible or prospective father-in-law for a while (*ibid.*, p. 587). He, of course, becomes informed about each camp, its wealth, its working conditions, and so on.

Moreover, Bogoras mentions that in the slack season, the father of the camp may leave the herd in charge of the younger members while he goes visiting and gossiping (p. 554). Bogoras remarks in this connection that the herdsmen come into camp giving details about the animals, pastures, drinking places, mosquitoes, reindeer flies, and the like—that is, they transmit ecological information important to decisions about herding the animals.

The animal migration cycle itself constitutes a device for information gathering as the herdsmen wander through the landscape observing conditions and coming in contact with other groups and sets of people.

It may be noted that whatever aboriginal trade existed was abruptly expanded by the Russians, who introduced new forms of trade from 1614 on and eventually broadened their activities over the entire area. In Bogoras' time, Russian trips for trade, by horse in summer, by dog sledge in winter, took place regularly.

By means of these various agencies it would appear that Chukchi herdsmen are generally well informed regarding conditions in both neighboring and more distant camps. To some of the festivities and ceremonies persons are invited, sometimes even by personal messenger (!, Bogoras, p. 374), from considerable distances. Bogoras mentions people gathering from as far as 50 miles away, and says that in one extreme case, a man, winner in a race, ran home, a distance of 500 miles (p. 265)! It seems clear, then, that any herder or herders under stress confront a perfectly rational and well informed choice as to how he or they may best cooperate with the neighbors and their herds to maximize his or their own security.

At the same time that a man is aware of the possibility of herd aggregation, he avoids this choice as long as possible. He attempts to keep his herd independent and to increase it as best he can, that is, to maximize it by improving his herding technique, increasing the capture of wild or tame reindeer, encouraging mating between wild deer and his own herd, and so on.

This behavior is reinforced by the ideology, by values concerning the "strong" man (Bogoras, pp. 639 ff.) , the "good herdsman," sheer physical strength, competitive physical accomplishment (see pp. 264–267, 553, 674) , violence (pp. 45 ff., 614, 639, 641, 679, etc.) , all of which are useful assets for the enormous physical labor of herding under the great variety of difficult technical conditions of the Chukchi environment. Expressions of these values are repeated in innumerable contexts such as at religious ceremonies, games, races and wrestling matches, or shamanistic performances, and in the tales (see Bogoras, 1910) . Feats of strength, acts of prowess, violent and heroic behavior, excessive endurance and expenditure of energy are all trumpeted, especially in the tales, and more particularly in those regarding war, the ultimate aim of which, it must be recalled, was the acquisition of reindeer herds, the capture of the labor supply attached to them, and the control of the territory on which they were grazing (see Bogoras, pp. 158 ff., 267, 543, 552–554, 562, 571, 589, 610, 639, 645–660, etc.) .

These, however, are no mere statements; they also reflect permeating behavioral characteristics. Throughout the ethnography itself, as well as the tales, quarrels, fights, rages, murders, violations, and madnesses are mentioned (Bogoras, pp. 45 ff., 264–266, 267, 419, 426–428, 548, 553, 561, 565, 573, 586, 613–614, 639, 641–645, 662–666, 668–676, etc.; see also Odulok, 1934, chaps. 10, 11) , almost all involving physical expressions of strength aimed at conquest. Competitive feats of strength are the core of wrestling, jumping, crawling, and racing matches, such as the stone- or log-carrying races (see Bogoras, pp. 264–268) ; of archery contests; of running for endurance (Bogoras, p. 265, mentions cases of Chukchi overtaking bucks running at full speed and of Lamut keeping up with reindeer running for life, and with dog teams for ten to fifteen miles and, in one case, for forty miles!) ; even of herding itself. When a man is defeated in any of these endeavors, he may spend months or years practicing the skills involved, strengthening himself, increasing his endurance, and so on (Bogoras, p. 267) , so that he may, perhaps, prevail in the next confrontation.

In other words, permeating Chukchi culture and society are a

set of values and institutions which drive men to practice behaviors and foster qualities that are highly serviceable ecologically
in the struggle to survive under subarctic conditions. These values
and institutions, especially the apparently very frequent quarrels,
tend to set man against man; to send him off on his own; to push
him to show that he, alone, can outdo others, can be a supreme
herdsman and manager. Men who cannot compete and quarrel in
the ideal Chukchi manner are considered "weak" (Bogoras, pp.
424, 583), even "soft to die" (*ibid.*, p. 417). Men who reject or
cannot cope with the fierce competition may commit suicide
(*ibid.*, pp. 417, 560–565), may become shamans (*ibid.*, pp. 416,
420–421, 424),[11] or may become transvestite "wives" of "stronger"
men. A homosexual female may become the "husband" of a vigorous young woman, who may even bear children to the former
through the services of a man also married to her, at the behest
of the female "husband," in typical Chukchi "group marriage."[12]

Herd Capture

Turning again to the avoidance of minimum range limits, herds
may also be increased, not by joining them, but by acquiring new
animals. One technique available to a small holder, especially a
"violent" man, is, in late summer and especially in the fall, to ap-

---

[11] It is fascinating to note the Chukchi rational awareness of labor needs. In a
small, and especially in a poor, family which cannot easily attract male labor, a son
who psychically is somewhat inclined to turn to shamanism is consistently dissuaded
from doing so by his parents because they need his labor power. In a large and
rich family, however, where there are a number of sons, among whom, incidentally,
the herd will have to be divided, a shamanistically inclined son will be encouraged
to enter the profession. His labor will, relatively, not be missed, or, at least, the
amount of labor lost through the time and energy consumed in becoming a shaman
and in practicing his art can be readily tolerated. In any case, if need be, other
labor—adoptive sons-in-law, paupers, assistants, and, formerly, slaves—will tend to
gravitate to the camp.

[12] Through suicide—whether by one's own or, at demand, by another's hand—the
really weak, the unstable, the hysterical, the sick, the inept, the superannuated are
removed from the consuming population, leaving the stronger and healthier personnel. Through shamanism, the unstable and hysterical, but often reasonably strong
and apt, can find a channel of service to the community, compensating for their inability to compete in other ways, while using their available physical skills. Through
transvestite, homosexual marriage, a homosexual can actively perform—physically
more strongly than a woman, if a man—in the role of the other sex, and can thus
contribute appreciably to the welfare of the society.

proach the large herd of a rich man with his own small herd and to drive it in among the former, more or less as if by accident (Bogoras, p. 614). As the herds are being sorted out again, the poorer man removes his own animals and appropriates a number of the rich man's as well. The rich man knows this has happened but cannot prove it, because, in his large herd, he has not yet been able to earmark a considerable proportion of both older animals and particularly the spring fawns with his own ownership mark.

Needless to say, herd capture is accompanied by intergroup hostility, quarreling, even, occasionally, active fighting and killing (Bogoras, p. 614, calls the Kolyma shore a coast of quarrels), and, of course, separation of groups, so that they disperse out into the pasture areas again. Fighting and killing, on the whole, are however avoided. It would seem that they are avoided, especially by the rich man, for two reasons. First, he must insure his own health and life and those of the herd laborers of the camp in order to guarantee the well-being of the herd and the other members of the camp. Second, he wants to avoid sizable sudden increments in his own herd (by overcoming the poor herdsman and taking his herd), especially if it has already reached the upper limits of the optimal range, lest his herd be in danger of exhausting food resources.

It would be interesting to know whether herdsmen in the middle range of herd sizes fight and kill more freely than really rich herdsmen because they can afford to take on increments of reindeer. It must be recalled that the Chukchi herders are quite rationally aware of the natural and technical necessities of reindeer herding. I would guess that fighting and killing might occur where a rich man could successfully add a poor man's herd to his own and still remain within the optimal herd size, but the data are wanting to prove this[13] (see Odulok, 1934, chap. 11, for a possible case).

Here, too, of course, we find ideological reinforcements for the aggressive behavior of either side in the Chukchi concept of the

[13] With sufficient time, indications of this sort might be elicited from Bogoras' text by cross-referencing various mentions of given individuals so as to acquire fuller case histories of individual herdsmen.

"violent man" (Bogoras, p. 614), a concept which gives ideological strength to a number of other behaviors, some of which will be mentioned below.

Herd Acquisition through Assistantship

A third way of increasing herd size, or even of beginning a herd if one has none, is to become an "assistant" to a rich man (Bogoras, pp. 615 ff.). Assistantship is a contractual relation between a man without a herd or with a very small one and a man with a considerable or large herd, who often hires assistants from afar (ibid., p. 349). The assistant, if without a herd, is usually a single man, spalled off from a camp too small to maintain or need him. If he has a few animals, he is a man with a wife or a small nuclear family (see Odulok, 1934, last chapter; Bogoras, p. 621). The data suggest that the potential assistant has received information about, or has even investigated, the labor needs of richer men in order to guide his choice; in view of the modes of communication discussed above, it is highly probable that most persons are fairly well informed about the composition of herds and needs of their herders in a sizable area about them. The data are insufficient, however, to determine whether entering into an assistantship and herd aggregation are alternative solutions to a man's herd size problems. I should guess that the choice depends on the herd composition and size and the labor situation of neighboring camps.

In any case, the assistant's contract involves his giving labor to the rich man, the strong man, and in return his receiving food supplied from the rich man's herd for himself and his family, as well as pay in the form of a small number of doe fawns a year, usually from 5 to 10. With this annual increment, in a few years he can have 100 does, or in a period of fifteen years or so he can build up a herd of perhaps 300 or more does, well above the upper limit of the minimal range in most circumstances (Bogoras, p. 622; the "master of the camp" is said to have 3000 or more). It is at about this time that he may split off from the large herd with his own little one in order to increase his herd independently in a pasture area unoccupied or as yet unused. The ideology, as we have said, reinforces this splitting off by underlining the desirability and propriety of a herdsman's having independence; of his being a man of substance who is a "front man" in his own encampment, a "strong man" who can support a family in style, albeit Chukchi style, a "violent man," a "master of the camp" (Bogoras, pp. 612 ff.) .

It should be noted that quite a number of such assistants, starting poor, become rich men. Bogoras says that he met a number of men who had moved from poverty to riches in the possession of thousands of reindeer, and were themselves in turn being helped by poor assistants (p. 622) . In other words, looking at the system as a whole, rather than at individuals, we see it functioning to produce rich men at a relatively steady rate, in response to long-range favorable ecological conditions.

Not every assistant goes off, however, after accumulating a small herd of his own. He may stay permanently with the large herd in two ways. First, he may become like or actually a member of the family (Bogoras, p. 617) , either by marriage to the master's daughter or possibly by adoption (*ibid.*, pp. 556–560) . Second, he may be the one master herdsman left with the herd when the camp master dies, so that he becomes the *de facto* if not the *de jure* owner of the herd and camp.

Several things must be noted about the assistant. First, the largest number of assistants are young men (Bogoras, p. 618) , but relatively inexperienced breeders. The institution of assistantship can be regarded as an exchange of youthful brawn for more elderly brain; that is, the youthful assistant gives his muscle power in exchange for the herd owner's experience, which he then has an opportunity to learn. It functions as a training institution to create capable independent herdsmen who can go forth and multiply herds successfully (see *ibid.*, p. 622) .

Second, a smaller category of assistants consists of men who have met with misfortune in their own herds and make an exchange of their own experience for the social security benefits that the rich man can afford them and their families. Such assistants appear to be afforded considerably more respect and good treatment than the youths, who are often even maltreated as a kind of test of their endurance, as it were (Bogoras, p. 617) . Thus, the assistantship functions, in some cases, also as a social security institution serving to utilize optimally the best available manpower (cf. the case in Odulok, 1934, e.g. p. 70).

Third, assistantship functions to redistribute personnel according to the distribution of resources; that is, reindeer. It may be recalled, in this connection, that grazing-plus-fallow cycles range between perhaps eight and twenty-five years, periods corresponding roughly to the length of the assistantship. Herd aggregation also serves, in part, to redistribute personnel according to resources, in contrast to herd capture, which redistributes reindeer according to personnel (and, of course, reindeer food supplies). Thus, assistantship may be regarded as an institution to adjust labor to the labor market.

Assistantship formerly was complemented by the capture of prisoners in warfare. The leading warriors were wealthy men, and, needless to say, invariably "strong men" and "violent men," characteristics corresponding to their ability to get and to hold large herds. War captives, as assistants, might ultimately be incorporated into the family by marriage to a herdsman's daughter (Bogoras, p. 617), thus ultimately having rights in the herds and probably becoming independent herders, a point we return to below. Until that time arrived, they contributed to the maximization of the rich man's herd, and, possibly, of several herds.

Herd Acquisition through Courtship and Marriage

Assistantship is not the only institution for beginning or acquiring herds and hence redistributing reindeer according to the long-term variations in their food supply, nor the only one for distributing labor, especially youthful, untrained labor. Courtship and the early period of marriage, especially for men, function in the same way. A young man or his representative (Bogoras, pp. 579, 583–584) sometimes spends weeks or even months before his marriage, and sometimes up to three years (depending on the size of the father-in-law's herd and his potential access to it) after his marriage, in such service (*ibid.*, pp. 584–587), often laboring intensively under the severest physical circumstances and the harshest abuse from his prospective and then actual father-in-law (*ibid.*,

p. 583). Thus his strength, endurance, and capabilities for work, for increasing herds, are tested and bettered. Only when he has really proved himself, and in the course of so doing added to his father-in-law's stock, is he not only allowed the full rights of marriage and independence, but also rewarded with animals of his own, while the wife also takes some of her own. The groom may be allowed the "freedom of one day," i.e., the permission to capture reindeer from the herd and put his own earmark on them (*ibid., p.* 586). Alternatively, if labor be short in the father-in-law's camp, the groom may be adopted into the camp as a "continuous dweller," that is, as son-in-law and heir prospective, thus permanently redistributing labor according to resources as well as maximizing his herd holdings (*ibid., p.* 587). However, as Bogoras remarks (*ibid.*), young men "want to look carefully into the quality of the possible reward before being committed to the marriage."

It may be noted that during the entire period of courtship and early marriage, the young man, like the young assistant, is receiving training and at least some support. One may hypothesize that the length of the pre- and postmarriage service correlates with the rate at which the man grows to the point where he is sufficiently strong and vigorous to challenge both the strength and the experience of his father-in-law, whether by sheer success or in actual quarrels. Such a moment is the time for the bride's father to let him and his wife go. Men with little capacity and little promise of growth are probably soon expelled from the prospective father-in-law's camp.

The data suggest that love is economically quite rational in that young men tend to discover their love for girls whose fathers are well heeled, or at least relatively so (see Bogoras, p. 587). This is especially the case since this form of marriage occurs among the wealthier rather than among the poorer families, among which the marriage contract of infants, mentioned above, is more frequent. Such contracts tend to reflect herd joinings. It may be noted that young women are much attracted, romantically, by the size of the herd of the prospective husband or father-in-law (*ibid., p.* 597).

Older men, remarrying or taking second wives, observe very abbreviated or no bride services, since their capacities are already well known and they have been long established as successful herdsmen with wives (Bogoras, p. 586), and cannot, in any case, leave their home herd. The very fact of being able to support a second wife is itself an indication of prior success. In some cases, where the first wife is childless or where her children have already left the camp, the second marriage is an effort to beget more children (*ibid.,* p. 600), a reflection of the camp's labor needs and of herding success. If the herder be already a man of sufficient mark, the prospective second father-in-law may simply hand over the daughter without question. The Chukchi attribute second marriages to economic motivations—a woman to go with each herd.

Women, too, are economically rational in their selection of husbands in that, so far as choice rests with them, they search for strong and successful herdsmen, able runners, expert hunters, and the like. They also resist, even violently, an unproved man. Such resistance on a woman's part often sparks the man in question to feats of violence, endurance, and strength—proofs of ecologically useful manhood and love—to acquire her (Bogoras, pp. 581–582).

In sum, the modalities of courtship; the ideals of manhood held by woman and of womanhood held by men; the roles of males as defined by males and of females as defined by females—all contribute, directly or indirectly, to motivate behavior functioning to increase herd size and maximize adaptation to the environment through creating herds of optimal ranges of herd size.

MEANS FOR CONTROLLING OR REDUCING THE SIZE OF LARGE HERDS

We turn now to the technical and social institutions for controlling pressures against the upper range limits of herds or even for reducing herd size.

In this connection, the population dynamics of reindeer are illuminating. Does produce young at the end of their first year, that is, in the fawning period of the spring after the spring of their own birth. They continue to bear for twelve to fifteen years (Bogoras, p. 75). In a large herd—how large Bogoras does not specify, though the calculations below give us an estimate—the calving rate is about 20 to 30 a day (*ibid.*, p. 79). An average 15 per cent of the young die (*ibid.*, p. 78) during the period directly after their birth, except under bad weather conditions, when they die by hundreds. Most of the fawns that survive the first days live into adulthood to reproduce in turn.

Fawning lasts from mid March to the end of May (Bogoras, p. 78), or about 75 days. If all does in the herd were pregnant, the maximum rate of calving would be 13 1/3 fawns per 1000 does per day. Bogoras' "large herd," producing 20 to 30 fawns daily, must then have from about 1500 to 2300 does, a total herd of roughly 3000 to 4600 animals. Assuming that all does are *not* pregnant, I may, for the sake of the argument which follows, posit a lower rate of say 850 to 900 fawns per 1000 does in the calving season. These are reduced to 722 to 765 by the 15 per cent average mortality. About half of the remaining fawns, or 361 to 383, will be doe fawns. Assuming that perhaps 10 per cent of these may prove to be sterile, may be seized by human or animal predators, or may be slaughtered, the number of female fawns ready for breeding within the year is 325 to 345, or an increment of between 32.5 and 34.5 per cent of breeding does a year added to the nonconsumable part of the herd. A large proportion of the male animals may eventually be slaughtered, whether as fawns or as bucks.

Table II presents idealized figures of herd growth based on the assumptions made above and using Bogoras' data, my hypothetical calculations, and both the minimum increment rate of 32.5 per cent and a possible 35 per cent rate. The table gives parallel figures of doe increments for large herds; assistants' herds which, at least during the number of years for which the figures are calculated, form part of some large herd; and small independent herds. With regard to the assistants' herds, it is assumed here that the assistant is yearly receiving what appears to be the smallest animal payment made by the camp master, that is, five does.

Several points should be noted in connection with the table. First, an assistant is also paid in food by the rich herdsman for whom he works. He therefore has to remove neither does nor

TABLE II. Increments in Number of Does in Various Kinds of Herds

A. At 32.5 per cent increment rate[a]

	Does available to reproduce at beginning of year		New breeding does added to herd in year	Payments in does
Large herds:				
Year 1	1,000	yield	325	
Year 2	1,325	yield	431	
Year 3	1,756	yield	571	
Year 4	2,327	yield	756	
Year 5	3,083	yield	1,002	
Year 6	4,085	yield	1,328	
Year 15	51,513	yield	16,742	
etc.				
Assistants' small herds:[b]				
Year 1	0	yield	0	+ 5
Year 2	5	yield	1.6	+ 5
Year 3	11.6	yield	3.8	+ 5
Year 4	20.4	yield	6.6	+ 5
Year 5	32	yield	10.4	+ 5
Year 6	47.4	yield	15.4	+ 5
Year 7	67.4	yield	21.9	+ 5
Year 8	94.3	yield	30.6	+ 5
Year 9	129.9	yield	42.2	+ 5
Year 10	177.1	yield	57.6	+ 5
Year 11	239.6	yield	77.9	+ 5
Year 12	322.5	yield	104.8	+ 5
Year 13	432.3	yield	140.5	+ 5
Year 14	577.8	yield	187.9	+ 5
Year 15	765.6	yield	248.8	+ 5
etc.				
Small independent herds:				
Year 1	10	yield	3.3	
Year 2	13.3	yield	4.3	
Year 3	17.6	yield	5.7	
Year 4	23.3	yield	7.6	
Year 5	30.8	yield	10.0	
Year 6	40.9	yield	13.3	
Year 7	54.1	yield	17.6	
Year 8	71.7	yield	23.3	
Year 9	95.0	yield	30.9	
Year 10	125.9	yield	40.9	
Year 11	166.8	yield	54.2	
Year 12	221.1	yield	71.8	
Year 13	292.9	yield	95.9	
Year 14	388.8	yield	126.4	
Year 15	515.1	yield	167.4	
etc.				

[a] The average growth rates of large herds and assistants' small herds are *minimum* rates; those of small independent herds are *maximum*.

116

TABLE II—*Continued*

B. At 35 per cent increment rate[a]

	Does available to reproduce at beginning of year		New breeding does added to herd in year	Payments in does
Large herds:				
Year 1	1,000	*yield*	350	
Year 2	1,390	*yield*	473	
Year 3	1,823	*yield*	638	
Year 4	2,461	*yield*	861	
Year 5	3,322	*yield*	1,163	
Year 6	4.485	*yield*	1,570	
Year 15	66,720	*yield*	23,352	
etc.				
Assistants' small herds:[b]				
Year 1	0	*yield*	0	+ 5
Year 2	5	*yield*	1.75	+ 5
Year 3	11.75	*yield*	4.1	+ 5
Year 4	20.8	*yield*	7.3	+ 5
Year 5	33.1	*yield*	11.6	+ 5
Year 6	49.7	*yield*	17.4	+ 5
Year 7	72.1	*yield*	25.3	+ 5
Year 8	102.4	*yield*	35.8	+ 5
Year 9	143.2	*yield*	50.1	+ 5
Year 10	198.3	*yield*	69.4	+ 5
Year 11	272.7	*yield*	95.4	+ 5
Year 12	373.1	*yield*	130.6	+ 5
Year 13	508.7	*yield*	178.0	+ 5
Year 14	691.7	*yield*	242.1	+ 5
Year 15	933.8	*yield*	326.8	+ 5
etc.				
Small independent herds:				
Year 1	10	*yield*	3.5	
Year 2	13.5	*yield*	4.7	
Year 3	18.2	*yield*	6.4	
Year 4	24.6	*yield*	8.6	
Year 5	33.2	*yield*	11.6	
Year 6	44.8	*yield*	15.7	
Year 7	60.5	*yield*	21.2	
Year 8	81.7	*yield*	28.6	
Year 9	110.3	*yield*	38.6	
Year 10	148.9	*yield*	52.1	
Year 11	201.0	*yield*	70.2	
Year 12	271.2	*yield*	94.9	
Year 13	366.1	*yield*	128.1	
Year 14	494.2	*yield*	173	
Year 15	667.2	*yield*	233.5	
etc.				

[b] Including increments from reproduction and from camp master's minimum payments, but not from thefts.

bucks from his increasing herd to feed himself and his family, if he has one. Hence, the increment rate not only of the does (because of the gift increment), but also of the total herd, is larger than the growth rate for either of the other types of herd, since no bucks are slaughtered.

Second, the small herder, assuming a hypothetical start from scratch, would take several years, *under the most favorable circumstances,* to reach the number of does just above the minimal range limits. During those years he might suffer from any or all of the hazards to small herds discussed at length above. The increment rate shown is, then, maximum and likely to be much lower, especially when the total herd is considered, since he and his family must take their food from the quite small absolute increase. The percentage effect of taking two or three animals from this increase is much greater for the small herds than it is for the large, where the number taken out for food is nowhere near the same proportion as in the former (see below).

Third, the rate of human population growth is necessarily very markedly slower than that of reindeer. Therefore, in general, the consumption of reindeer cannot increase at the same rate as the reindeer increase, even if reindeer are consumed in additional uses such as for skins for trade. Among the wealthy herders, reindeer accumulate in such huge numbers as sooner or later, or continuously, to require techniques or events to limit herd sizes. It can be seen in the idealized figures of the table that the number of does of a herd *alone* would reach the maximum limit of permissible herd size in six years, starting with 1000 breeding does.

It is in view of this situation that the great epidemics and climatic excesses affecting both man and animal[14] which, judging by

---

[14] Bogoras mentions "periodic epidemics" (p. 40) and the following catastrophes:

1850	syphilis epidemic (p. 41)
1880	famine (reduction of animals for climatic reasons?) (p. 29)
1884	smallpox epidemic in the lower Kolyma area (pp. 26, 40, 82)
1899	smallpox epidemic (p. 719)
1900	measles epidemic (pp. 29, 40–41)
1901	famine (p. 101)
1901	hoof disease epidemic on the Omolon (p. 73)
1900–1901	drastic winter with loss of about half of herds in northern area (p. 27)

(Footnote continued on next page)

Bogoras' casual mentions (pp. 27, 29, 40, 41, 48, 73, 82), seem to
have occurred roughly every twenty to thirty years, as well as the
lesser summer and winter epidemics (see above), and annual flu
epidemics for over one hundred years (*ibid.*, p. 41), may be said
to be functional, even though obviously not intended by the Chukchi. As I have pointed out, the epidemics not only kill off humans
and animals, but tend directly or indirectly to affect the larger
herds more severely, thus effectively exercising a control over the
almost limitless growth near the upper range limits suggested in
the table. Needless to say, this "method" of herd control is totally
unpredictable, so that, from the point of view of the individual
herdsman, the reduction may be catastrophic, as in the case of the
man who lost 3000 reindeer in three days (see above). But from
the point of view of the human population, as such, the reduction,
if not excessive, is "adaptive" to the environment, and the stricken
herdsman, with the compelling Chukchi values, is driven to begin
his cycle of herd aggrandizement again.

Herd Division

An extremely important procedure, both technical and social,
for exercising control over the herds near the upper range limits
is herd division. I have already discussed the division of herds re-

---

no date   famine (p. 82)
no date   scab disease epidemic (p. 81) with the example of the wiping out of a
           herd of 3000 animals in 3 days
    Hoof disease occurs more or less yearly, killing reindeer by the score (p. 80). It
should be recalled that an epidemic affecting the human population lethally also
reduces herds, since the labor for maintaining the herds is lost; for example, in the
smallpox epidemic of 1884, one-third of the human population was killed (pp. 26,
719) and the wild reindeer were replenished by the tame (p. 82); and in the measles epidemic, children, important as herd helpers, died, with the result of scatter-
ing the herds (pp. 40–41). The 1901 hoof disease epidemic greatly reduced herds.
1901's severe winter did the same. Bogoras mentions that the smallpox epidemic of
1884 was only the latest of several. He says that famine occurred at least every other
year on the Kolyma among the Russian and Russianized native population (p. 716).
He speaks of periodic epidemics (p. 40); epidemics every ten or fifteen years (p.
35); epidemics which reduced the conquerors (Russians?) as well. He quotes an
old man of Indian Point as saying (p. 36): "The spirits . . . take care that the
people of this country shall not multiply. In olden times war was sent down to ward
off increase. After that, in spite of the abundant variety of sea-game, famine would
come and carry off the surplus. At present, with the fulsome supply of American
food, the disease comes down, and the result is exactly the same."

volving about the departure of full-term assistants. The larger the
herd, the more assistants will it have, and hence, the more frequently will assistants depart with small herds. The table shows
that, even with minimum payment in does, such a small herd may
amount to a considerable number of beasts after some years, provided no major catastrophes affecting the larger herd have also
affected the assistant's animals. Starting empty-handed, an assistant might achieve an ideal 765 does or so in fifteen years, but given
any of a series of herd-reducing occurrences, the increments would
be reduced throughout, so that his actual achievement after fifteen years would be more like that supposed for four or five
years earlier at the idealized rate of 32.5 per cent; that is, somewhere between 177 and 239 does. This theoretical number cor-
responds to the number mentioned by Bogoras as being more or
less characteristic of the size of herds with which an assistant went
off to herd alone (p. 622: 100 does in a few years, 300 does in fifteen). Periodic removal of assistants from a large herd would of
course depress the rate of absolute growth of the large herd well
below that posited in the table.

Besides spalling off parts of the herd by the departure of assistants, there are other types of herd division. A master herdsman,
or "master of the camp" or "strongest one," as Bogoras (pp. 612–
614 *et passim*) calls him, recognizes when his herd is getting too
large to be sufficiently mobile or when it is likely to outrun food
resources in any given locale. He has two alternatives.

The first procedure he may use is to divide the herd among his
closest relatives, or, failing these, less close relatives; the second is
to put parts of the herd in charge of those assistants most closely
tied to the camp, especially by incorporation into the family group
by marriage or adoption. Division of the herd among close family
members is much preferred. Sons and brothers, at least ideally,
are possessed of blood which is thicker than water. In fact, however, the blood appears to thin as soon as the son or brother has
gone off to new pasture lands with his part of the divided herd.
Sooner or later, it becomes a *de facto* if not a *de jure* new herd,
and hence also a new camp and an independent self-maximizing
economic unit. The old man complains bitterly that the son or

brother has behaved ill. He threatens to go forth to recapture his herd, but in fact never does. Of course he does not! On the one hand, he does not intimately know the territory where the herd is situated, and, on the other, he would ruin his own resources if he brought it back. The purpose of splitting it off in the first place would be defeated. The same fissioning process takes place with the trusted assistants, naturally. This arrogation of herd rights to oneself is of course reinforced by the ideology, especially by incentives to quarrel and to be violent in the protection of one's own interests.

The fissioning is, needless to say, also a social one, since new camps linked through males are constantly being created—the foundation, indeed, for the patrilateral kinship ties of the Chukchi.[15] Fissioning by herd division contributes to the spacing out of both reindeer and human populations, and, hence, to maximizing the use of the total resources of the area in a wider variety of ecological niches.

Several techniques of herd control and reduction have been previously mentioned in other connections. Herd captures remove a number of animals from the large herd. The killing of pregnant does—both reducing the breeding stock and removing any potential new breeder—has also been mentioned. Giving of prizes at races, usually as a gift from a wealthy donor, also removes a certain number of animals from a herd (Bogoras, p. 264).

Again, when a young man has worked more or less time for his prospective and new father-in-law and is finally released from service, he is given a part of the herd (Bogoras, p. 586). Bogoras

---

[15] I have referred above to the difficulty of designating the form of Chukchi kinship. However, a number of references made by Bogoras, especially to fire boards and their inheritance (pp. 348–353), reindeer earmarks (p. 677), and generally the relationships between herds, on one hand, and fathers-sons, brothers, and other male kinsmen (e.g., p. 678), on the other, suggests strong patrilateral, if not patrilineal, ties (see p. 537). Antropova and Kuznetsova (p. 820) speak of the "father's line" with respect to fire boards, which were also symbols of the camp and its masters, even when camps split among a number of sons.

Given the central articulatory position of men in the total ecological picture I have described, and the fact that women are tied to the movements of the men as well as to their successes and failures of all sorts, one should be able to predict kin features based on ties through males rather than through females. This is, of course, confirmed by the data.

gives no statistics. This practice redistributes animals according to labor available, while also reducing the herd size.

Sacrifice

Perhaps one of the most important means of herd reduction is sacrifice. Larger sacrifices are made by men with greater herds. The main sacrifices occur in the late summer and early fall (Bogoras, p. 372) when the herd and the hearth are rejoined for the coming winter, a notable ceremonial occasion represented in a variety of symbolic forms translating the economic and social ties of kinship into ideological paradigms, for example, the fire boards as paradigms of the patrilateral kin ties along which cooperation and mutual support are most likely to occur (see Bogoras, especially pp. 350–354).

It may be noted that although these sacrifices are religiously and ceremonially sanctioned, they also serve significant practical ends: providing food and supplying fawn skins (the best for the purpose) for clothes and for trading as well (Bogoras, p. 372). Male fawns and large bucks are killed, each accompanied by a female, "wife" fawn (*ibid.*, p. 373) —plainly a device reducing the number of potential breeders and, hence, the rate of herd accumulation. Bogoras notes, however, that *poor* herders usually slaughter only a couple of bucks or a single (male?) fawn; that is, they keep the females, breeding or potentially so, in order to increase the herd. Incidentally, when fawns are killed an opportunity for drinking milk is provided, since it can then be taken from the mothers (*ibid.*, p. 374).

The importance of the rich breeders in the major ceremonies is made explicit by Bogoras (p. 375). Rich men invite guests from far and near, sometimes including foreign tribesmen. As remarked above, invitations may be sent out, even by personal messenger, so that there is no excuse for the visitors' absence. A fawn is killed for each guest as a gift, with precedence for women and strangers! The first arrival gets two or three, the rest one, unless they ask for more, in which case more are given. It is dangerous to refuse, since the guest may bewitch him who refuses—again a sanction acting in support of resource distribution and herd size control. A rich man may kill as many as 100 to 120 fawns at such a time, one-third or more going to the guests, a half of the rest to the camp, and the remainder for trade. Bogoras remarks that only later, after a time interval and under conditions which he does not specify, do the guests make presents to the host. Foreigners give dissimilar commodities in return, also at a later date. But poor men, be it remarked, do not give returns (Bogoras, p. 375) ; for them, it would seem, the redistribution is final, and it spares them a certain amount of killing in their own small herds.

Smaller sacrifices occur all year round. For example, there is the sacrifice connected with the establishment of the permanent winter house, at which two or three animals are killed. Again, there is a sacrifice at the time of the winter solstice (Bogoras, p. 376) ; one to the sun between the first and second lunar months of the Chukchi year; one between the "first" and "second" summers, when the herd is being driven to summer pasture; or, again, sacrifices are made on any unusual occasion such as before beginning a trip, on returning from a trip, at markets for the good will of the local spirits, for protection by or against unusual spirits (*ibid.*, p. 377) ; and there is also the young moon sacrifice, which removes a few reindeer monthly (*ibid.*, p. 378) .

There is, thus, a continual series of killings which are religiously sanctioned and have the dual effect of supplying food over and beyond the secular kills and of siphoning off excess animals from the herds, especially the larger ones. Furthermore, there are the antler ceremonies, three or four a year, at each of which a number of deer are killed. Bucks of different ages produce antlers at different times of the year. Thus, they provide a steady source for the ceremonially used antlers (Bogoras, p. 377) and, by the same token, they are continuously removed from the herd to provide food.

Another series of sacrifices revolve around death, burial, and continued commemoration at the grave of the deceased, apparently for years. For example, on the second day after the open-air burial, prepared food is distributed by the family of the deceased to many camps, within a radius of fifty miles (Bogoras, p. 530) . But also reindeer are killed (*ibid.*, p. 531) . If the family is rich,

each guest, including children, gets a reindeer—in effect, cutting
out that part of the herd work load which the dead man may have
been responsible for, again a mechanism for adjusting herd size
and labor to each other. At the same time, of course, the herd is
diminished. On other occasions the herd may be divided among
kinsmen heirs (*ibid.*, p. 678). Poor men kill only a few reindeer
and distribute them only to their friends, as one would expect
from what has gone before. Five days after the ceremony, another,
the feast of antlers, takes place. Antlers also become important as
grave goods, but the best ones come from wild reindeer—an ideological stimulus to successful hunting—or from those domesticated bucks that produce palmated antlers—an incentive to raise
such more effectively.

Trade

There are still other, and mostly new, social institutions which
contribute to herd decrease. One of these is the meeting of Russians and Chukchi at annual fairs, for whose festivities the Chukchi, especially the rich herders, slaughter large numbers of beasts,
a case of 1200 at one time being recorded. Another is trade
among the Chukchi and between the Chukchi and the Americans
or especially the Russians, particularly for furs of both adult and
young reindeer (and other animals as well), in return for metal
goods, tea, sugar, flour, and even guns, which are aids in hunting.
A third comprises various types of connubial arrangements with
Russians in the outpost towns. The Russians are supported by a
flow of meat supplies, skins, and peltries. The trade and marriage
institutions, according to Bogoras (pp. 592–594), lead to the continual slaughter of probably hundreds or thousands of animals.

The main traders and intermarriers, needless to say, are wealthier Chukchi, those with larger herds whose upper limits have to
be controlled. In these instances, the control over the upper
ranges of size is exercised by means of exchange with the Russians
for advantages in addition to that of pruning the herds down to
an optimal range—advantages such as women, tools, weapons,
foods, and delicacies. It should be pointed out that the great increase of Chukchi herds and the expansion of the Chukchi spa-

tially appear to have been contemporaneous with the Russian contact and acculturation in that area beginning in the first half of the seventeenth century.

CONCLUSIONS

Much more might be said, more institutions, more customs, more values, more ideological paradigms brought into the scope of this analysis. For example, it would be of interest to pursue the ecological significance of polygyny, *de facto* polyandry, "group marriage," inheritance, feuds, and so on. All, I believe, tend to confirm the interpretation given here with startling uniformity and neatness. For present purposes, the analysis above is sufficient to indicate the operation of a self-equilibrating system whose fundamental, environmentally undetermined given is reindeer use. I have shown that a whole series of institutions contributes to keeping herd sizes within a rather broad range of optimal values. The institutions serve to redistribute resources in reindeer as environmental conditions warrant, in an elaborate system of herd joining and herd division. Concomitantly, these institutions operate to redistribute various kinds of labor—young men's, old men's, strong poor men's, young women's, older women's, and so on—according to the continuing short- and long-term ecologically determined flux of resources and labor needs, and in a generally highly rational manner, mostly conscious.

I have also briefly suggested other types of transfers and conversions, as between wealth, strength, and prestige. To these, polygyny may be added, especially since courtship service, as I have said, is abbreviated or absent during the acquisition of plural wives, if indeed they are not freely tendered to the prestigeful, the violent, the strong, the "master of a camp." These transferables or convertibles are reconvertible into reindeer or into labor when these are needed.

I have also shown how the values attached to violence, strength, prestige, and the like, constantly impel people to increase their wealth and hence to foster their physical continuity as a people in a harsh environment.

I have, in effect, described the Chukchi in terms of systems, cybernetic, or servomechanism concepts. Cultures, approached from the ecological point of view, appear to be singularly accessible to systems analysis. Systems analysis seems to facilitate wholistic[16] socio-cultural descriptions without falling into the trap of organicism; without having to posit purpose or final causes; without having to assume consciousness of participants *a priori*. It seems to afford a much more effective way of relating all kinds of phenomenologically diverse variables to one another than older approaches, as I believe this and other papers in the present volume show. Finally, it lends itself to much more precise and operational demonstration of propositions, especially by means of pointing toward appropriate quantifications.[17]

In conclusion, a word about the fact that we are dealing here with an animal resource. I am not certain that the qualities of being animal determine specific socio-cultural characteristics different from those dependent on being a plant: some parallels were drawn in this paper with swidden systems. However, the mobile and durable characteristics of animals, the fact that they can be used in a variety of types of exchange both as representation of value and, in themselves, as actual value, that is, as food, seems to me important. I suggest that some of the extreme individualistic, aggressive, and competitive traits of the Chukchi are connected with the necessity for individual competence and resourcefulness in dealing with these large, half-wild animals aggregated into herds which are immensely difficult to maintain, handle, and utilize.[18]

---

[16] Wholistic descriptions in terms of general system theory are referred to in Bertalanffy (1956, p. 6) and are extensively discussed in Hall and Fagen (1956, pp. 21–22, 26–27).

[17] See, in connection with systems approaches to functional analysis: Baggett, 1964; Collins, 1964a, 1964b, and the last paper in this volume; Leeds, 1963; Vayda, 1961a, 1961b; Vayda, Leeds, and Smith, 1961.

[18] It is interesting to note that the Eskimo, on the whole, are reported as friendly, cheery, and the like; not quarrelsome, cantankerous, violent, antagonistic, and hostile like the Chukchi. At the same time, they do not have a pattern of exigent herding like the Chukchi, but must, for the most part, operate more individually and with respect to more individually occurring resources, i.e. game. I believe that herein may lie some of the reasons for the difference in temperament and ideology between the two peoples.

REFERENCES

ANTROPOVA, V. V., and V. G. KUZNETSOVA. 1956. The Chukchi. In *The Peoples of Siberia* (M. G. Levin and L. P. Potapov, editors; English translation, S. Dunn, editor), pp. 799–835. University of Chicago Press, Chicago, Ill., 1964.

BAGGETT, S. 1964. A functional analysis of the Mexican military. MS. William Jennings Bryan Prize Paper in Political Science, University of Texas.

BERG, L. S. 1937. *Natural Regions of the U.S.S.R.* English translation, O. A. Titelbaum. The Macmillan Co., New York, N. Y., 1950.

BERTALANFFY, L. VON. 1956. General system theory. In *General Systems, Yearbook of the Society for the Advancement of General Systems Theory, 1,* 1–10.

BOGORAS, W. 1904–1909. *The Chukchee.* Jesup North Pacific Expedition, vol. 7 (3 parts). Am. Mus. Nat. Hist., Mem. 11. Brill, Leiden, Netherlands.

BOGORAS, W. 1910. *Chukchee Mythology.* Jesup North Pacific Expedition, vol. 12. Am. Mus. Nat. Hist., Mem. 11. Brill, Leiden, Netherlands.

COLLINS, P. 1964a. *The Logic of Functional Analysis in Anthropology.* University Microfilms, Ann Arbor, Mich.

COLLINS, P. 1964b. Towards a reconstruction of functionalism; The aim of functional analysis. Read at annual meeting, American Anthropological Association, Detroit.

CONKLIN, H. C. 1957. *Hanunóo Agriculture; A Report on an Integral System of Shifting Cultivation in the Philippines.* Food and Agriculture Organization of the United Nations, Rome.

CZAPLICKA, M. A. 1914. *Aboriginal Siberia; A Study in Social Anthropology.* Clarendon Press, Oxford, England.

DOLGIKH, B. O. 1960. *Rodovoi i plemennoi sostav narodov Sibiri v XVII veke.* Trudyi Instituta Etnografii, new ser. V, 55. Izdatyelstvo Akademia Nauk, Moscow.

HALL, A. D., and R. E. FAGEN. 1956. Definition of system. In *General Systems, Yearbook of the Society for the Advancement of General Systems Theory, 1,* 18–28.

Karta Narodov. 1956. Geological Ministry of the U.S.S.R., Moscow.

LEEDS, A. 1961. The Yaruro incipient tropical forest horticulture— Possibilities and limits. In *Antropológica,* Suppl. Pub. No. 2, *The Evolution of Horticultural Systems in Native South America —A Symposium* (J. Wilbert, editor), pp. 13–46. Editorial Sucre, Caracas.

LEEDS, A. 1963. The functions of war. In *Violence and War; with Clinical Studies* (J. Masserman, editor), vol. 6 of *Science and Psychoanalysis*. Grune and Stratton, New York, N. Y.

LEVIN, M. G., and L. P. POTAPOV, editors. 1956. *The Peoples of Siberia*. English translation, S. Dunn, editor. University of Chicago Press, Chicago, Ill., 1964.

MURDOCK, G. P. 1957. World ethnographic sample. *Am. Anthropologist, 59* (4), 664–687.

ODULOK, T. 1934. *Snow People (Chukchee)*. Behavior Science Translations. Human Relations Area Files, New Haven, Conn., 1954.

VAYDA, A. P. 1961a. Expansion and warfare among swidden agriculturalists. *Am. Anthropologist, 63* (2), 346–358.

VAYDA, A. P. 1961b. A reexamination of Northwest Coast economic systems. *Trans. N. Y. Acad. Sci.,* II, *23* (7), 618–624.

VAYDA, A. P., A. LEEDS, and D. B. SMITH. 1961. The place of pigs in Melanesian subsistence. *Proc. 1961 Ann. Spring Meeting, Am. Ethnol. Soc.,* pp. 69–77. University of Washington Press, Seattle, Wash.

Camel Pastoralism in North Arabia and the Minimal Camping Unit

LOUISE E. SWEET

Department of Anthropology, State University of New York,
Harpur College, Binghamton, New York

TRADITIONAL ACCOUNTS of the north Arabian Bedouin tribes have emphasized the fluctuation between tribal unity and disunity, intertribal conflict, and internal feuding. They have thereby given a confusing and contradictory picture of a desert pastoral society at once cohesive and divisive, aristocratic and equalitarian, communalistic and intensely individualistic. More recently an attempt has been made to characterize this polarity of Arab Bedouin society in more rigorous terms: it shows "the potentiality for massive aggregation of agnatic units, on one hand, and atomistic individualism on the other." It is said to lack stable or corporate segmentary organization below the level of the tribe, although segmentation processes along agnatic lines, ordered by genealogical relationships and ideology, form its basic structural design (Murphy and Kasdan, 1959, p. 21).

I should like to propose here that recognition of a relatively stable social unit smaller than the tribe may help to dispel some of the confusion over the internal structure and cohesion of Bedouin tribal society, and may clarify the nature of minimal camping units in relation to other units of the tribe. This smaller unit, the tribal section, governs a number of aspects of the techniques and economics of camel pastoralism in north Arabia, and it shows features of corporate structure and process in relation to the control of productive resources. Control and protection of resources

129

is vested in the section and administered through a redistribution system. The section is flexible in size and internal organization in response to ecological conditions and is corporately organized for nomadic grazing movement as well as for the defense of its herds and their aggrandizement by predation. This is in contradiction to the statement that in Bedouin society "there are no lineages in the sense of bounded groups having a continuing and cohesive base in corporate rights and duties" (Murphy and Kasdan, 1959, p. 24).

Attention to the empirical data that are available on the techniques and economics of camel pastoralism in north Arabia, rather than merely to the logic of kinship, blood feud, and parallel cousin marriage, requires notice of this structure and of its relation to the camel as the strategic resource of the Bedouin tribes.

I shall deal first with the camel, its capacities and requirements, its role in Bedouin economy, and then shall endeavor to show how adaptation to these factors is related to the organization of the societies dependent upon this animal and to the corporate structure of the tribal section. (See Appendix, section 1.)

ECOLOGY AND CAMELS

The steppes and desert of north Arabia have been occupied for some three thousand years by camel pastoralist societies. From time to time they have overrun the agricultural societies on the northern rim of their range or have given rise to oasis-based kingdoms to the south. Within the arid regions in which their culture developed, however, the Bedouin camel-breeding tribes have maintained a distinctive pattern and a dominant position over other societies and settlements in their territories by virtue of their ability to exploit the grazing ranges into which other local economies cannot spread, and by virtue of their fighting strength, mobility, and control of communication routes. The camel is their basic resource and tool for dominance. The Bedouin tribes of camel-breeding specialists, such as the Rwala, Shammar, and Mutair, are to be distinguished from the non-Bedouin peoples in the same region who use the camel for transport and labor, but whose econo-

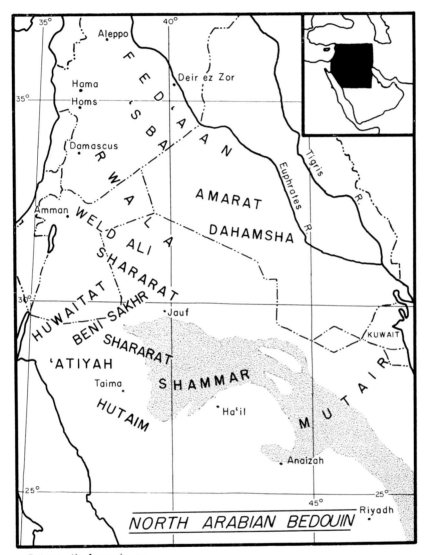

Robert K. Argersinger

BEDOUIN TRIBES OF NORTH ARABIA

The stippled area indicates the Nefud, the chief grazing area of the
Shammar Bedouin

mies are based upon shepherd pastoralism, agriculture, commerce, or specialized services and crafts. (See Appendix, section 2.) The northern tribes are also to be distinguished from camel breeders of south and southeastern Arabia, whose herds are smaller and whose usages are somewhat different. The discussion here will be confined primarily to the better-known northern tribes, particularly the Rwala, the Shammar tribes of the Nejd, and the Mutair.

The camel is the largest of the domesticated animals of Arabia. Its range and scale of uses, its specific adaptations to desert conditions, and its limitations are the foundations of Bedouin culture. As a source of food it provides both meat and milk, but for the Bedouin the camel is more significant as a milk producer. In the desert and steppe environments of north Arabia few other food resources are available. Game (gazelle, lizards, birds), plants (truffles, the semḥ seed), and locusts are sporadically utilized, but they are seasonal in availability, difficult to procure, and sparse in yield. The camel herds provide a more stable food supply. But camels mature slowly and reproduce slowly as compared with other domestic dairy and meat animals such as sheep and goats. A female camel is bred for the first time in her sixth year, and then only once in two years produces a single offspring. If this offspring is a male cub, it is more often butchered than kept, in order to conserve the mother's milk for human use (Johnstone, 1961, p. 294). Milking camels are the heart of the herd and are never sold. The female gives milk for 11 to 15 months, and it is this unique lactation period that makes camels the only dependable year-round source of food. The yield per animal, however, is small, varying from 1 to 7 liters per day according to season and pasturage (Musil, 1928b, pp. 88–89). In order to meet subsistence needs in milk, minimum herd size must therefore be maintained and the herd must be managed so that both pregnant and lactating females are available to ensure a continuous supply; hence there is strong pressure to increase herd size.

The literature on the Bedouin provides no clear information on the minimal number of animals required to support a family. There is apparently great variation in wealth in camels, but there are also many facets of interdependence and customary means of supporting the poorest folk. One example may suggest a median figure. My Dosiri Bedouin informant in Kuwait in 1959 regarded his family as relatively secure and well off with about 18 female camels, half of which were pregnant and half giving milk. In addition to these, his family had at least two strong baggage camels for transporting the tent and equipment and bringing water, as well as a few riding camels. He felt his family to be well enough supplied with milking camels to be able to lend some to kinsmen who had no fresh animals. The British estimates of tribal herd strengths about 1917 are based on allowing 20 camels as an average figure per tent (Great Britain, Admiralty, 1917, p. 77). Subsistence needs satisfied from the milking camels are, however, only one aspect of the use of camels by the Bedouin. Nor is milk their only food.

Although camels also provide meat, this is rarely, if ever, a part of the daily Bedouin diet, but rather is a feature of the ceremony of hospitality and of sacrifices on such special occasions as the return of successful raiding parties or the fulfillment of vows. There is no way to gauge the possible frequency of such contexts in which a camel would be butchered for a feast. Musil notes that usually the only meat eaten by the Rwala Bedouin is camel meat, but it is a luxury (1928b, p. 96).

The transport uses of camels—for riding, carrying domestic equipment, and fetching water—are probably of as great general significance as the food uses, since these uses and capacities of the camel enable the Bedouin to penetrate grazing ranges inaccessible to small-animal breeders, to migrate over greater distances, and to mobilize mounted warrior parties. The diversified uses of camels are reflected in differences between milking, baggage, and fine riding types as well as between breeds distinctive in color and build and characteristic of different tribes and regions of Arabia. Mention should also be made of the use of hair and hides for tents and especially the largest water bags, and of the fat.

Camels are more commonly used for meat in Egypt, throughout the north Arabian oasis towns, and in the urban centers of the Levant. Moreover, the work capacity of the camel to carry freight, 150 to 300 kilograms per animal (Musil, 1928a, p. 453), and to pull plows or irrigation apparatus is utilized extensively in commercial and agricultural activities of other Arabian societies.

Hence among the Bedouin breeding or acquiring camels for sale exerts additional pressure to maximize the herds. Exchanging camels (males and old or barren females) in the oasis town markets or selling them to the itinerant merchants moving among the tribes is as important as predatory tactics in obtaining supplies of arms, grain foods and condiments, domestic hardware, and textiles. It should be noted here that camel pastoralism in north Arabia appears to have developed long after the rise of the ancient oriental civilizations (Mikesell, 1955), and therefore has operated in continuous contact with complex, inter-regionally supplied economies in which money and market systems of exchange only recently developed. This contact cannot be ignored as an influence on Bedouin camel breeding and herd building, as well as on Bedouin social structure. However, there is no clear evidence that the tribesmen buy or sell camels among themselves at all.

For the Bedouin the camel is thus a multipurpose resource for food and other materials, a valuable commodity for exchange, a means of heavy transport, and a fast-moving durable mount for defensive and offensive movement. In combination, these features are superior to those of any other animal in Arabia and render the Bedouin superior to or independent of non-Bedouin societies in the same region at strategic points of interaction with them.

The capacity of camels to tolerate extremes of heat and lack of water, to thrive on desert plants beyond the capacities of other domestic animals, and to cover great distances in the course of nomadic grazing supports Bedouin life in the outer ranges of the ecological niche of desert pastoralism. But the climate and rainfall regime of north Arabia and the geographical distribution of permanent watering points enforce an annual migration pattern which, after winter in the interior desert, converges upon summer camping places in the vicinity of settled areas. The range of a pastoral society in north Arabia thus includes winter pastures, permanent watering points for summer, and access to an urban market. These are the basic features of the tribal territory, and it is the relatively stable dominance over such a territory, with its other inhabitants, over time by a group of genealogically related agnatic segments which identifies the Bedouin tribe. The Rwala tribal territory, for example, extends from the vicinity of Damascus, their summer camping zone, to the southeast between the Wadi Sirhan and the Anaizah highland, and into the sand desert of the Nefud, south of Jauf oasis, a distance of some 800 kilometers (Raswan, 1947, p. 5).

The great size of tribal territories and the long nomadic grazing treks are features of camel pastoralism. Müller says the normal migration range of the camel tribes is about 600 kilometers and in some years may reach 700 or 800 (1931, p. 97). Such extensive ranges seem to be required because of sparse and sporadic distribution of vegetation and the variable rainfall patterns—the cyclic patterns of years of drought and years of abundance, and the annual variation within one tribal grazing zone.

Desert vegetation provides three categories of plants on which the herds depend for forage: annual grasses and plants, xerophytic surface perennial shrubs, and perennials which survive the dry, hot months by root and bulb adaptations. The Bedouin rainfall and plant lore recorded by Musil and others indicates that the full growth cycle of these plants, providing the most abundant pasturage through the year, requires a sequence of good rains from early October until the final storms that may occur in mid April or May. The failure of the early rains in any area, especially those of November, affects the later development of plants, especially the annuals, and spells trouble for the herds. An abundant growth of the annual plants, particularly from March to mid April, is especially necessary for the kinds of pasturage that will result in abundance of milk from the camels. If the autumn and winter rains fail or are meager for two or three years running, then the growth of annuals will fail altogether (Musil, 1928*b*, pp. 8–16). In such years of extreme drought affecting a whole tribal area, the tribe must move into better-favored areas. Such an emergency emigration may be accomplished by peaceable agreement with allied tribes (Dickson, 1949, p. 46) or by threat or use of force against others.

The number of camels which the north Arabian tribal territories can carry in view of the pasturage and rainfall variation is not known in any systematic or accurate fashion. The few figures available are scarcely more than estimates. One that is given for the Rwala is perhaps suggestive: in the 1930's (1936?) they were

said to number 35,000 persons in 7000 tents, and to own some
350,000 camels (Raswan, 1947, p. 36). This was a year of extreme
drought, and the Rwala lost many camels before they successfully
threatened and negotiated their way into the territory of a neighboring tribe for the season. Montagne has characterized the north
Arabian area as "overpopulated" and says there is intense competition for pasturage (1947, p. 23). But such competition and temporary tribal emigration seem rather to be features of the drought-
end years of a rainfall cycle. (See Appendix, section 3.) Though
camels are bred in many other parts of Arabia, the north Arabian
steppes and deserts are the optimum breeding areas, if the location there of the greatest herds and the most powerful Bedouin
societies is an adequate measure.

Within a tribal territory the rainfall pattern varies each year
in such a way that areas of good pasturage one year may be barren the next. A sector occupied by some agnatic segments or families of a Bedouin tribe may be more favored than that of other
segments or families. Though it is logical to suppose that freedom
of access to adequate pasturage is a condition of tribal life, how
this is regulated within the tribal structure of north Arabian Bedouin society has not been fully understood. It is not patently de-
ducible, for there are at least two possible modes: (1) independent movement of the minimal property-holding and camel-herding
units of extended or joint families, and (2) coordinated and cooperative movement of larger units composed of a number of
genealogically related families. Determining which mode is operative requires a clearer understanding of the structure of Bedouin
society than is now available. The discussion below of the significance of the tribal section as a corporate unit may contribute to
the solution of this problem.

FISSIONING IN THE SOCIAL ORDER AND ECOLOGY:
THE CAMPING UNIT

Security depends on striving to maintain and increase the size
of the herds that support any given social unit, in order to counteract any hazards of the habitat (drought, disease, accident) and

other factors that may tend to reduce the herds below the survival limits for man. These limits, however, are set not only by the subsistence and domestic transport use of camels by the Bedouin, but also by their exchange value for equipment and supplementary foods (chiefly dates and wheat) taken into the desert, and their military use for offense and defense. A "surplus" of camels is required above subsistence needs. When the slow breeding rate of the camels, failure of pasturage, or loss by theft and raid threatens the security of a unit, its members have recourse to certain actions which are to a considerable extent formalized in Bedouin society. First, they may secure replacement or increase by predation upon the herds of others. The institutionalization of raiding other Bedouin tribes for camels, with its elaboration of tactics, etiquette, division of spoils, celebration in sacrifice and poetry and song, strikes one as an elaborate "take-away" ceremony comparable to the "give-away" feasts of the northwest coast Indians of North America. Raiding, too, results in the reciprocal distribution of economic goods between societies (Sweet, in press). Predation against non-Bedouin tribes is equally widespread and is prevented only by the payment of tribute or protection fee, often also in camels. Secondly, in times of poor pasturage a Bedouin unit may move with its herds to a more fortunate area. As we have seen, tribal emigration takes place under conditions of widespread drought, but localized droughts may have the same effect upon smaller segments of the society. It would seem that the asserted freedom of minimal lineage groups, families, or even siblings to split from their kinsmen and nomadize by themselves or to join, through the custom of establishing "neighbor" relations, other sections or tribes than their own, is a means of adapting to unfavorable habitat conditions for grazing in local areas, at least temporarily. Thirdly, persons or families who have lost their herds entirely or who have never succeeded in acquiring enough camels to support themselves may join other more fortunate families in various client or free servant roles. Fourthly, new grazing territory or well points may be seized. There is as yet no evidence of such seizure by a unit smaller than the tribe. Finally, Bedouin may partly or completely abandon specialized camel breeding by moving out of the ecological niche in which it flourishes and becoming sedentary or diversifying their economy with sheepherding. Such a process has taken place among Shammar tribes who moved in the nineteenth century across the Euphrates to the Jazira region of Syria.

A pastoral society of atomistically fissioning lineages, uncommitted to any scale of corporate organization or structure other than the tribe, accords well with the mobility required under desert conditions. Such kin groups, however, are vulnerable to predation or competition for pasturage from analogous units which are larger. This implies competition within the tribal structure and territory which does not seem to accord with other facts. Within the Bedouin tribal territory the grazing areas are systematically exploited, herds are managed, and camels or other wealth are distributed within structures which encompass a number of minimal lineages, and which also have means of acting upon or bringing pressure to bear upon vengeance unit operations within their organizations at times of crisis. These are the tribal sections (*fakhd*). Their functions are economic as well as political; in evolutionary perspective, it seems likely that they could well be classed as petty chiefdoms (cf. Sahlins, 1961, p. 327) rather than as segments of "tribal" societies. Musil regularly refers to these units as "clans."

For the exploitation of its territory a Bedouin tribe is divided into a number of segments or sections, the residence units of the peoples of the tribe. Through the annual regime of nomadic movement, each section moves in systematic relation to analogous sections. Dickson says that the Mutair sections set out from their summer camps on the wells, which are "jealously treasured possessions" of the sections (1949, p. 46), one after the other. A serial order of migration is implied, each section separated from the others; in orderly fashion they occupy the pasture areas. The migration proceeds rather slowly, especially in years of abundant pasturage, and the distances between sections apparently allow enough time for the growth of annual plants in the pasture areas, in the course of a few rains, to recover. There is probably a fan-like dispersal of the Mutair sections rather than a rigid serial order of march; Dickson provides very little detail. Musil's accounts of the Rwala indicate quite clearly a parallel movement of sections across the tribal territory (1928*b*, p. 165 *et passim*). Constant communication between the chiefs of sections circulates information on the conditions for grazing and sources for water. A similar regular movement of sections is implied for the Shammar tribes of the Nejd (Montagne, 1932, pp. 71–72). The cyclic movement of the sections thus appears to have a close relation to the variations of the habitat within the tribal range.

Control over and defense of the camel herds is a concern of the whole section. Individual "ownership" of camels has been emphasized to the point of obscuring the operation of social control, vested in the office of the chief and administered through a redistributive system. (See Appendix, section 4.) As a group of genealogically related lineages, a section brands its camels with a common sign. Of the Shammar, Montagne says, "Each section is an association which defends in common its camels, each marked with the same brand" (1932, p. 71). Musil describes the special section herd of the Rwala group with whom he traveled (that of the tribal chief), and seems to imply that other Rwala sections also maintained such herds of white camels, built up from animals selected from raid booty as well as by natural increase. (They are not the total herd of the section, but a selected group under the trusteeship of the chief.) These herds are sources of pride and prestige for the whole section and are guarded by outstanding young men selected from the members of the section lineages (Musil, 1928*b*, pp. 335–336). The herds of a section thus include two categories, the sectional herd and those of varying size and composition which belong to individuals and families. It is unfortunate that no more is known of the distribution of camels within Bedouin economy.

In their position as the dominant power groups of the north Arabian steppes, Bedouin groups also own or control through tribute relations a portion of the products of oasis cultivators. Among the Shammar, at least, the ownership of date palm gardens in oasis settlements is vested in the section; the agreed tribute portion of the harvest is transmitted to the section chief, who then distributes it among the kin groups of his section (Montagne, 1932, p. 71). Among the Rwala a distinction must be made between garden properties in oases owned by chiefly families and the protection tribute paid to the tribe (and probably section) by agricultural settlements or subordinate tribes. In either case, however, the tenant or tributary contributions are subject to distribution among the tribesmen by the chief.

This redistributive role of the section chief is a marked feature of Bedouin society. It functions not only with respect to the obligations of hospitality and the distribution of valuable goods received from outside the section structure, but also in calling upon the collectivity to support the individual. Thus the section chief might call together the prominent men of his unit and assess each man, in proportion to his herds, camels to replace those that a fellow section member had lost in a raid or for other reasons (author's field notes, Dosiri informant, Kuwait, 1959). The chief is expected to see that every needy family has at least the minimum requirement in camels for keeping up with the section. While the section is nomadizing during the winter and spring, selection of grazing areas and of camping places is made in the chief's tent with the collaboration of the leading men of the unit. The chief's tent serves as a collecting point of information of all kinds, but particularly that which bears upon the grazing conditions and security lying ahead of the line of migration. Travelers, couriers from other chiefs, members of independently roving bands of the Salubba peoples, and scouts sent out by the section chief seek him out or are brought to him to report their observations. Although the decision to move and where to move is signaled by the chief, an occasion when he must demonstrate his astuteness, the group may, as one incident in Musil's accounts indicates, override the chief's decision (1928a, pp. 203–204). His authority is by no means despotic, and his status is maintained largely by his demonstrated ability in the economics of herd management, as well as by his generosity, and his success in leading the unit on major predatory raids.

Smith has noted that the "tribe" on the march moves with all the precautions of war (1885, p. 55). Presumably he was referring to the nomadic trek of the section during the winter grazing season. Pasturage scouts and guards move ahead of the group and are organized to defend the other section members and its herds as they move in a body together. In the camp, security and pasturage conditions dictate the camp pattern. Among both the Mutair and the Rwala the tent clusters of kin groups are more or less compactly placed, depending in part upon the terrain and the likelihood of raiders. When a season of consistently good rains has brought forth abundant vegetation, the family and lineage components of the section may pitch their tents close together, since the herds may all be grazed nearby. But in a year of poor and scanty distribution of vegetation, some dispersal of the section according to its subunits is enforced, so that the grazing herds may range over a wider territory. When predators are expected and a more compact encampment is established, the clustering of tents in kin units, with their couched camels, at 200- to 400-yard intervals makes for maximum security and mobilization, as Dickson says of the Mutair. At such a time a balance between the greater mobility of small units and the greater security in gathering numbers of such units together is achieved. Though the raiders may make off with peripheral herds, it is more difficult to pillage the whole camp before resistance can be mobilized. The Shammar likewise order their camp settlements in kin units, and often the whole is surrounded by the tents and animals of nonmembers (clients, herdsmen, merchants, blacksmiths) moving under the protection of the clan section (Montagne, 1932, pp. 72–73).

One of the confusing aspects of earlier accounts of Bedouin society is the lack of distinction among raiding, warfare, and vengeance action. If these activities are distinguished, the function of the tribal section in organized raiding operations emerges more clearly. And the raid itself appears as an institutionalized means of increasing or restoring the herds of the section, or ensuring the "surplus" necessary for maintaining regional dominance. Elaborate rules govern the prosecution of raids between Bedouin tribes, all of whom stand in some degree of kinship relation to one another in the ideology of common genealogical descent. The more closely two mutually raiding tribes are considered to be related to each other, the more the rules restrict taking advantage of prime conditions for attack. The major objective of raids is the capture of camels, particularly adult females. Other property in tents and desirable furnishings may be seized in rare instances of complete rout of the defenders; but even in such cases a raided group will not be completely wiped out or pillaged. The men defending will flee rather than fight when the odds are clearly against them, and women and children must be left with sufficient camels to get them to their nearest kinsmen in neighboring sections. Various rules of restitution also protect the camels and property of persons living with the raided section who are not members of that kin group.

Though raiding relations are formally declared between *tribes*, the organization of raids takes place in the tribal sections, and the raids are necessarily directed at sections of other tribes. The taking and retaking of camels through raiding seems then to serve as a means of circulating or distributing a scarce resource over a wide area (Sweet, in press).

The ancient pattern of northward drift of the camel pastoralist societies out of the less favorable ecological setting of southern and central Arabia and into the better-watered steppes of north Arabia, and the probable southern origin of camel breeding in such less favorable areas (Mikesell, 1955), suggest on the one hand that the raiding complex is an adaptive feature. It offsets the slow reproductive rate of camels, in an area where large herds are an economic and political advantage and where in fact ecological conditions make large herds possible. On the other hand, it may be that the raiders' preference for adult female camels simply by-passes losses due to the localized effects of habitat hazards as well as other factors. That is, in the prolonged and difficult work of breeding and raising camels in a desert environment subject to cyclic periods of drought, the acquisition of an adult female camel suitable for breeding saves five or six years of labor.

The sizes of tribal sections vary widely among the Rwala, Mutair, and Nejd Shammar. This variation probably reflects to a considerable extent ecological differences among the tribal territories which are significant for breeding camels. Of the three Bedouin groups, the Mutair territory lies farthest south and east, and their sections range in size from 20 tents to 200, though most fall between 50 and 100 (Dickson, 1949, pp. 564–566). To the west and slightly north of the Mutair, the Shammar tribes of the Nejd range in section units that average between 200 and 300 tents each (Montagne, 1932, p. 73). The Rwala Bedouin, the most powerful of the north Arabian tribes and representative of the Anaizah group, move in sections that range from 150 to 800 tents, most of them numbering between 300 and 500 (Great Britain, Admiralty, 1917, p. 50). About 1917 the observation was made that the Shammar tribes were not so rich in camels as the tribes of the Anaizah group, but that they must have possessed on the average 20 to 30 camels to a tent, or, having 4000 tents, a total of at least 80,000 animals (*ibid.*, p. 77).

A few general features of the internal organization of a tribal section should be mentioned. The agnatic lineages of a section are ranked relatively to each other; that is, the office of section chief is vested in a chiefly lineage as distinct from non-chiefly lineages. Such hereditary rights in an office may, as Montagne notes, be held through eight to ten generations and then be lost to a rising rival lineage (1932, p. 70). At any one time, however, the lineages of a section are ranked, and the larger the section, the more internal segments, each also ranked, it may contain. ("Fissioning agnatic segments," "prominent families," "subsections" are terms common in the literature that seem to refer to such ranked internal segments of a section; at present the single ranking distinction between chiefly lineages and others is all that can be made, but the possibility of further ranking mechanisms should be considered.) These kin groups who move together and camp together in the section are "fixed lineages" in the sense of the term proposed by Bacon and are to be distinguished from the "sliding lineage" or the egocentric vengeance unit (*khamsa*): the two do not necessarily coincide (Bacon, 1958, pp. 123–134).

At this point there is a regrettable gap in the descriptive data

needed to relate this lineage structure to the actual camping units
and economic activities. There are few detailed descriptions of
the composition of particular tent clusters in a camp or of their
herds and herding. One can only say that the members of a
"fixed lineage" within the section camp together and comprise
one or more extended families. The family cluster of tents within
it (*ahl*), together with its nonmember dependents, if any, is the
minimum or "real" herding unit. The kinsmen of this cluster are
likely to be "the descendants of one grandfather" (author's field
notes, Dosiri informant, Kuwait, 1959). This will give several
possible combinations of brothers, fathers and sons, uncles and
nephews as heads of families, forming a camping unit of close
kinsmen for which parallel cousin marriage would be an advantageous means of intensifying internal cohesion.

There is clearly unequal distribution of wealth in camels among
Bedouin families, in terms of ownership, but kinship obligations
tend to equalize to some extent the access to the camels or to their
products. All writers on the Bedouin distinguish between the majority of "ordinary" poor tribesmen and the minority of wealthy,
most but not all of whom are of chiefly lineages. Apart from this
there is very little to indicate how, except from good fortune in
the natural increase in herds and in raiding, one man may become
more wealthy in camels than another. Good fortune is transitory,
however, and Western observers have also remarked upon the
"fatalism" with which a man may face loss of his wealth through
raids. Only the chiefs, whether of tribe, section, or subsection,
display their economic power in slightly larger tents and finer
equipment.

Besides the core of member patrilineages and their family components, a tribal section includes other persons or families. There
are likely to be fellow tribesmen from other sections; there may
be refugee families or individuals of other tribes. As fellow Bedouin, these are members of the '*aṣiil* or caste of noble tribes, the
camel-breeding specialists, who dominate the north Arabian desert. The greater the reputation and power of a section and its
chief, the more likely it is to attract such reinforcements. There

are also individuals or families from the non-noble or subordinate tribes; the men of this category are usually the herdsmen of the camels. There are also the blacksmith families, the slaves, and the Salubba guides and hunters, the lowest caste of Arabian desert society. Under optimum conditions in north Arabia, such as Musil saw among the Rwala, the tribal section is a mobile petty chiefdom, heterogeneous in composition, and ranked in structure, but organized around a central core of genealogically related patrilineages. It may number five hundred tents and some twenty-five hundred or more people, and control and depend upon more than ten thousand camels.

Everywhere, however, in accounts of the society or in contact with the people themselves, the "individualism" of the Bedouin is noted. When a man has acquired camels, a tent, and a wife, he is not obliged to remain with his father's or brother's or uncle's cluster—an attitude which he expresses assertively—but may independently move with others. A poor man who has no camels seeks a wealthier man and works for him as a herdsman. Each year he receives an animal or two as part of his compensation, and he expects, after seven or eight years of good fortune, to be independent (author's field notes, Dosiri informant, Kuwait, 1959). Such data tend to reinforce the impression of economic "individualism" in Bedouin society. A minor lineage chief within a section, disgruntled with the section chief's treatment of him in the distribution of largess or the collection of tax camels, may remove his kin group from the section temporarily. Such fissioning has been emphasized as a major trait of Bedouin social process, and less attention has been given to data which just as clearly underline the cohesion of Bedouin social units within the key structure of the tribal section. Even after so critical an event as murder, membership in the section is retained by the violator and his kinsmen, and there are customary means of return to it after exile in a distant tribe as fugitives from vengeance. A quarrel at the wells resulting in homicide may split such a small body of kinsmen, the *khamsa* or vengeance unit of the murderer, from the section and send it into refuge with another tribe until the blood price can be arranged. Once it has been settled, however, the kinsmen are welcomed back with feasting and celebration. "For do they not return who might have been lost?" (Musil, 1928a, pp. 489–493) .

Summary

The size, strength, mobility, endurance, and lactating capacity of the camels provide the subsistence base for Bedouin society; for many families, milk may be the only food for several months of the year. In the north Arabian steppes and deserts where conditions for specialized camel breeding are at their optimum, the herds are larger than elsewhere in Arabia and the camping units tend to be correspondingly larger.

The extremes of desert life and dependence upon the camel enforce mobility of the social units, of which the smallest and most mobile is the extended or joint family and its herds. This unit, however, is also the most insecure because of factors tending to deplete the herd: the slow reproductive rate of camels in the face of environmental hazards, the need for supplies produced outside the pastoral economy for which camels must be exchanged, and the threat of raid. Hence three other units of organization within the tribal boundary are functionally significant: the section, composed of a core of ranked lineages; the separate or "fixed" lineages themselves; and the "sliding lineage" or egocentric vengeance unit (khamsa). The section appears to be the maximum unit governing the maintenance of herds in the subregions of the tribal grazing range, and also to be the minimum unit for security against predatory raiders and for the effective mobilization of retaliatory measures to gain animals and to keep the size of the group's herds at maximum. Conditions which demand the dominance of the larger-scale units of organization over the lesser and more atomistic include not only protection from and aggrandizement by predation, but adjustment to such fortuitous hazards as the habitat presents. Likewise, intersectional relations and the relations to other societies, their markets and governments, foster this dominance and the dependence of the smaller units upon the larger. It can be said, then, that the effective minimal camping unit of

Bedouin society is the tribal section. The variability of desert grazing conditions, however, demands flexibility in social arrangements; hence fissioning into lineages and families serves as a means of meeting threatening conditions, and it is ideologically emphasized throughout Bedouin society.

ACKNOWLEDGMENTS. The writer would like to express appreciation to Grace L. Wood Moore for suggestions improving earlier versions of this paper, and to Anthony Leeds for stimulating and careful criticisms leading to the final version.

Field notes gathered from interviews with Bedouin tribesmen and others were taken in Kuwait in 1958–1959, in the course of field research supported by a grant from the Social Science Research Council. The writer's gratitude is also owed to the Kuwait Oil Company for providing opportunities to interview men of pastoral background and to travel widely in Kuwait, and to the hospitality of the State of Kuwait.

APPENDIX

1. SOURCES

Ethnographic and ecological data in this paper are based primarily upon the works of H. R. P. Dickson, Doughty, Müller, Montagne, and Musil cited in the references. In all cases, the writers were in Arabia at times and under circumstances of political upheaval. Only Doughty and Musil actually lived and moved with Bedouin groups for any length of time; Müller and Montagne were involved in forwarding the policies of the French mandate government in Syria after the first World War, and Dickson was similarly engaged as a British political resident stationed at Kuwait. At these times the "normal" flow of economic life was obscured by pressures and activities of the Great Powers. Musil's journeys, spanning the period from 1900 to 1915, likewise reflect the overlay of political tensions developing in the rivalry between the Shammar Rashidi emirate and the rising Saud hegemony.

None of the sources on the Bedouin provide the intensive descriptive and analytic detail needed today for a well developed essay of this type. The culling of anecdotes and of interpretations of poems, and the collating of diary-recorded observations provide the data used here, an awkard and uncertain procedure at best.

2. "Bedouin"

In the use of the term "Bedouin" I have followed Musil (1928*b*, p. 45) and, so far as I know, the usage of the 'aṣiil tribesmen themselves. It designates the tribes who are engaged predominantly in camel breeding and who, in particular, share a common ideology of descent expressed in the traditional tribal genealogies. Two great genealogical plans group Arabian tribes respectively as the descendants of *Ishmael* ("North") or of *Yoktan* ("South"). To what extent these genealogies reflect historical connections would be a matter of lengthy dispute with those historians who accept this interpretation as their major import. Peters (1960) has, on the other hand, demonstrated clearly their immediate political and ecological significance for the Bedouin tribes of Libya. In north Arabia, tribes with genealogies, whose members "know their ancestors," as an Utaibi told me in Kuwait, are 'aṣiil or noble. These are the tribes with which the present paper is concerned. North Arabian desert society is not, however, homogeneous. The steppes and deserts are inhabited by oasis dwellers, small-animal breeders, and a number of pariah or ignoble tribes, peoples who may or may not breed camels exclusively. The Awaazim, Hutaym, and Shararat are among the latter. The blacksmith caste and the Salubba hunters are also to be found in the region, living among or in the tribal territories of the noble tribes. The *control* of wells, pasturage territories, caravan routes, minor settlements is held largely by the Bedouin tribes. This does not exclude others from passage or use, provided the customary arrangements have been made with the dominant tribes, through their chiefs.

Relations between the Bedouin tribes and others are clear and explicit along general lines. The former do not intermarry with the latter, and in particular would not allow their women to do so. Intermarriage between Bedouin tribes is not uncommon, however, especially between chiefly lineages. Moreover, many of the non-noble tribes are "clients" or "serfs" of the Bedouin tribes, or pay tribute to them. Such subordinate tribes are frequently sheep and goat breeders, and some may be engaged in managing properties in flocks of sheep for the Bedouin.

3. Rains, Vegetation, and Grazing

Buxton (1923) is the only source I am aware of for an ecological study of desert life from the biologist's point of view which applies to north Arabia. This supplements and confirms the water and plant lore of the Bedouin, which is most extensively recorded in Musil's several books, together with his own observations.

The plant life of the desert is of two major kinds, annuals and perennials. During the rainy season, from early October until May, depending upon the abundance of rains through the fall sequence, green forage is available for the animals, and water in pools, crevices, wells, or at shallow depth is available for man. With green, lush growth camels need not be watered for as long as 30 days. When the rains cease and heat and aridity dry the annuals to straw and hay and the perennials lose their sappiness, the return to permanent watering places takes place. Camels, as well as other animals, subsist on the dried forage in summer, but require water once every three days or oftener, depending on the heat.

The distribution of vegetation in "areas" is known only for Kuwait (V. Dickson, 1955) and from a few remarks in Musil. The latter mentions that the sand desert area of the Nefud means to the Shammar, in fact, the vegetation area of the *raza* shrub, a good source of forage for camels as well as fuel for the Bedouin (Musil, 1928c, p. 19). Philby, incidentally, has said that the northeastern parts of the Rub' al Khali desert have vegetation areas recognized, named, and exploited by the Murra Bedouin sections (1933, p. 131). Musil's accounts of his exploratory journeys, apart from the Rwala section which often served as his base, list the grazing plants found in various areas, and the lack of them because of failure of rains in a local area over a number of years. There are very few passages in his books which suggest or state that there is *competition* for pasturage between groups whether tribal or subtribal. Rather, the first concern of the migrating group is to locate the best pasturage and water resources ahead of them. Scouts are sent ahead to do so, information is collected from all travelers, and word is sent to other groups. The intense interest of pastoralists in vegetation and water conditions was impressed upon the writer in her contacts with Bedouin in Kuwait. After every trip made to some outlying sector of Kuwait, her informants inquired as to what plants she had seen, how widely and high they grew, if water was standing in pools, if animals were drinking from pools.

The general body of literature on the Arabian pastoralists suggests that, rather than competition leading to conflict, a kind of squatter's rights process takes place: once a good pasture area has been located and settled on by one group, others seek elsewhere, unless the abundance is sufficient for all. But the sectional movement of migration, parallel or serial relative to others, seems to reduce considerably any random searching. Sections *seem* to have customary lines of movement, favorite sites, which however vary over years with the sporadic distribution of rain. Any pasturage seems to be left before it has been eaten out or trampled down completely. Both Müller and V. Dickson suggest explicitly that the camps so move in order to conserve the plants for the future (Müller, 1931, p. 97; V. Dickson, 1955, p. 116). Dickson also says that pastures left for two weeks or so recover; that is, the annuals especially continue to sprout and develop, if the sequence of rains keeps up through the season. In some areas where reeds grow heavily in the vicinity of brackish swamps, the Bedouin may burn them off in summer to improve the fresh growth for pasturage in the following winter (Musil, 1928*a,* p. 337).

4. HERD MANAGEMENT AND OWNERSHIP

Apart from the section herd, camels are clearly held by individuals. Whether the concept of ownership is as fully developed as that of "private ownership" in our sense may be seriously doubted. I have given in the text the general information I have found which indicates that the "herds" carrying the brand of a large kin group, the clan or section, are or may be regarded as communal property in no small sense. Their defense is certainly a concern of the whole section. Men rally to defend the whole herd. In management, inheritance, and other respects, however, camels are held in herds in the name of the head of a household; a man of an extended family which owns twenty camels speaks of them as "our camels," but in referring to a kin cluster of two brothers and their uncle, he will say each man has his camels. These herds, whether small or large, are kept together when couched at night before the owner's tent, and if the "owner" is wealthy in animals they are under the care of a herdsman who is responsible only for those particular animals. However, the herdsmen appear chiefly to lead their particular animals out to graze and to return them to the family tent cluster; in the grazing range, the animals of several owners move or mix together. The location of pasturage is a whole section concern. I think the problem is not one of apparent conflicting principles which must be solved by deciding that the section herds are either communally or privately owned. Both these relations to camels can operate, and grazing and security conditions, death of a family head, maturing or marriage of a son are among the varying conditions which call for the operation of one or the other relationship to ensure the consistent and continuous management of the animals. A man who is "wealthy in camels" is the trustee of a herd in the interest of those who are attached to him as kinsmen, clients, servants, slaves, and so on. But this is a hypothesis for the substantiation of which much more information is necessary. This is an area of great weakness in our knowledge of Bedouin economy.

References

BACON, E. 1958. *Obok; A Study of Social Structure in Eurasia.* Viking Fund Publ. Anthropol., No. 25. Wenner-Gren Foundation for Anthropological Research, Inc., New York, N. Y.

BUXTON, P. A. 1923. *Animal Life in Deserts.* Edward Arnold, London.

DICKSON, H. R. P. 1949. *The Arab of the Desert.* George Allen and Unwin, London.

DICKSON, V. 1955. *The Wildflowers of Kuwait and Bahrein.* George Allen and Unwin, London.

DOUGHTY, C. M. 1937. *Travels in Arabia Deserta.* Random House, New York, N. Y.

GREAT BRITAIN, ADMIRALTY. 1917. *A Handbook of Arabia.* I. *General.* H. M. Stationers' Office, London.

JOHNSTONE, T. M. 1961. Some characteristics of the Dosiri dialect of Arabic as spoken in Kuwait. *Bull. School of Oriental and African Studies, University of London, 24,* 249–297.

MIKESELL, M. K. 1955. Notes on the dispersal of the dromedary. *Southwestern J. Anthropol., 11,* 231–245.

MONTAGNE, R. 1932. Notes sur la vie sociale et politique de l'Arabie du Nord: Les Semmar du Negd. *Rev. études islamiques,* pp. 61–79.

MÜLLER, V. 1931. *En Syrie avec les Bédouins.* E. Leroux, Paris.

MURPHY, R. F., and L. KASDAN. 1959. The structure of parallel cousin marriage. *Am. Anthropologist, 61,* 17–29.

MUSIL, A. 1928a. *Arabia Deserta.* American Geographical Society, New York, N. Y.

MUSIL, A. 1928b. *Manners and Customs of the Rwala Bedouins.* American Geographical Society, New York, N. Y.

MUSIL, A. 1928c. *Northern Neğd; A Topographical Itinerary.* American Geographical Society, New York, N. Y.

PETERS, E. 1960. The proliferation of segments in the lineage of the Bedouin of Cyrenaica. *J. Roy. Anthropol. Inst., 90,* 29–53.

PHILBY, H. ST. J. B. 1933. *The Empty Quarter.* Henry Holt and Co., New York, N. Y.

RASWAN, C. 1947. *Black Tents of Arabia.* Creative Age, New York, N. Y.

SAHLINS, M. D. 1961. The segmentary lineage; An organization of predatory expansion. *Am. Anthropologist, 63,* 322–345.

SMITH, W. R. 1885. *Kinship and Marriage in Early Arabia.* University Press, Cambridge, England.

SWEET, L. E. (In press.) Camel raiding of north Arabian Bedouin; A mechanism of ecological adaptation. *Am. Anthropologist.*

Native Cattle Keeping in Eastern Africa

W. W. DESHLER

Department of Geography, University of Maryland, College Park, Maryland

ONE OF THE DOMINANT ASPECTS of the cultural landscape of the semiarid zones of both eastern and western Africa is the large number of cattle kept by the tribes of these areas. In eastern Africa such tribes as the Masai, the Suk, the Karamajong, the Nuer, and others maintain herds of from four to ten cattle per person. These are spoken of as the "cattle complex" peoples. In these cultures, otherwise diverse, cattle take on an extreme importance. Cattle play a part in tribal ceremonies, and their possession gives prestige. (I am purposely avoiding use of the term wealth.) Cattle have esthetic value, and in some of the tribes men may feel an emotional attachment to them, taking as a second name that of their favorite ox or bull.

There are to us as Western Europeans some puzzling aspects of this emphasis on cattle. Early workers in trying to probe it devoted their attention to the ceremonial role of cattle. Later workers have regarded cattle as the basis of a network of mutual obligations (Colson, 1955) and as important for their contribution to subsistence (Schneider, 1957). Among the most thorough examinations of cattle-keeping societies in eastern Africa is that of P. H. Gulliver (1955). There are cattle-keeping societies of West Africa which show similar culture traits. D. J. Stenning has demonstrated this in his work on the Wodaabe, a pastoral Fulani group of Nigeria (Stenning, 1959). Study of the cattle problem to date has been done almost entirely by anthropologists.

Though the ceremonial role of cattle and the relationships of mutual obligation and social structure lie outside the field of research competence of a geographer, subsistence and its relation to physical landscape do not. The contribution of cattle to subsistence in these societies is more subtle than the literature makes it appear.

A basic question related to that of subsistence is that of herd size. The herds are so large as to produce long-run land deterioration and so would appear to decrease the land resources available. Stock-reducing programs developed by governments in the hope of alleviating the land damage have been repeatedly and effectively opposed by African cattle keepers. This indicates a deeply felt need for large cattle herds. The social anthropologists suggest that the underlying reason for large herd size is that cattle are a form of social security. They observe that at any time many of a man's animals are out on loan to friends and dependents and that the possession of many cattle extends the man's network of mutual obligations. This observer accepts the proposition as a partial explanation of herd size and further suggests that these strong values placed on the possession of large numbers of cattle are related to the utility of cattle in solving problems of survival for the tribe. In effect I am suggesting that the social attitudes toward cattle are related to and may have arisen from subsistence or survival imperatives.

An analysis of field observation of one of the "cattle complex" tribes can be of use in understanding these problems. This paper will discuss the subsistence contribution of cattle and the problem of herd size among the Dodos (sometimes written "Dodoth") , one of the northern Karamajong tribes of Uganda (see map) .

The Dodos inhabit 3000 square miles of semiarid highland in northeastern Uganda. They subsist through a combination of stock raising, tillage agriculture, and gathering. In the tribal area there are 20,000 people and 75,000 cattle. The densely settled areas tend to have 4 to 5 cattle per person.

The majority of both people and cattle live in the eastern half of Dodos country, which has an annual rainfall of 18 to 25 inches, with a dry season of 6 to 8 months. The potential evaporation is

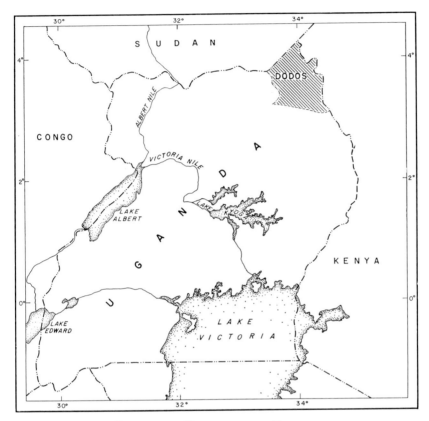

LOCATION OF DODOS COUNTRY, UGANDA

at least twice the rainfall. The vegetation consists of small areas of scattered tree-grassland surrounded by larger tracts which have degenerated under overgrazing into thorn thicket with few grasses. This is in no sense productive cattle country.

The western half of Dodos country carries few people and had carried no cattle for thirty-five years because it was until the late 1950's infested with tsetse fly (Deshler, 1960). The fly carries livestock trypanosomiasis, a disease fatal to cattle of the area. This western country is potentially more favorable for cattle than eastern Dodos. It receives 30 to 40 inches of rainfall and has a dry season of from only 3 to 5 months. Its vegetation consists of scat-

ZEBU CATTLE AT A WET-SEASON GRAZING GROUND

156

HERDSMEN AND CATTLE ON A DRY-SEASON LANDSCAPE

157

tered deciduous trees with an understory of tall grasses which provide richer grazing than is available in the east.

The Dodos practice an extensive agriculture, which takes the form of a shifting cultivation. Calculations made from maps of Dodos family fields indicate that slightly over one acre per person is in cultivation. In many cases the settlement unit, an extended family, will clear and cultivate a large 20- to 40-acre patch which is subdivided into areas for each man; these are further subdivided into patches for each wife and other working woman.

When possible the group uses two tillage areas adjacent to their stockaded settlement and corral. The first area is cultivated for two to three years, then the second area for a like period. This cycle is then repeated. At the end of the second cycle soils are so depleted that the settlement moves, up to 15 miles away and where possible to an area which they have used in the past and remember as satisfactory. Again two potential cultivation areas are used and the cycle is said to be repeated. Under this system fallow must be long and any cultivation patch should be in use for only about one year in ten.

The main crops planted, *Sorghum vulgare,* the tall common sorghum, and *Pennisetum typhoideum* or bulrush millet, occupy about three-fourths of the total acreage. Smaller amounts of corn, eleusine millet, gourds, and tobacco are planted.

Dodos crop yields vary widely as a result of the erratic rainfall. Here is a tropical steppe climate in which at one station annual precipitation over the short period of record has varied from 10 to 25 inches. The precipitation varies in timing as well as in amount, and accordingly effective growing seasons have ranged from 1 or 2 months up to about 5 months. The crops planted require 4 months or more of growing season. Since growing seasons vary and often are less than this, crop failure here is common. Tillage agriculture does not consistently produce food adequate to supply Dodos subsistence needs.

Cattle are owned by extended family groups. The average settlement contains 25 to 30 people. Groups of this size would own herds of from 70 to 130 cattle. In the drier parts of Dodos there were 4 to 5 cattle per person, whereas in the more humid regions

STARVING CATTLE AT A DRY-SEASON WATER HOLE

This was a year of 10 to 20 per cent herd mortality during the drought. The boys have dipped water from the hole and are pouring it into a trough.

of the west along the margins of a tsetse-infested country as few as 2 cattle per person were found.

The cattle of eastern Dodos are kept in the home areas during the rainy season. At this time as many as 60 to 80 people per square mile and 300 to 400 cattle per square mile will be found over large sections of the country. After a few months of such stock concentration the home areas become thoroughly grazed over and the main herds are dispersed to early dry season grazing grounds. The milking herds are kept in the home corrals as long as possible. As the dry season progresses, the once ubiquitous water holes begin to dry up, and the cattle are moved to grazing grounds with access to the diminishing number of water holes. Late in the dry season there may be as few as a dozen and a half water holes for the entire 3000 square miles of the tribal territory. At this time cattle will be watered every other day and on occasion every third day. The countryside takes on a dead brown aspect, dust storms are common, and the grazing is so thin as to be invisible to anyone but a Dodos herdsman and his sharp-eyed cattle. Cattle lose condition during the dry season, and mortality from starvation and from malnutrition-associated ailments in some years reaches 10 to 15 per cent of the herds. Weight loss during the dry season will amount to 60 to 100 pounds for a 650-pound animal. The cattle receive no supplemental feeding, but live on the rough grazing throughout the year.

Under this regime of cattle keeping, animals require six to seven years to attain full growth. At this time bulls will weigh 600 to 700 pounds, and cows will be a hundred or so pounds lighter. (In the United States under present systems of management 900-pound steers are produced in 18 months and are fattened to 1100 or so pounds in a further 4 to 6 months.) Nearly all animals gain weight during the rainy season and lose some appreciable part of it during the following dry season. Young animals grow during only a few months of each year, so that the attainment of full growth is considerably deferred.

The Dodos make use of their cattle in a number of ways. Milk is drunk both fresh and soured. Cattle are bled; the blood is drunk fresh or cooked into a blood pudding or sausage. Cattle are killed for meat, and the meat is used when animals die from most causes. Cattle are sold to the government cattle buyer for money, and during the dry season most of this money is spent for purchase of corn meal and sorghum. The largest cattle sales are made during the dry season, when animals are in the poorest condition.

There is a commonly held belief that some tribes of the "cattle complex" peoples use vast quantities of milk and blood and tend to live entirely on these items. Several of the tribes, Dodos among them, are supposed to eat quantities of meat. This is a belief which the tribes themselves tend to encourage.

The actual productivity of the herds is influenced by factors in addition to the physical environment. One important consideration is the age structure of the herds. A stock census taken during 1953–1954 counted separately the preceding year's calf crop, those animals under one year of age. Twenty to twenty-three per cent of total herd population were found to be under one year of age. Mortalities among young cattle are known to be high, and from these clues we infer that cattle populations here are similar in demographic configuration to human populations of the area. Birth rates are high, as are death rates, especially among the young. Since these animals take six to seven years to mature, there are relatively few mature animals in the herds, and so relatively few animals fully productive in terms of milk and meat.

MILK PRODUCTION

Roughly 20 per cent of Dodos herds are milk cows. Like other East African zebu animals, they are in milk for 330 or so days a year. Milk production varies greatly with food and water intake. During the wet season these animals will give roughly a pint of milk morning and evening after the calf has fed. During the dry season this drops off so that 4 to 6 cows together produce less than a quart of milk a day. Unimproved animals kept on government farms produce 300 to 400 pounds of milk per lactation (Colonial Office, 1953). Under range conditions the quantity produced is somewhat less. (Production in the United States is around 8000 to 12,000 pounds per lactation.) The total production from the cows of the Dodos herds at these rates is of the order of 15,000 to 16,000 pounds (roughly pints) per day, or under 1 pint per person per day. This is about 300 calories. Actually there is adequate milk, a pint to a quart per person per day, during the wet season, and little during the long dry season when productivity per animal is low. At this time the cattle are away from the settled areas and are kept at the dry-season cattle camps, not accessible to most people.

BLOOD PRODUCTION

Western European squeamishness to one side, raw blood is a high-protein food. The Dodos and many other peoples prize this as a delicacy and possibly also for its symbolic value. One hears the phrase "Men drink blood." Prized though it is, production is limited. Animals are bled by shooting a small arrow into the jugular, and the blood is gathered in a gourd. Animals are bled about once a month during the wet season, less frequently and with caution during the dry season. One to two pints is taken from an adult animal. About half a pint is taken from sheep and goats, which are bled by making a cut over the eye. Maximum possible blood production would provide less than a pint per person per week. Actual consumption is much less. Young men who work with the herds use more blood than the rest of the population. Women and children receive very little.

MEAT PRODUCTION

There are, as might be expected, no precise data on Dodos meat consumption, though there are sufficient clues to enable us to establish with some confidence an approximate level of consumption, and certainly the upper limits. There were roughly 75,000 cattle during the mid 1950's (over 90,000 by 1963–1964). The cattle population had been growing slowly for some years before that time. The annual calf crop, then, must be slightly more than the total of animals removed from the population in most years.

BUTCHERING

About 15,000 calves, animals one year and under, were counted
in the 1953–1954 census. The number of animals removed by
death, sale, or trade is then of this order. Of these deaths, about
half would be of immature animals, here sufficiently small to make
little contribution to meat supply. About 7000 reasonably mature
animals were removed from the herds annually. Of these, 3000
were sold out of the area as beef animals. The remaining 4000 or
so animals died or were killed for local meat consumption.

It is most of these latter animals which provided meat for the
Dodos. There are records of less than 1000 animals butchered per
year, but this figure is known to be grossly under the total. The
beef available to the Dodos can come from as many as 4000 animals, and the meat per 600-pound animal is about 200 pounds,
often less. The total beef available per person is, at this rate, up
to 30 to 40 pounds per year. Immature animals provide roughly
a further 10 pounds per person. At lean beef caloric rates, the
contribution to Dodos subsistence is up to 150 to 200 calories per
day. During much of the year people eat meat once a week or
less. The main dietary contribution is in protein rather than in
calories. However, this amount of meat provides only a modest
protein intake for the year.

The accompanying graph shows in rough fashion the seasonal
consumption of cattle products. The seasonal shifts in consumption of milk, meat, and blood are based on field observation
throughout the year and are reasonably accurate. The caloric contribution shown is inferred from the census data and available information on productivity per animal. It is to be considered very
approximate. If the information on food intake were more adequate, it would be perhaps more useful to show it as protein
rather than caloric intake, in that these are high-protein foods.

With respect to the Dodos the reports of high milk-blood-meat
consumption from cattle do not fit the facts. The total of these
products can make a contribution to Dodos diets of not more than
600 calories per day and for only short seasons. This would be
available if there were even distribution. In fact, the herds are
away from the settled areas for much of the year, so there is a
large measure of maldistribution of cattle products. There is

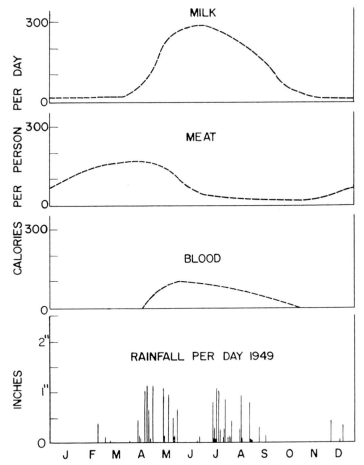

INFERRED SEASONAL CONSUMPTION PATTERNS FOR CATTLE PRODUCTS, DODOS
(HOME AREAS ONLY)

shortage in the settled areas, while at the dry-season cattle camps there may be surplus and wastage of these perishable products.

Dodos diets are not heavy in calories. These people most likely exist on less than 2000 calories daily for many months of the year. There are other periods when food is gorged, and at such times a man is seen to consume one and a half to two pounds of meat at a sitting. Here is the probable origin of the high meat and milk consumption myth. Semistarved men working for a European hunter or traveler eat prodigious amounts of meat when it is shot by the European. The erroneous assumption is made that this behavior is customary. The reality is that from these landscapes large quantities of cattle products cannot be obtained. Some contribution is made by sheep and goats, but no quantitative information existed on the population of these animals at the time of field study.

I have attempted to demonstrate the contribution of cattle products to Dodos subsistence. As we have seen, it is modest and probably less than a quarter of total food intake. Grain and gathered products make up most of the remainder. The basic question remains: Why do Africans of the "cattle complex" tribes keep and feel they require such large herds of cattle? A partial, though not complete, answer would be that the production per animal is so low that large herds are necessary to produce even modest amounts of milk, meat, and blood. This is supported by a Dodos answer to the question: "I need many cattle so that my children have enough milk."

ALTERNATIVE MODES OF SUBSISTENCE

In order to probe the question further, we must examine the alternative and supplemental modes of subsistence. I find from field study that grains provide the major portion of the diet among these people. The grains used are sorghums, small millets, and corn. Crop yields are of the order of 2 to 5 bushels per acre, and total yields are such that in many years the grain harvest is adequate to meet home needs for only 4 to 7 months of the year. When the supply of grain is exhausted, additional grain is begged or borrowed from relatives in more fortunate areas. When these sources fail, cattle are traded to other tribes for grain, or as a last resort are sold to the government cattle buyer for cash, which is largely used to purchase whole grain or corn meal. It is probably significant that cattle and meat are traded for grain, a further indication that grain is really the basic food.

Gathering is a further mode of subsistence and seasonally is of considerable importance. Items gathered vary from week to week throughout the year and range from termites to wild onions, wild spinaches, fruits, and grasses.

The significant fact of Dodos subsistence is that annual food shortage is a severe problem. Famine is still felt as a distinct threat to survival. Grain supplies in dry years are not adequate to see the tribe through the drought period; gathered products are sparse at this time of year and often are not storable. Livestock, largely cattle, are the one means of hedging against possible famine. In a severe drought they die of starvation and are eaten or the meat is traded. In the worst possible case they can be killed as needed to provide food for the tribe. It would seem to this observer that livestock are the one food available which can be stored on the hoof until needed. Livestock are a form of famine insurance, and this is certainly one of the bases of the high valuation placed on them by this tribe.

If the famine hedge concept proves to be one of the real factors underlying large herd size, there are some practical implications which might be of use in making it possible for administrations concerned with land problems among the cattle-keeping tribes to reduce herds. The argument is that the large herd size is related to the threat of recurrent food shortage. It would seem that if the felt threat of annual food shortage were to be removed by improved crop yields and by improved meat and milk yield per cow, it would be possible for the tribes to meet their subsistence needs with smaller herds and to survive dry seasons. This writer recognizes well that the main problem in matters of technical aid is not the technology—this can usually be readily developed; the real problem is that of acceptance by indigenous people. Acculturation is complex.

The other areas inhabited by tribes of the "cattle complex" have equally severe climatic regimes. Livestock productivity is about as low as that in Dodos, and the alternative modes of subsistence provide equally little product. It is suggested that the concept of livestock as a famine hedge or famine insurance might be applicable in these other areas and that it warrants further examination.

REFERENCES

COLONIAL OFFICE (BRITISH) . 1953. *The Improvement of Cattle in British Colonial Territories in Africa.* Colonial Advisory Council of Agriculture, Animal Health and Forestry, Publ. No. 3. H. M. Stationers' Office, London.

COLSON, E. 1955. Native cultural and social patterns in contemporary Africa. In *Africa Today* (C. G. Haines, editor). Johns Hopkins Press, Baltimore, Md.

DESHLER, W. W. 1960. Livestock trypanosomiasis and human settlement in northeastern Uganda. *Geograph. Rev., 50* (4) , 541–554.

GULLIVER, P. H. 1955. *The Family Herds.* Routledge and Kegan Paul, London.

SCHNEIDER, H. K. 1957. The subsistence role of cattle among the Pakot in East Africa. *Am. Anthropologist, 59* (2) , 278–300.

STENNING, D. J. 1959. *Savannah Nomads.* Oxford University Press, London.

Animals and Social Types in the Exploitation of the Tibetan Plateau

JAMES F. DOWNS

Department of Anthropology, California State College at Los Angeles, Los Angeles, California

ROBERT B. EKVALL

Burke Memorial Museum, University of Washington, Seattle, Washington

TIBET, one of the last non-Western civilizations to survive the impact of Western technology and ideology, presents to the social scientist a number of incongruities, the most apparent being the development of a remarkable cultural, linguistic, and social homogeneity within an area in which one would expect a high degree of diversity and socio-political separatism. This paper explores the role of certain categories of livestock which make possible the exploitation of the area and which foster and maintain this homogeneity.

ENVIRONMENT

The distinctive feature of Tibetan geography is altitude, most of the area lying as it does from 10,000 to 24,000 or more feet above sea level. High mountain ridges separate relatively fertile valleys one from the other. High plains, well above the limits of agriculture, divide farming districts. In some areas at certain times of the year, vast areas of bog create impassable barriers to travel. Deep gorges, narrow valleys, and numerous swift-flowing rivers all contribute to the difficulties of communication between districts within Tibet. Almost all of the country lies near, and much of it above, the upper limits of agriculture. At certain times of the year, snow and the condition of the footing on trails make

169

travel impossible. At best, any journey in Tibet becomes a hazardous undertaking, and a long one.

Such natural conditions might be expected to contribute to at least a degree of cultural, linguistic, and social diversification based on varying ecological adjustments, such as are found in other mountainous areas, including the southern slopes of the Himalayas (Iijima, 1961). However, Tibet displays a cultural and linguistic unity which is most impressive and which extends from China proper to the Kashmir and from Sinkiang to northern India.

In addition to geographic factors which would seem to inhibit the development of homogeneity, current ethnologic argument suggests that the Tibetan plateau and its escarpments have been peopled by refugee groups fleeing from all points of the compass —China, India, Burma, and central Asia—into the mountains. Though it is to be expected that various refugee groups would make roughly similar ecological adjustment to the refugee environment, it cannot be assumed that such adjustments would occur in identical fashion among peoples of different biological, linguistic, social, and cultural backgrounds.

Certain unifying elements within modern Tibet have been noted by almost every observer, whether missionary, adventurer, or scientific investigator. Wherever Tibetans are encountered, they exhibit a determined adherence to a dominant religious system and an addiction to trade and commerce. In a subjective sense it might be said that Tibetans are generally characterized as deeply religious traders. In a more objective sense, we can argue that religion and trade are motivations for, and at the same time provide important mechanisms for, maintaining homogeneity in an environment which does not favor, and would seem to inhibit, its spontaneous development.

RELIGION

In a recently published work one of the coauthors of this paper (Ekvall, 1964) has characterized some of the observances of Lamaism (the Tibetan form of Buddhism) as space-object oriented. In a behavioral sense this means that the foci of religious observances —monasteries, shrines, or persons—require that the worshipers act through space toward a definite object. Thus, each monastery dominates a particular area. Shrines, religious personages, gods, or demons are phenomena of a specific area. Some of these are nation-wide, others are entirely local. In either case they require of the worshiper actions which move through space actually or symbolically, for example, bowing toward a specific monastery in prayers, circumambulating particular shrines, or making pilgrimages to certain holy places.

Pilgrimage plays an extremely important role in Tibetan religion. It may be said that every Tibetan, like every Moslem, is a committed pilgrim. In the Tibetan case, however, the pilgrim does not have a single destination. He visits many national and local religious centers. In the course of visiting the many monasteries, shrines, or religious personages, a devout Tibetan may well visit almost every part of Tibet. Nor, for the devout, are such pilgrimages a once-in-a-lifetime requirement, for they are constantly repeated to acquire merit and receive particular blessings. Thus Tibetan religion makes travel mandatory. If conditions prevailed which prevented large-scale travel, not only would the present form of Tibetan religion be changed, but the role it plays in Tibetan culture would be drastically impaired.

Ideally a pilgrimage should be made on foot, with the pilgrim begging or carrying his own supplies. This mode of pilgrimage has two advantages according to Buddhist doctrine: by the expenditure of his own physical energy the pilgrim makes the trip more merit-worthy, and by avoiding the burdening of riding or pack animals he is conforming to the Buddhist ideal of compassion for all sentient beings. However, relatively few Tibetans observe these rules strictly. The idea that pilgrims from nomadic tribes ever traveled otherwise than on horseback was considered a joke by our Tibetan informants. Even non-nomad pilgrims tend to temper the letter of doctrine by recourse to a number of "adjustments." Well-to-do pilgrims may simply form a caravan with pack animals carrying supplies and equipment, and the pilgrims themselves riding on horses or yaks. Frequently such caravans are organized to combine trade and piety. In many cases, the caravan may be broken up a few days short of its destination, trade goods packed on mules rented from local residents, caravan animals pastured, for a fee, with nearby nomads, and the trip completed on foot. The more devout or less well-to-do pilgrim may in fact make the entire trip on foot, but usually attaches himself to a trade or pilgrim caravan, exchanging labor—gathering fuel, tending animals, pitching tents, and the like—for protection, food, and the right to have his supplies carried on one of the caravan's pack animals. Even the most devout pilgrim usually follows the caravan routes, begging his food from the caravans and seeking protection from bandits. Many pilgrims literally "hitchhike" along these routes, begging or exchanging services for food. The pilgrims themselves are the medium of a rather large-scale exchange of goods, inasmuch as they often bring valuables to present to the monastery of their destination and frequently engage in trade to finance their trips.

TRADE

Remote and inhospitable as it may be, Tibet is part of a world-wide, two-way network of commerce that links Tibetan markets with Wall Street quotations and the perfume laboratories of Grasse. In addition, the high plateau is the scene of an intricate system of exchange of commodities among the different areas of Tibet. Tea and manufactured items enter Tibet from the east. They are transshipped from the Chinese trade system to the Tibetan system for distribution throughout Tibet as far as the borders of India and the Kashmir. From India manufactured goods enter through the Himalayan passes and thence proceed to Lhasa for redistribution. From Tibet flow wool, musk, fur, hair, and so on, as raw materials to be used in foreign factories. Within Tibet certain districts are noted for their special products, which may even have a nation-wide market. For example, the ironwork and printed books of Derge are found throughout the country; and the fine tent cloth woven near Jekundo is valued and sought everywhere. Food, grain, meat, butter and other dairy products, woven goods, ironwork, leatherwork, manufactured goods, special agricultural products, and livestock are constantly passing in exchange from area to area.

This trade has not developed an exclusive merchant class or trader class in Tibetan society. Though certain men or families may engage more actively in trade than others, every Tibetan is, in addition to whatever other roles he may play, a trader. The nomad makes a yearly trip to the farming areas to trade animal products and livestock for grain and farm produce. Villages organize cooperative buying and trading groups which undertake long journeys, the profit from which is divided among the members of the corporation. Monasteries detail monks to engage in trade and organize trading caravans. The nobility, supported by rents and dues, enter into trading arrangements as actively as do commoners. As every Tibetan family does, or expects to, place a son in the monastic community and also is involved in trade, we can see that these two factors serve to crosscut social divisions, and transcend environmental pressure toward separatism. Trade and religion, affecting all Tibetans, serve to encourage a continuous movement of goods and persons throughout Tibet. They reinforce the need for a common ecclesiastical and secular language and provide an opportunity for constant exchange of ideas.

Confronted with the basic characteristics of the Tibetan environment, which tends to discourage travel, we are forced to ask, By what means are these two systems, trade and religion, maintained? It is at this point that we must turn to the role of the animals by whose strength and on whose backs Tibetan commerce and pilgrimage exist.

THE DOMESTIC ANIMALS OF TIBET

The Yak

The domestic yak of Tibet (*Poëphagus grunniens grunniens*) is related to the wild yak (*Poëphagus grunniens mutus* Przewalski), which less than a century ago was distributed from eastern Ladakh to western China and from the southern reaches of the

Himalaya to central Asia (Harper, 1945, p. 361). This distribution is coterminous with that of Tibetan culture. Although it can be said that wild yak occur where there are no Tibetans, it can also be said that Tibetans rarely occur where the wild yak does (or did) not exist. The domestic yak has a somewhat wider distribution than its wild cousin, to which it is occasionally bred, by accident or design. Like the wild yak, it is essentially a high-altitude animal, able to survive the terrible winters of the high plateau and get sustenance from the rough and sparse herbage of the highlands up to 16,000 feet or more above sea level. From the yak the Tibetan harvests meat, milk, blood, butter, cheese, hides, hair, and fur, as well as horn for utensils; and he depends on the yak for pack transport and riding. Its usefulness is limited by its inability to adjust to even relatively low altitudes (White, 1946, p. 356).[1] Moreover, it obstinately refuses to learn to walk head to tail on trails, preferring to huddle together with its fellows, even when fully packed. This precludes its use on narrow trails leading out of Tibet, and into the lower valleys of the country. Thus travel by yak is limited to areas where the animals will not push each other off cliffs and where the tendency of yaks to bunch and herd while traveling does not create unacceptable damage to the loads they carry, or despoliation of roadside fields.

Although it is clear that domestication of the yak is the essential factor which permitted Tibetan culture to extend its range of exploitation into the country above the upper limit of agriculture, the nature of the yak makes the use of other animals imperative if both upland and lowland areas are to be jointly exploited.

The Cow

The Tibetan cow is not essentially different from the cattle to be found in China or India (Phillips *et al.*, 1945, pp. 47–61), although it tends to be somewhat smaller and grow heavier coats of hair. By and large its primary function is to serve as a breeding

---

[1] Reliable information, gathered under experimental conditions, relating to the agricultural potential of the yak and *dzo* is extremely limited. The authors have included in the References all the literature in English on the subject of which they have knowledge: Phillips *et al.*, 1945, 1946; Rothwell, 1928; White *et al.*, 1946; Zawadowsky, 1931.

foundation for producing hybrids. It is in many senses a poor farmer's animal, and considered less valuable than other types of cattle found in Tibet. It does produce a modicum of milk, butter, cheese, meat, and hides, as well as traction power for plowing, and is sometimes used as a pack animal. It is not a good weight carrier, nor is it as hardy as the yak. It has a low resistance to the extreme climate of the highlands and is not well adapted to herd life, requiring more shelter and care than the yak.

Horses (Equus caballus)

The vast majority of Tibetan horses can be divided into two types, differentiated more by conditions under which the animals are raised and kept than by any inherent biological characters.[2] Horses raised in the farm districts are generally larger and more robust than those found among nomads of the high country. They are not able to withstand the rigors of highland climate and maintain these qualities. Lowland horses tend to have somewhat smaller and tougher feet, which makes them useful on the rocky trails of the valleys and the slopes. The highland horse is kept in great numbers by the upland nomads and is, in fact, the same horse as those found in the valleys. Nomad horses tend to have wider and thinner hoofs, suitable for the plains and bogs of the uplands. They are also said to be faster and more spirited than horses found in the farm districts. The difference, it should be emphasized, lies in the fact that lowland horses are kept under cover and fed at least some grain and/or turnips when grazing is at its poorest, whereas the nomad horse exists in herds in the open, gaining and losing condition as the forage waxes and wanes. The nomad herds not only serve as a breeding pool for Tibet, but also supply thousands of mares each year to the mule-breeding centers in China. In Tibet the horse is primarily a riding animal. It is seldom packed and never killed for meat, nor is it milked. The mane, tail, and hair of mares may be cut off for sale as horsehair, but the hides are never sold. The hide of an exceptionally good

---

[2] Phillips (in Phillips *et al.*, 1945) gives a clear and concise description of the various horse and pony types of western China and Tibet, although Ekvall believes he has confused the Ch'ing-hai and the Nan-fan breeds.

horse may be stuffed and offered to a monastery as a religious of-
fering. Caravans of horses are never assembled because horses require that each animal be led, whereas numbers of mules, yaks, or
other animals can be driven along a trail by as few as two or three
men.

The Donkey

Extremely common in China, the donkey is less common in
Tibet, and its distribution is limited to farming communities.
The animal is a "jack-of-all-carrying-trades," being used to carry
wood, dung, and water, to help with the plowing in emergencies,
or to pack manure to the fields. It is also pressed into commercial
service as a pack animal by farmers contracting to transport wool
over short distances for Indian wool buyers. Occasionally, in preference to walking, the Tibetan seats himself on, rather than
mounts, the nearest available donkey to go short distances.

Sheep and Goats

These two animals produce wool, hair, skins, milk, and meat.
There are two types of Tibetan sheep: the large, wide-horned animal which appears to have significant infusions of wild sheep
blood, and which is the typical sheep of the nomads; and a smaller
animal with finer, shorter wool and short curling horns, more
common in farming areas. In parts of Tibet, the nomad-type
sheep is often used as a caravan animal in the salt trade. Each animal can pack up to thirty pounds (Smith, 1949, p. 215), and in
general they require little attention on the trail. The boatmen
who navigate the rapid rivers of Tibet depend on a sheep to carry
their personal belongings while the men carry their skin boats on
portages (Thomas, 1950, pp. 156–157).

Hybrids

The yak-cow, horse-donkey, large-small sheep combinations express the clear dichotomy of the Tibetan environment. The yak
enables the Tibetan to exist and carry on a remarkably adequate
subsistence economy in high altitudes where conditions preclude
agriculture or extensive employment of lowland animals. The

horse, which, it would appear, came into Tibet from the steppes of central Asia, is able to exist in large numbers in the highlands and thus provides a pool of animals which could not be maintained on the restricted pastures of the farming communities. The cow, a lowland animal, is largely restricted in use to the farming areas. The donkey, coming into Tibet from China and perhaps India, serves a variety of purposes in the lowlands. All these animals are employed in transport. However, all of them have limitations which preclude their widespread use between and across ecological zones. Though each animal plays an important role within a specific environmental situation, none of them alone, nor any of them in combination, can overcome the obstacles to long-distance travel in Tibet. Such travel must necessarily adjust to a variety of environmental conditions. Therefore exclusive dependence upon these animals could be expected to contribute, by default, to isolation and consequent cultural diversification. Using only these animals, cross-country travel would be immeasurably more difficult than it is. Caravans would have to transship goods onto the backs of different animals as trails entered a new environment. Failing this, most of the traffic between ecological zones would have to move on the backs of that most adaptable animal, the human being. However, the Tibetan has brought into play his knowledge of hybridization to produce intermediate types of animals suitable for work in either of the extremes of Tibetan environment.

The yak-cow. The first-generation cross between the yak and the cow is the *dzo,* a general term which will be used here, although the Tibetan language contains a number of terms for this cross, depending on the species of the male parent or the degree of removal from the primary cross. The *dzo* displays the expected hybrid vigor, being somewhat faster than the yak and carrying one-third more pay load than could be expected from either parent. Moreover, it is able to travel higher than the cow and lower than the yak. It is also more tractable than the yak and it is easily trained to walk head to tail on narrow trails or, in open country, to walk its own path without jostling. The 1950 price of a *dzo* in good condition was about one-third higher than that of a yak, a relation which seems to have remained constant over long periods of time and in various areas despite inflation and deflation and different currency systems. Although the female *dzo* is fertile, the male is sterile.

The mule. The yak, cow, and *dzo* are relatively slow animals despite their weight-carrying capabilities. It is often advantageous for either pilgrims or traders to have caravans made up of faster animals which can cover more ground even though the loads are lighter. Neither the horse nor the donkey is suitable for this task. To fill this role, the mule, another hybrid, is used. The mule is the offspring of the horse and the donkey. Usually the male of the mating is a donkey (jack), although the opposite cross, known as the hinney in America, is relatively common in Tibet. Both sexes in the mule are generally sterile, so that the supply of mules, like the supply of *dzo,* depends on constant crossbreeding of two species. The mule, as compared with the horse, has better hoofs, keeps in condition on less food, is more phlegmatic, and, within limits, is more easily trained and handled. It is a better weight carrier than either the horse or the donkey, and faster than the latter. Compared with the donkey, it is far better adapted to the extremes of the upland areas.

The Ecology of Hybridism

Thus we have in Tibet a roster of animals of various species, each able to perform under specific environmental conditions, but generally not suitable for extensive employment under other conditions, or between areas of different environment. By crossing these species the Tibetans have produced two hybrid types able to perform, as it were, across the boundaries of ecological zones. The yak is clearly a high-altitude weight carrier and dairy animal. The cow is a relatively low-altitude farm beast. The horse, though found in both high and low lands, is bred more efficiently in the upland meadows and steppes, and it is in this area that it is found in greatest number. The donkey is limited to a variety of lowland farm tasks and is of little value in the uplands. The yak-cow hybrid combines weight-carrying capability, trail wariness, milk productivity, and an ability to perform in high altitudes and in relatively low country as well. The donkey-horse cross contributes to pack transport a degree of speed which is sometimes desirable. It functions well on narrow trails, is easily handled, and is not at too great a disadvantage in the high country.

The Social Structure of Hybridism

Thus far we have tried to show how trade and religion serve as motivations which foster Tibetan unity. We have further argued that these systems are dependent on a means of transportation which can overcome the difficulties of travel due to the extremes in Tibetan environment. This means, we have argued, is provided through the utilization of several species of animals suited to various environments, and through the crossbreeding of these species to obtain hybrids which are suitable for transport and other uses in a much wider environmental context than is either of the parent species. There are, then, three general classes of animals to be considered in Tibet: upland animals useful in areas where agriculture is impossible; lowland animals which are adapted to lowland environment; and intermediate types suitable in both the upland and lowland environments. Can we postulate that Tibetan society will reflect, in its structure, the same kind of environmentally oriented tripartite division? From the data gathered in this research program, the writers agree that this is indeed the case.

TIBETAN SOCIAL STRUCTURE AND ENVIRONMENTAL ADJUSTMENT

Rong-ba or Farmers

Rong is the Tibetan word applied to the areas within which agriculture can be practiced. Rong-ba is the term applied to the people who live and work in the agricultural areas, that is, the farmers. In the valleys of Tibet, wherever agriculture is possible, there are farming villages. The farmers raise barley, wheat, peas, and some root crops. The agriculture is plow agriculture, so that a number of plow animals—yaks, cows, mules, or dzo—are kept. In addition, donkeys are used and horses are kept for riding. Usually small sheep herds are maintained for their wool, which is converted into cloth for clothing. Dairy products, hair, and hides are taken from the yak, *dzo,* and sheep. Winter supplies of meat and dairy products in excess of home production must be obtained from the nomads of the uplands. In addition, hair, fur, wool, hides, and lambskins to be taken on trading expeditions made up by the *rong-ba* must also be obtained from the nomads. The more well-to-do farmers, however, may maintain separate herds in the nearby mountains to supply these items and reduce their dependence on the nomads. The nomads also bring new breeding stock of horses and yaks into the valleys.

Drog-ba or Nomads

The *drog,* in Tibetan, refers to the area above the upper limits of agriculture. Ekvall has translated the word in a very general sense as "wilderness." The *drog-ba* are the people who inhabit the wilderness. These plains and mountains above the limits of agriculture support a nomadic pastoral population which does no farming, depending instead on herds of yak, sheep, *dzo,* and horses for support. In the fall, before the nomad goes into winter camp, he drives some of his animals into the valleys to trade for grain and other farm products and, to a lesser extent, for manufactured items traded into or produced in the farming areas. In addition to meat and livestock for breeding purposes, the nomad brings dairy products, wool, furs of wild animals, hides, hartshorn, and lambskins, which are traded to the farmers for consumption or to stock-trading caravans made up in the valleys. He seldom buys mules from the farmers because the yak performs the necessary transport work in the uplands. The nomad also gravitates toward raiding; frequently nomads serve as caravan escorts (often an arrangement which allows the nomad to obtain money or goods in return for not attacking a caravan, thus functioning as an escort against himself) .

Sama-Drog or Farmer-Herder

A third social type clearly illustrates a relation between Tibetan social structure and environmental adjustment. Neither farmer nor true nomad, the *sama-drog* exploits areas close to farming regions which are not extensive enough to support the large-scale pastoralism practiced by the so-called *drog ch'en* or "great" *drog-ba*. The *sama-drog*, as does the nomad, lives year round in a tent in order to care for his herds. Usually he keeps sheep, yak, and *dzo*, although in some reported cases only yak and *dzo* were kept. It is significant that the *dzo* are proportionately more numerous in *sama-drog* herds than they are in either the herds of the nomads or the livestock of the farmer. This appears to be the natural consequence of maintaining yak herds close to farming areas where bulls of the common cow breed can be obtained for breeding to yak cows. *Sama-drog* families are invariably related to farming villages. The *sama-drog* is usually the uncle or younger brother of a more prosperous than average farmer. In many cases his herds include animals belonging to less well-to-do farmers who pay a fee to have surplus animals, not needed for farm work, pastured and cared for. Periodically, the *sama-drog* brings animals and animal products into the valley to his relatives, for their use and for trade. The herds are thought of as belonging to both the herding and the farming elements of the family. In some cases, particularly in Kham and Amdo, the herder winters with his family in the village, returning to the higher pastures in the spring and summer.

The *sama-drog* serves to supply the farmer with meat and animal products which the farmer could not produce on his own restricted pastures. It is from the herds of the *sama-drog* that pack animals are obtained for periodic trading caravans formed in the valleys. It is from these herds that a significant number of *dzo*, needed to maintain the trade from the lowlands to the highlands and from outside Tibet, over the passes, into Tibet, are derived. It might be noted here that *dzo* caravans are most common in the China-Tibet trade, less common in central and western Tibet, but again very important in the extreme south, where Tibetan trade flows to India. The existence of the *sama-drog* facilitates trade in yet another way. It is common for caravan managers to trade off their weak stock while still in the farming area before proceeding into the relatively uninhabited highlands, where worn-out or injured pack animals and their loads would have to be abandoned. The *sama-drog*, by his existence, permits the farmer to buy these animals and assign them to his herding relatives for rest and recuperation, and eventual resale to subsequent caravans. The restricted pastures near farming villages would not be sufficient to maintain any great number of resting animals.

Thus we see a complex system of animal exchange between various socio-ecological types which results in the maintenance of the various pure species and hybrids needed to facilitate transport in this difficult terrain.

SUMMARY

Tibet cannot be totally exploited by agricultural peoples using the agricultural and animal husbandry techniques of the adjacent lowland areas. Exploitation, however, has been extended above the upper limit of agriculture by the domestication of the indigenous yak and by the breeding of specially adapted sheep, which serve as a foundation for a remarkably adequate nomadic pastoral economy. The entire area is bound together by a network of trade and pilgrimage which is dependent, not only on the yak, but on hybrids which are able to work efficiently in both highland and lowland environment.

The nomads, as a distinct socio-ecological type, maintain large herds of yak, horses, and sheep which not only are sufficient to their needs, but supply surplus animal products and breeding stock. These eventually, in considerable numbers, come into the hands of the farmers, who constitute another socio-ecological type, to be used or placed in trade. In exchange for these products of highland pastoralism the nomads receive agricultural products and manufactured goods from the lowlands. Manufactured goods are brought into, or distributed within, Tibet by caravans made up, in large part, of the mule and *dzo* hybrids, offspring of the mating of upland and lowland animals.

The nomads maintain basic herds of yak cows and mares which are essential to this crossbreeding, and these are bred respectively to the lowland bulls of the common cow and to jacks possessed by the farmers. The *sama-drog*, as the third socio-ecological type, intermediate in character, serve as a repository for surplus stock, accumulated in the lowlands as the result of farmer-nomad trade. In addition, the *sama-drog* actively breed the all-important *dzo*, so essential to the caravan system. The *sama-drog* also provide facilities for the rehabilitation of caravan animals and their return, in due time, to the trade routes. This constant interchange of animals for breeding, hybridization, and rehabilitation makes possible the formation of the long-range caravans on which trade and religion—the two primary unifying impulses of Tibetan society—depend.

These three socio-ecological types, based entirely, or in large part, on differing styles of animal husbandry, adapted to particular environmental settings, make possible the total or near total exploitation, by people sharing common cultural patterns, a common language, and a unique civilization, of the Tibetan plateau, a vast and inhospitable area of great environmental diversity.

ACKNOWLEDGMENTS. The information on which this paper is based was gathered by the authors during several months of round-table and personal interviews with Tibetans from various parts of Tibet who are resident at the University of Washington and cooperating with the University's Chinese and Russian Institute research project on Tibet. Ekvall, who has eight years' experience in eastern Tibet, served as the linguistic focus and co-interrogator, besides contributing information from his own experience. Downs acknowledges the support tendered by the American Council of Learned Societies for certain parts of this work, while he was resident at the University of Washington.

REFERENCES

In the voluminous literature on Tibet, many facts mentioned in this paper have been mentioned or described. The authors have made no attempt to cite such material. Unless accompanied by specific citations, statements in this paper represent information gathered from Tibetan informants or taken from Ekvall's field experience.

EKVALL, R. B. 1964. *Religious Observances in Tibet; Patterns and Function.* University of Chicago Press, Chicago, Ill.

HARPER, F. 1945. *Extinct and Vanishing Mammals of the Old World.* American Committee for International Wild Life Protection, New York, N. Y.

IIJIMA, S. 1961. *Agriculture and Land Tenure in Nepal.* Tokyo. (In Japanese.)

PHILLIPS, R. W., R. G. JOHNSON, and R. T. MOYER. 1945. *The Livestock of China.* U. S. Department of State, Publ. No. 2249, Far Eastern Series No. 9. Washington, D. C.

PHILLIPS, R. W., with I. A. TOLSTOY and R. G. JOHNSON. 1946. (No title.) *J. Heredity, 37,* 163–170, 207–245.

ROTHWELL, G. B. 1928. *Report of the Dominion Animal Husbandman for the Year Ending March 31, 1927,* p. 85. Dominion of Canada, Department of Agriculture, Ottawa, Canada.

SMITH, N. 1949. *Golden Doorway to Tibet.* Bobbs-Merrill Co., New York, N. Y.

THOMAS, L., JR. 1950. *Out of This World.* Greystone Corp., New York, N. Y.

WHITE, W. T., with R. W. PHILLIPS and E. C. ELTING. 1946. Yaks and yak-cattle hybrids in Alaska. *J. Heredity, 37,* 355–358.

ZAWADOWSKY, M. M. 1931. Zebu-yak hybrids. *J. Heredity, 23,* 297–313.

Herds and Herders in the Inca State

JOHN V. MURRA

Institute of Andean Research, Huánuco, Perú

AMERICAN CIVILIZATIONS, like sub-Saharan ones, owe their development to the skilled manipulation of human energies, unaided by mechanical devices like wheels or domesticated animal power. To this Afro-American model, the llama is the only exception. In a comparative, cross-cultural sense, the most significant aspect of its utilization is as a beast of burden: it will carry up to a hundred pounds and will travel as far as ten or twelve miles a day loaded (Tschopik, 1946, p. 533; compare Acosta, [1590],[1] bk. 4, ch. 41; 1940, p. 338, with Tschudi, 1891, p. 106; see also Maccagno, 1932, pp. 28, 48) , and does not require any fodder beyond what it finds growing in between the bunches of *ichu* grass. The animal may lie down and refuse to budge when tired or overloaded, but it is otherwise docile and easy to manage, and requires few drovers.

Still, the llama's contribution to burden bearing in the Andean economy should not be exaggerated. Many places lacked llamas in pre-Inca times, and although state policy called for the extension of herding to new areas, they were still scarce, particularly in the North. To the Andean elite, the llama appeared clearly inferior to human beings—who could be made to carry more and farther and in collaboration with one another, and who were more sensitive to fulfilling the requirements of ideology, as well as to the whip.

---

[1] The dates in square brackets following the names of sixteenth- and seventeenth-century authors refer to the year of first publication or writing; the second, modern date refers to the edition used by the writer for the present paper.

Alpacas were too small to use as pack animals, but their wool was finer, a quality which in Andean economics was highly valued since textiles functioned in so many contexts beyond the ornamental or utilitarian (Murra, 1962). And of course all camelids were eaten; their meat was frequently preserved as *charki*. Leather and fur, sinew and dung, all had their efficient uses, which need not detain us here, for they are conveniently described in the *Handbook of South American Indians* (Gilmore, 1950, pp. 429–454).

There is no indication in our sixteenth-century sources that llamas and alpacas were viewed in any obsessive, ostentatious ways that might appear "irrational" to the ethnocentric. They were highly valued not only economically, but as a gift from one's kin or a grant from the mighty; their lungs and entrails were scrutinized for omens, and seed potatoes were bathed in llama blood before planting; one hundred white spotless beasts were sacrificed periodically for the welfare of the state; and in the South herders felt a kinship to a fabulous llama of long ago. In modern times (Arroyo Ponce, 1953, p. 81) folklore collections include praise and propitiatory songs to be offered on "branding" day:

> Don't say this is any old day
> —it's the day of our tawny llamas.

The Europeans who invaded the Andes did not leave us the texts of their sixteenth-century parallels, but we know that songs, prayers, and offerings were common then (Poma, [1615], 1936, pp. 318–319 [320–321]). So were artistic representations in various media: ceramics and stone, life-size silver statues or wall paintings. We see no "llama complex" in such behavior; it seems well within the range of men's ordinary concern for an important element in their life.

Ricardo Latcham, in the twenties, and Gilmore in his article in the *Handbook* (Latcham, 1922; 1936, p. 611; Gilmore, 1950) have assembled whatever information was available on the zoology and the domestication history of these beasts. Since their summaries, the camelid-hunting horizon has been pushed back by Cardich's archeological work to more than 8000 years ago (Cardich, 1958, 1960), long before pottery or agriculture. The date of domestication is still unknown, but through inference from coastal remains, the taming of the llama was a fact in the highlands by Chavín times, 1000 B.C. (Bennett and Bird, 1949, pp. 126, 142). Junius Bird has suggested that a growing interest in wool on the part of coastal weavers was possibly the major incentive for the domestication of lamoids (*ibid.*, p. 260; Bird, 1954, p. 3), but at the present stage of highland studies it is conceivable that the huanaco and alpaca were tamed locally, by those who had come to know their habits through 5000 years of hunting.[2]

It has been suggested that the locus of domestication was the Lake Titicaca area (Latcham, 1922, p. 82), where we find the heaviest concentration of both wild and domesticated species. The area is part of the high *puna* steppe which begins around the eighth degree below the equator and rises and widens as one moves south into Bolivia. It has many grassy slopes and plateaus providing ample pasture at altitudes where even the most frost-resistant tubers will not bear. Above 14,000 feet there are few towns, or ruined prehistoric settlements; only the isolated houses of the herders and their corrals (Bowman, 1916, pp. 5, 46, 52, 96; Tello, 1959, p. 23).

Troll and other geographers have emphasized the unique qualities of the dry and very high *puna* ecology and its culture-historical significance. Troll finds a close correlation between *puna* conditions and the distribution of domesticated camelids. "In a biological sense, llamas and alpacas belong to the biotype *puna*"; when these animals are found elsewhere, as in Ecuador or Chile, he considers them marginal, "artificially" introduced by the Inca state (1931, p. 266; 1958, p. 29).

Other scholars have pointed to the much wider distribution of the wild huanaco, closely related to the llama, and living at lower altitudes all the way to Tierra del Fuego (Latcham, 1922, pp. 7, 75-78, 82; Tello, 1942, p. 607; Horkheimer, 1960, pp. 42-43). Though the chroniclers of the invasion record that the llama was "a friend of cold climates," "flourishing in the snow and dying in

---

[2] See Valcárcel's insight on the matter (1922, p. 15), and Troll's apparently independent conclusion (1931, p. 271).

hot country," they also provide ample evidence that the animals were frequently driven to the coast, loaded with highland staples to be exchanged for maize, or for ritual purposes. Occasional transhumance is suggested for the years when climatic circumstances made the coastal *lomas* bloom, and the highlanders brought their herds down to what became islands of succulent range in the middle of the desert (Tello, 1942, pp. 607–608; Troll, 1958, p. 12). Other beasts remained on the coast, carrying guano from the islands to the irrigated fields, and one reference mentions a herd of 600 head belonging to a Lupaca *mitmaq* colony settled in a coastal oasis (Garci Diez, [1567–1568], f. 61r). Since highland herds fed on natural range, special arrangements would have had to be made to feed such coastal animals.[3] Replacements were always welcomed and were driven down from the sierra, as needed, while the older animals ended in the soup pot.

As one studies the llama and its uses, one keeps coming back to the high Andean area, between 8000 and 13,000 feet, including most of southern Peru and Bolivia. This is not only the optimum habitat of the domesticated camelids; it is also the country where people were most ingenious in their domestication of a wide range of frost-resistant tubers and grains and where they developed unique preservation techniques for potatoes and meat. Tubers and llamas, *chuñu* and *charki*, went together as staples in Andean nutrition and economics (Murra, 1960; Troll, 1931). Ideally, Andean man considered his vertical habitat to include both agricultural and grazing zones.

It should be noted that no separate pastoral economy or nomadism, away from tuber agriculture, had developed anywhere in the Andes (Troll, 1931, pp. 263–264; 1958, p. 12; Horkheimer, 1960, p. 27). Herding was thought of in age-grade terms:[4] most of the herders (*awatiri* in Aymara and *michik* in Quechua) were, and still are, young people of both sexes. Sometimes they herded for their immediate families, at other times they worked off the

---

[3] Zárate saw coastal animals fed on maize ([1555]. bk. 3, ch. 2; 1853, p. 485). See also Gilmore, 1950, pp. 432, 436.

[4] Poma, [1615], 1936, pp. 203 [205], 205 [207], 207 [209], 226 [228]; Valcárcel, 1937–1941, vol. 2, p. 37. Today, when peasant herds are much smaller, herders are usually women and children (Tschopik, 1946, p. 521).

reciprocal obligations of their kin group. Where the herds were sizable, or where the range was distant from the village, the herders would be assigned to their chores on an adult, full-time basis. How and when this transition took place, who volunteered or was picked for this duty, generally considered to be of low status, what the opportunities may have been to leave the range eventually— as yet, all this cannot be reconstructed. But we do know that full-time herders, even if they spent most of their lives in the *puna*, high above the peasant settlement, continued socially to belong to the village. Their isolation did not deprive them of their automatic rights of access to agricultural lands, which were worked for them by their kin (Poma, [1615], 1936, pp. 245 [247], 315 [317], 321 [323]; Ortiz, [1562], 1957, pp. 326, 331; Garcilaso de la Vega, [1604], bk. 5, ch. 11; 1960, pp. 162–163) .

COMMUNITY AND PEASANT HERDS

To consider now the social structure within which the lamoids and their herders had been fitted, we note first that we are dealing here with a true state, having a redistributive economy, whose revenues were derived not from taxing the peasant's own produce, but by conscripting his energies for work on state fields and pastures. Thus there were at least *two dimensions to Andean animal husbandry:* that of the defeated ethnic groups, now a peasantry, and that of the Inca state. Access to animals and to herding services must be viewed in both contexts.

Second, the llama is the only animal treated in this symposium, the data on which come from a period now four and more centuries past. This affects comparability: the kind of functional and behavioral details available for contemporary cultures are rare in our sixteenth-century European sources. Fortunately, in recent years we have gained access to local, bureaucratic accounts of particular valleys or ethnic groups, that make no attempt to generalize about "the Inca" as a whole, but provide us with the raw, first-hand data about particular herds and their herders.

The most revealing of these accounts, by Garci Diez de San Miguel, deals with the densely populated western shore of Lake

Titicaca, where an Aymara-speaking kingdom, called the Lupaca, had arisen in pre-Incaic times.[5] Its center was Chucuito; it was one of several principalities in this southern highland area, which was generally known as Qollasuyu. The Qolla had a reputation throughout the Andes as *the* llama breeders, and those of Chucuito controlled vast herds of llamas and alpacas. The 3242 Lupaca households of the township of Xuli reported a "community herd" of 16,846 head in 1567 (Garci Diez, [1567–1568], ff. 31r, 60r), which may or may not have included those animals earmarked for particular families or *mallku,* the ethnic leaders. Nearby, the township of Hilaui reported only 2122 beasts for 1470 households (*ibid.,* ff. 31r, 56r), but the over-all feeling in the area was that llamas were the main resource and that in Inca times they had been even more numerous. "There were not enough pastures, there were so many animals in those days," said Cutinbo to his interviewers. He was old enough to have taken part as an adult in Inca affairs.

Although it is the best and most detailed report we have had so far from the llama country, Garci Diez' account is sketchy on peasant and household data. His informants were the traditional Lupaca lords, whose authority had been diminished by both Inca and European domination since the days when the Cari dynasty had ruled much of Qollasuyu (Cieza de León, [1550], bk. 1, chs. 100, 104; 1862, pp. 443, 445; [1550], bk. 2, chs. 41, 42, 43; 1943, pp. 157–159, 163–165). Their testimony reflected their nostalgia for past privileges and their apprehension that the Europeans might find out how large Lupaca resources really were. Still, they spoke from within the culture, and not even the double filter of the questionnaire and the translation could eliminate the real people testifying about what mattered to them most.

Garci Diez' evidence on men and their beasts is recorded township by township and covers close to 20,000 households. The value of the account increases if we recall that the Lupaca region is also

[5] This report, now in the Archivo de Indias, Sevilla, has been transcribed by Waldemar Espinoza, of the Universidad Nacional del Centro, Huancayo, Perú, and published by the Casa de la Cultura del Perú, Lima, 1964, with the assistance of the Institute of Andean Research. See also Helmer, 1951.

"covered" by the Aymara dictionary of Bertonio, compiled soon after the inspection of 1567 and extremely rich in pastoral detail (Bertonio, [1612], 1879). In this, as in so many other aspects of Andean life, the Europeans of the sixteenth century followed Inca precedent (Rowe, 1954, 1957) : unconcerned with the staple tubers, Incas and Europeans were awed by the size of the herds. It was here that the Inca state had found a pretext in the "rebellion" of the Qolla for the confiscation of many animals which later served as the nucleus of state herds.

The salient revelation of the document is that despite the long history of llama breeding in Qollasuyu, the frequent wars, and the emergence of a series of competing kingdoms, llama and alpaca herds were still identified with and herded by particular kin groups. Each of the seven Lupaca townships was bisected into Hanansaya and Lurinsaya, the traditional Andean moieties, and each of these was divided into a number of *ayllu*, or *hatha*. Each of the fourteen moieties had its own animals (Garci Diez, [1567–1568], ff. 41r, 32r, 37v, 43r, 56r, 60r) ; when the township of Xuli went from dual division to three phratries, each of the three set up its own flock (*ibid.*, f. 60r). The evidence is less conclusive on segregation by *ayllu* within such moiety herds, but at least at Acora "each *ayllu* keeps separate its own community cattle" (*ibid.*, f. 48r; Polo, [1571], 1916*b*, p. 156; Avila, [1608], ch. 20, ff. 85r–85v; 1942, pp. 110–111; see also Trimborn, 1928, p. 656).

The animals of a given moiety or *ayllu* were segregated according to sex and age.[6] The exact details are not yet available, but apparently pregnant does grazed separately from burden-bearing males and so did lactating females and their lambs. Within a herd, any individual llama or alpaca was publicly and ceremonially earmarked (Gonzalez Holguín, [1608], 1952, p. 110; Bertonio, [1612], 1879, vol. 1, p. 429) and known to belong to a particular household, but most of the year, out on the range, the animals grazed together, "all mixed up" (Ortiz, [1562], 1957, p. 326; Garci Diez, [1567–1568], f. 37v). The Lupaca lords and peasantry had many llamas: we hear of households that owned 20, 30,

---

[6] Bertonio, [1612], 1879, vol. 1, p. 57; vol. 2, p. 259. For contemporary practice see Maccagno, 1932, pp. 49–50, and Tello, 1942, p. 599.

even 500 beasts.[7] Some of the European settlers in the region, interviewed by Diez, were categorical: "all Indians, poor as they may
be, own llamas," but the local people testifying were more cautious: "generally all have llamas, some a hundred head and more
and some fifty, others twenty and ten and three and two and some
Indians have none, though not many" (Garci Diez, [1567–1568],
f. 47v). In fact, at Hilaui, in the same area, "the Indians who
have cattle are about half of the Aymara[-speaking] ones and the
others are poor and some have no blankets for their bed" (ibid.,
f. 55r). Many miles away to the north, in Huánuco, 100 people
living in two hamlets reported a herd of only 33 llamas among
them, 6 of which were the local ethnic leader's own beasts (Ortiz,
[1562], 1957, p. 326).

Obviously, many households and entire regions in the North
had no animals whatever, so the meaning and implications of herdlessness varied from place to place. In Huánuco, where agriculture was the major activity and llamas were scarce, lacking livestock did not imply destitution: here llamas were not a strategic
resource. The meaning was different in Lupaca territory, where
tubers and kinowa crops were significantly supplemented by herding. Here llamas were a major capital good, and most households
expected to acquire rights in llamas as part of successful participa-
tion in altiplano economic life. Minimum subsistence may not
have been threatened if one had no animals, but it was both an
economic and a social disability. Being herdless limited one's opportunities to weave and trade, both important since they were
the key to cloth, maize, beer, coca leaf, and other hospitality goods
needed in a society where, in the absence of money or markets, institutionalized generosity was the obligation and privilege of adult
and high status. Also, in an emergency, at times of drought and
frost, when the Andean tuber crops failed and famine threatened,
llama products could always be bartered for food.

Assuming that "generally all have llamas" was the cultural norm

---

[7] A slightly later [1574] census of household herds for the same area has now been
published in Garci Diez de San Miguel, 1964. Compiled by Pedro Gutiérrez Flores,
it lists the herds by household, lineage, and moiety. One household reported as
many as 1700 head.

for this area, there were still at least three circumstances in which one could be herdless: (1) when a young man was getting ready to set up his own household, through marriage, which in the Andes defined his adult status; (2) if one was alien to the Aymara-speaking community and thus "never" had had any llamas; (3) if one had lost all stock through some calamity.

1. By definition, the young in the Andes had limited access to strategic goods, nor did they owe services to the Inca crown in their own right; they "served" as part of their father's team. However, there is some evidence that at least in Qollasuyu, the young did acquire some llamas even before marriage. Bertonio reports that at two or three years of age the hair of the children was ceremonially shorn, and among the gifts were llamas known as *hinchuma* "given by the father to his son, by the uncle to his nephew" (Bertonio, [1612], 1879, vol. 1, p. 119; vol. 2, p. 134). Similar gifts were to be expected at marriage, and there are hints at bride-wealth (Morúa, [1590], bk. 3, ch. 32; 1946, p. 240; Poma, [1615], 1936, p. 67) : marriage was the moment to stake one's major economic claim within the household and *ayllu*. Unfortunately, how the young stated their claim to their kinfolk, how it was satisfied and when denied, how wide the network of kin participating—all these are not recorded. Additional mechanisms of transmission and of continuity of tenure must also have functioned at death, but all we hear of are the animals killed to accompany the deceased (Poma, [1615], 1936, pp. 257 [259], 296 [298]) .

2. The chroniclers do report some people lacking llamas for reasons other than their youth: the swamp-dwelling, fishing and gathering Uru, the aboriginal population of the shores of Lake Titicaca, who were kept in virtually caste-like seclusion, herdless and "backward," by the Lupaca elite (Garci Diez, [1567–1568], ff. 20v, 68v–69r) ; also some of the *mitmaq* colonists transferred by the Inca into the region (*ibid.*, ff. 31r–31v; Polo, [1571], 1916*b*, pp. 68–69) .

3. Others mentioned are *waqcha*, usually called the "poor" by the Europeans—those who had no animals by reason of epidemics, drought, mismanagement, or the absence of influential or numerous kin. Dangers of various kinds did threaten the herds: Tello

mentions a "law" that llamas sick with an extremely contagious
mange should be buried; one of the Lupaca lords, interviewed at
Acora by Garci Diez, mentioned a thousand head that had died
in a single year because of the frosts (Garci Diez, [1567–1568], f.
48r). But the meaning of herdlessness is best understood when
we look at the changing meaning of *waqcha*. Though "poor" may
be the later translation, the dictionaries compiled in the sixteenth
century hesitate: in Quechua, *huaccha* means "poor and orphan";
in Aymara, *huakhcha* was "poor and also orphan without father
or mother" (Gonzalez Holguín, [1608], 1952, pp. 167, 548; Bertonio, [1612], 1879, vol. 1, pp. 270, 371; vol. 2, pp. 144, 197;
Garcilaso de la Vega, [1604], bk. 5, ch. 9; bk. 9, ch. 3; 1960, pp.
159, 336; Valera *in* Garcilaso [1604], bk. 5, chs. 11, 15; 1960, pp.
162, 169). *Huacchayani* meant "to become impoverished and to
lack relatives" in Quechua.

For the herdless, there were apparently two ways to regain control of some llamas: (*a*) the "generosity" of some local ethnic
leader, and perhaps (*b*) the existence of community herds.

a) In Andean economics, reciprocity was extended to kinfolk
and fellow villagers in agriculture, housebuilding, and herding;
the actual lands and herds were perceived as inseparable from the
reciprocal services used to work and guard them. To paraphrase
Guamán Poma, a sixteenth-century Andean writer, there was no
need for charity (Poma, [1615], 1936, p. 220 [222]) since everybody had access to the strategic resources of the culture and to the
people who made them productive. If for any reason one could
not work off one's share, reciprocity did not stop: an old man's
llamas were tended for him by others (*ibid.*, p. 199 [201]); a
widow's herd grazed with her *ayllu* or moiety beasts (Garci Diez,
[1567–1568], f. 37v).

Such reciprocal services were also extended to the traditional
ethnic leaders, whether they were kin or not. The lord received
no tribute in goods, but was entitled to *mitta* help in the cultivation of his fields or the herding of his flocks; in return, he was
institutionally generous: "to those who served him well he would
give a live lamb and food . . . because if they are not given it, they
get angry" (Garci Diez, [1567–1568], f. 10r), according to the

Lupaca chiefs at Chucuito. "To all those who served him, he gave coca leaf, some food and llamas which they could eat or raise for themselves" (*ibid.*, ff. 42r, 53r). If the report is accurate, the lords would grant animals not only for consumption but also as the starting pair of a herd. The same pattern of chiefly "generosity" prevailed much farther north, where llamas were scarce. Cochachi, the minor leader of Rondo in Huánuco, who owned, he said, only nine beasts, when "he saw some poor Indians, he granted to them [presumably from the nine] one head among three households" (Ortiz, [1562], 1921, vol. 2, pp. 223, 227).

b) Perhaps there was another way of getting access to llamas, beyond the claim to one's father's beasts and to the lord's "generosity": the sources speak of community or *sapsi* herds (Poma, [1615], 1936, pp. 245 [247], 897 [911]), and these are distinguished from animals earmarked for particular households and the lords. They were "inspected" or counted in public twice a year: in May, soon after lambing, and in November, after being sheared (*ibid.*, pp. 245 [247], 257 [259]; see also Gonzalez Holguín, [1608], 1952, pp. 280–281; Bertonio, [1612], 1879, vol. 1, p. 57; vol. 2, pp. 258–259). Some of their uses have been recorded: among the Lupaca, the *sapsi* herd was a reserve flock which could be bartered off in case of famine (Garci Diez, [1567–1568], ff. 10v, 68r). From this herd, a lamb would be roasted for a visiting dignitary; sacrificial animals for the deities came from the same source, and both offerings were known by the identical Aymara term, *angru caura*.[8] Finally, in early European times "community" animals would be sold to pay the new money taxes or to feed the clergy. We know, then, that as ceremonial and consumption goods, community llamas did reach the peasant. The question that arises but cannot be answered from our evidence is: could such *sapsi* animals be allotted to particular households as capital goods, in case of calamity? In Aymara country, there was a ceremonial occasion once a year when young animals were "promoted" to the adult herds by the *phattiri*, "the official in charge of assigning the llamas." In both Quechua and Aymara, the verbs

[8] Bertonio, [1612], 1879, vol. 1, p. 119; vol. 2, p. 20. For modern llama increase ceremonies, see Tschopik, 1951, pp. 268–269, 275; Morote Best, 1951, pp. 144–146.

ppatachani and *phattami* relate to division, distribution, and the settlement of disputes (Gonzalez Holguín, [1608], 1952, pp. 280–281; Bertonio, [1612], 1879, vol. 2, pp. 258–259). It is conceivable that this was also the moment when a claim to some animals could be stated.

By analogy with land, this is possible. The herdless, at least in Qollasuyu, should be able to press a claim to such a strategic resource, not only before their kin but also to the wider community of their *ayllu* and moiety, much as they have a claim (Núñez del Prado, 1949, pp. 194–196; Chávez Ballón, 1958, p. 29) till today to the marginal and the long fallowed lands.

And yet, the availability of such reserve animals is in doubt in our sources, not only because herds need not follow the tenure rules applicable to lands, but also because of the conditions under which our documentation was recorded: the European inspector was too obviously eager to know the size of the "community" herds, while showing much less interest in animals identified with particular households. The Lupaca witnesses fenced, dodged, and if possible denied the presence of such herds, since they had reason to feel that inquiries about "community" resources were likely to lead to their confiscation by the Europeans or at least to heavy taxation on beasts that were "nobody's" by being everybody's. Thus Cari, the Hanansaya leader for the whole Lupaca realm, declared on folio 10v that "his" community herd was 400 head strong, but by folio 32r he had been forced to confess that at Chayata alone there were 2000. The opposite moiety reported "no more than five hundred, 173 [of them llamas], the rest alpacas," but soon there were 2030 and possibly more than 8000 (Garci Diez, [1567–1568], ff. 14r, 37v, 42v, 85v).

Some of this confusion clearly results from the effort of the Lupaca leadership to protect their resources, but not all of it. There was also the deficient translation from the Aymara: what did the "ladino" interpreter make of the Spanish word *comunidad?* Did he use the moiety, the *ayllu,* or the *marka* (town) as the equivalent? And how did he handle the conceptual differences in "ownership" and their relations to social organization held by the two cultures confronting each other in the inspection?

What is demonstrable so far is that around Lake Titicaca, the classic llama country, large herds were organized under *ayllu* and moiety sponsorship. Although a given alpaca may have been earmarked for a chief, a peasant household, or the community (Garci Diez, [1567–1568], ff. 37v, 136v), and some holdings were much larger than others, they all grazed together. Each household within this kin group maintained a variety of rights to the animals under its control, and minimally, each of these households had some access to some animals to which its claim was stronger than that of anyone else.

HERDING

Responsibility for a moiety herd was assigned to men, described as *principales*, leading men, by the Europeans, and *llama kamayoq* or *michiy kamayoq* in Quechua (Gonzalez Holguín, [1608], 1952, pp. 237, 355, 410, 618). The man interviewed by Garci Diez was don Luis Cutipa. He was in charge of the thousands of animals belonging to the Lurinsaya moiety and testified that the beasts were grazing three leagues away, community llamas all mixed with those of the lords, "those of private Indians . . . and those of some widows." When asked for the names of those whose llamas were mixed with the community's, he answered that he could not know the names of so many Indians.

Cutipa reported there were fifteen herders guarding the flocks of Lurinsaya: at the rate of 30 to 40 per man, claimed by the Lupaca (Garci Diez, [1567–1568], f. 72v), this would add up to 600 beasts. At the rate of up to 200 head per herder, claimed by a European informant of Garci Diez (*ibid.*, f. 81v), we would have a moiety flock of 3750, apparently a low estimate, contradicted by other figures in the same document (*ibid.*, ff. 60r, 85v).

Some of these herders were presumably young men sent out on rotation from each *ayllu* within the moiety (Garci Diez, [1567–1568], f. 43r; Poma, [1615], 1936, pp. 203 [205], 205 [207], 207 [209], 226 [228]; Cobo, [1653], bk. 14, ch. 6; 1956, p. 246), who performed herding duties as part of traditional reciprocity. While the herder was on duty, the moiety fed him; "his lands were worked for him by other Indians" (Ortiz, [1562], 1957, pp. 326–327, 331). While in the *puna,* he not only had responsibility for the ruminants in his charge, but was expected to make ropes of llama hair, hunt dangerous or edible game, collect feathers, and otherwise make use of *puna* resources (Poma, [1615], 1936, p. [904] 890). One wonders if such services could have been rewarded with a grant of the animals themselves.

By Inca times, and probably much earlier in Lupaca country, some of the herders were no longer just youths, but had become adult, apparently full-time craftsmen. They still came on rotation from the various *ayllu,* but the job of herding was not as easily subdivisible as agricultural work, and demanded more continuity. Thus Cari, the Hanansaya lord, had men herding his llamas coming from each of the seven townships in the realm. Of the 60 men sent to work for him at some time during the year, from Chucuito proper, 10 were assigned to herding (Garci Diez, [1567–1568], f. 9v). Cusi, his Lurinsaya opposite number, sent 17 to the pastures out of the 30 he disposed of, and 4 more came from Xuli, but then Lurinsaya herds are reported to have been larger (*ibid.,* ff. 43r, 84v, 85v). How long each herding *mitta* or turn lasted, how these men were selected for the job, cannot be stated now. Elsewhere in the Andes, where there were many fewer animals, there were nevertheless some men who spent full time in the *puna;* apparently some took their family with them, others were accompanied only by a child (Ortiz, [1562], 1957, p. 326). Herders had songs and celebrations of their own; they worshiped and sacrificed to *Urcuchillay,* the Lyre constellation, thought to be a multicolored buck who watched over the growth and multiplication of llamas.[9]

A further step in the social and economic differentiation of herders had also occurred around Lake Titicaca. The Chucuito account provides the first evidence that some herders were no longer members of their ethnic and kinship communities and had become hereditary pastoral retainers of the Lupaca chiefs. Martín Cari, the Hanansaya leader who testified before Garci Diez,

---

[9] Polo, [1559], 1916a, pp. 4–5, and those who copy from him even if they hate him: Jesuita Anónimo, [1590?], 1950, pp. 139–142; Morúa, [1590], bk. 3, ch. 51; 1946, pp. 285–286; Poma, [1615], 1936, pp. 315 [317], 321 [323]; Cobo, [1653], bk. 13, ch. 6; 1956, p. 159; Oricaín, [1790], 1942, p. 600.

stated that in addition to the ten herders who worked for him on rotation, there were ten others "given to his ancestors long ago, before the Inca had governed this land" (Garci Diez, [1567–1568], f. 9v). These ten "service Indians who were and still are in the *puna* . . . where the cattle are kept, which Indians have multiplied so that today they would be 50 or 60 with women and children . . . and the said town of Xuli, in ancient times, in addition to the stated above, gave to the ancestors of the witness, two men of service, who have been used, along with their descendants, by the witness and his ancestors. From the multiplication of those two, there are now nine, who served him in the herding of cattle." When Garci Diez arrived at Xuli, he inquired about the matter and was told that "to the grandfather of said Martín Cari, they gave certain Indians once and for all and today there are some of them who had multiplied and these he is using now" (*ibid.*, f. 58r).

Other sixteenth-century writers mention the *yana*, "perpetual servants" (Cieza, [1550], ch. 17; 1943, p. 69), who worked on the estates of the Inca kings. At least two of the best known sources (Sarmiento de Gamboa, [1572], 1943, pp. 228–229; Cabello Valboa, [1586], bk. 3, ch. 19; 1951, pp. 346–347) reproduce a legend according to which *yana* retainers had emerged in Inca times from reprieved "rebels" against the king. The present Lupaca data indicate that hereditary servitude is apparently pre-Incaic; that of seven townships at least two, Acora (Garci Diez, [1567–1568], f. 45v) and Xuli, had surrendered 10 households each to pastoral servitude in exile at the capital, in Chucuito; that the local Xuli leaders also benefited from the assignment of about 4 households (out of 1500) to *yana* status; that these *yana* were presumably Aymara-speaking, experienced herders, and not low-status Uru fishermen (*ibid.*, f. 59v); that the percentage of those "given once and for all" was low—less than 1 per cent of the population. Most of the herding, farming, and other services enjoyed by the leaders continued within the framework of reciprocity.

A question arises about the subsistence and other goods which the ethnic leaders supplied to the *yana* as contrasted with the *mitta* herders serving on rotation. The latter expected "once a year" some food, coca leaf, and beer in keeping with reciprocity obligations; presumably the *yana* had to be provided with full subsistence, but the details are missing. The impression one gets is that *yana* status did not end one's role as a cultivator: in Hilaui, "each of them has his own house although he serves" (Garci Diez, [1567–1568], f. 53r), but since his ties with his own *ayllu* were cut, the lands which provided the *yana* herder's subsistence were carved out of the chief's holdings and were worked either by his immediate family (Ortiz, [1562], 1957, p. 326) or by *mitta* peasants cultivating on rotation for the lord. It would be interesting to know if *yana* retainers were the "servants" who received llamas if "they served well," but this cannot be determined now, since the Europeans referred to *yana* and peasants on rotation as "Indios de servicio," interchangeably; both groups are also reported to have "received" food, wool, and coca leaf. At least in theory one can conceive of a significant difference between the two groups in their access to llamas: ordinary, *mitta* herders would get theirs from their kinship and ethnic group and/or the "community" herd, whereas the *yana* would be more dependent on their lord's whim.[10]

This distinction between *yana* and peasants assumes importance not only in terms of our efforts to elucidate the condition of Inca herders at the moment of European invasion, but also in terms of the larger debate on the nature of the Inca economy. Recently references which view the Inca as a slave society have become frequent (Núñez Anavitarte, 1955; Choy, 1960). The context and extent of hereditary retainership in Lupaca herding country, as reflected in Garci Diez' inspection account, is an important new entry in the debate: if the *yana* formed less than 1 per cent of the population and if they had access to lands and llamas, even if no longer in a kinship context, could slavery be considered as characterizing the economy?

NON-PEASANT HERDS

Beyond herding services, the *mallku* could claim further contributions of energy from the peasant community. Every year,

---

[10] Garci Diez, [1567–1568], 1964, f. 48v: "to those who were rich he gave nothing."

after the rainy season was over, hundreds of llamas were dispatched to the coast, carrying wool, potatoes, *charki,* and other highland commodities to be exchanged for maize, the indispensable ceremonial and beer-making grain. The drovers were men supplied from the various *ayllu:* "every year they give him forty or fifty Indians who go with llamas to bring him maize from Moquegua and Çama and Çapinota and Larecaxa for the provisioning of his house . . . and the trip takes them two and three months coming and going and once they return he uses them no longer. . . . And he gives them *chuño,* potatoes, and dried meat and *kinowa* and coca leaf so they can eat and he gives them wool so they can barter over there for themselves for whatever food they want" (Garci Diez, [1567–1568], ff. 9r–9v). Much of this "barter" or "trade" was more in the nature of transporting one's own harvest, since the maize producers were frequently themselves Aymara-speaking highlanders transplanted on a permanent basis to the coastal oases as *mitmaq* colonists, to ensure and regularize the Lupaca supply of maize. Throughout the Andes, regional differences in production were, by preference, handled by means of colonization instead of through barter and trade.

Nevertheless, some small-scale exchanges did take place. Those in Lupaca country "who had their own cattle" (Garci Diez, [1567–1568], f. 13v) went to the coast and to the *lomas* to barter on their own (Tello, 1942, pp. 607–608). The maize growers on the irrigated coast were eager for the highlanders' animals, their wool and meat. In ordinary years a llama could be bartered for as much as five bushels of grain, but when frosts had been severe in Qollasuyu and food scarce, the exchange value would fall to half (Garci Diez, [1567–1568], f. 58v). Throughout the Andes small interzonal markets functioned, with llamas, *charki,* and wool always on the list of items bartered (Ortiz, [1562], 1921, p. 228; [1562], 1956, p. 306). When money was introduced after the European invasion, priests noted that people would buy llamas with money for sacrificial purposes (Arriaga, [1621], ch. 4; 1920, pp. 43–44), if they had none of their own. Offerings of llamas were made to shrines like Quimquilla, in Huarochirí, that were considered responsible for the multiplication and welfare of the animals. This shrine had its own herd (Avila, [1608], ch. 24, f. 95r; ch. 9, f. 75r; 1942, pp. 123, 96), as did many other holy places listed in the chronicles. We should probably distinguish them from peasant and *kuraka* flocks, as a separate form of llama control at the ethnic, local level.

Shrine herds are reported to have been quite large, 500 head and larger (Hernández Principe, [1623], 1923, p. 46); they were used for sacrificial and hospitality, as well as utilitarian, purposes. In the Huánuco and Chucuito accounts we find little mention, in fact denial, of any such shrine resources (Ortiz, [1562], 1920, pp. 29, 31, 41), but elsewhere in the Andes we frequently hear of isolated individuals, sometimes several, who devoted full time to the pasturing of beasts dedicated to sacred aims. As late as 1621, an inspection in the region of Recuay found two shrines, each the responsibility of a separate *ayllu*, each with many hundreds of llamas at its disposal. "The inspector took pity on them and since they had confessed their crime he lowered the number of the llamas to 150 for the Carachuco shrine and 200 for Huari Carhua, no more, from a much larger quantity" (Hernández Principe, [1621], 1923, p. 46). The Jesuits who undertook the destruction of Andean religion at Huachos at about the same time claimed they had found "twenty, even thirty men and women . . . who were busy in the service of the shrine; these [the community] protected from the *mitta* chores at [the European mines in] Huancavelica. And to disguise what they did from the Spaniards, they hid them from childhood on and did not baptize them so they would not appear on the books of the priest" (Teruel?, [1613], 1918, p. 185).

The reason why the existence of shrine herds was denied in the 1560's was not only the fear of punishment for continuing heathen practices, but also the danger of loss, through confiscation, of any resources once earmarked for Inca institutions, now illegal. There is a notable reticence among Garci Diez' informants at Chucuito about any herds that may have been assigned to the Inca state, its church, or the royal dynasty. Yet all these had existed in many parts of the Inca realm, and their pastures were still remembered in Cobo's time, a full century after the European invasion (Cobo, [1653], bk. 2, ch. 10; 1956, p. 74).

STATE HERDS

State herds and state pastures were set up in the "provinces" rich in llamas; some areas which had never had llamas before acquired them (Cieza, [1550], bk. 2, chs. 13, 17, 7; 1943, pp. 46, 60–61, 258). Since the Yauyos region was poor in grazing facilities, each administrative subdivision was granted pastures in the Cochorbos country to the south (Jiménez de la Espada, 1881, vol. 1, p. 78). Similarly, Polo tells us that state pastures in Lupaca country were administered separately from those in Pacasa, south of the lake; beasts from one could not graze on the range of the other (Polo, [1571], 1916b, p. 62). Church flocks also had their own pastures, separate from those of the crown. According to Polo, who knew the llama country well, crown and church herds were known as *qhapaqllama*, the herds of the mighty, while peasant and ethnic animals were *waqchallama*, those of the weak (Polo, [1561], 1940, p. 136; [1571], 1916b, p. 62; Poma, [1615], 1936, p. 897 [911]).

Such labels reflect the ideological stance of the Inca elite. After the conquest and the emergence of Tawantinsuyu, the Inca state, an effort was made to promote a legal fiction, according to which all llamas and alpacas became the crown's creatures, much as the wild huanacos and vicuñas were *intipllaman*, the animals of the Sun. All lands and other strategic resources were similarly defined as "belonging" to the state. This did not correspond to functional reality: a large, if undetermined, proportion of the animals remained in the peasants' and their *kuraka's* hands, particularly in the South, much as most lands in the highlands continued at the disposal of the local ethnic community.

Still, the fiction had its uses: it could be argued that the llamas which had not been alienated had been beneficent grants of a generous monarch, "gifts" which justified in reciprocal terms the new obligation to "serve" the state; a "rebel's" herds could be "reclaimed" and granted to the deserving; all wild lamoids, which were herded by no one, were reserved for the king's beaters. The fiction made it possible for the state to issue an edict that wild does caught by the beaters should not be killed, only shorn, a decree which the Europeans tried to reintroduce without success as early as 1557.[11] It is also claimed that in Inca times no one could hunt on crown lands, and all hunting territories, *moya,* were so defined (Hurtado de Mendoza, [1557], 1953, p. 62). Even if permission to hunt or to gather timber or fodder was granted, this "license," issued in one jurisdiction, was not valid in another (Polo, [1571], 1916*b*, p. 88; Ortiz, [1562], 1920, p. 179). One wonders how strictly this could be enforced in Andean conditions; the main function of such a definition of "wild" things was probably that the state could claim actual tribute, in kind, of feathers, fish, eggs, vicuña, and deer *charki* which had been raised by no one and were hence the king's; while the peasant household had a still untouchable, old-Andean right to keep all its own production, owing only its *mitta* energies and time to the state.

There is no reason to believe that the peasantry ever accepted this version of Inca statecraft. Before the Inca conquest, the various Aymara-speaking groups in the Titicaca region had fought each other and had never been unified. Quarrels and raids between these groups were common (Cieza, [1550], bk. 2, chs. 24, 62, 63; 1943, pp. 95, 237, 242; Garcilaso de la Vega, [1604], bk. 3, chs. 11, 14; 1960, pp. 98–99, 102–104). The Inca state began its expansion beyond Cuzco into this area, stepping in where bitter, age-old rivalries had made united action impossible, and proclaimed Pax Incaica: the local boundaries between the pastures of ethnic groups were to be set up and enforced (Polo, [1561], 1940, p. 194; Falcón, [1580?], 1918, p. 149; Garcilaso de la Vega, [1604], bk. 2, ch. 13; 1960, p. 61) ; many of the llamas were confiscated to form the nucleus of Inca state herds (Polo, [1571], 1916*b*, p. 62) ; others were granted as spoils to the Cuzco soldiers, individually. A century later, in the 1560's, the long memory of the folk still recalled this plunder (Matienzo, [1570?], bk. 2, ch. 14; 1910, p. 179). According to Santillán, it was still possible at that time to identify the original owners by the animals' *señales* (Santillán,

---

[11] There is a hint that such ceremonial definition of wild animals is pre-Incaic. Avila's informants at Huarochirí told him that annually, in November, just before the rains, the men would go hunting. The huanacos caught would be turned over to a shaman, the hunters keeping only the tails. After the hunt came celebration and dancing. It was hoped that the rains would coincide with the dance ([1608], ch. 11, f. 106r; 1942, p. 138) .

[1563–1564], ch. 54; 1927, p. 45), the nature of which is not clear, but may have been the color or some other local characteristic. The claim of Inca state control of all resources may have been made, but we also hear of frequent revolts by the Lupaca and other llama breeders against Cuzco rule.

The distribution of captured llamas as spoils in the southern campaign was a fond memory to the Inca royal lineages. It was re-enacted ceremonially in the royals' initiation rites, when the cadets chased llamas which were later divided among them, "as after victory." Royal grants of llamas to individuals created a further category of tenure in animals beyond state and church herds; they may have originated in the division of military booty (Betanzos, [1551], ch. 10; 1880, p. 59; Bandera, [1557], 1881, p. 98), but eventually were made for services rendered and as a sign of special favor at accession to the throne. When, late in pre-European history, king Wayna Qhapaq faced a discontented group of royals, llamas and cloth were granted to appease the rebels (Cabello Valboa, [1586], bk. 3, ch. 22; 1951, p. 376). Garcilaso claimed such herds were very small, "barely enough for them and their families," whereas P. Pizarro estimated the grants at from 50 to 100 head. Cobo claimed that such grants were made from the community herds (Cobo, [1653], bk. 12, ch. 29; 1956, p. 123), but after the original looting this seems unlikely. Most of Cobo's information on llamas was taken from P. Pizarro and Polo; the latter, who still found sections of the Inca administrative machinery functioning, is categorical in affirming that whatever beasts were distributed did not come from community herds. Polo and Cobo agree that llamas granted by the crown could not be alienated nor divided among the heirs. Like royal land grants, such herds were inherited by the kinfolk of the first grantee and used by them all (Polo, [1561], 1940, p. 136; [1571], 1916b, pp. 61, 75, 128; Cobo, [1653], bk. 12, ch. 29; 1956, p. 123).

The limited European vocabulary available to describe the kinds of administrative reciprocity found in the Andes forced our sources to speak of "grants" and "gifts" when referring to issues of state llamas made by the kings to the local lords. Thus, Cari of Chucuito claimed that the king "gave" him annually 200 or

300 llamas so that he could feed the "passengers" traveling through Lupaca territory on government business (Garci Diez, [1567–1568], ff. 10r–10v). The confusion is greater in Cusi's report, from the other moiety: the llamas were given to him so he and his people and the travelers could eat; but then, Cusi was very young and had no firsthand experience with the Inca state (*ibid.*, f. 16r). The issue is clarified 25 pages later in Garci Diez' account: the Inca "gave" the lord "some clothes or other things of value and some llamas and maybe a silver glass to drink from." This matches what other sources tell us of royal generosity: the emphasis was not on quantity but on status proximity of the "gift" to the royal personage. The local lords may have been granted some llamas from the royal herd and even some herders (Ortiz, [1562], 1956, p. 45) for their personal use, but the 200 to 300 mentioned by Cari are an administrative issue, not a grant: in so far as the state road to the south passed through Cari's territory, the crown was responsible for the provisioning of wayside facilities. The ethnic lords may have been charged with the administrative responsibility of supervision, but economically such installations were a burden on the state herds, not on local resources.

The pack animals of the crown carried supplies from the provinces to the capital and then outward when needed. They could not always replace men, since logs, rocks, or other bulky and heavy units were beyond their strength or ability to cooperate. In the northern part of the country, one hears that even maize traveled from Caxamarca to Cuzco on human backs, and so did Huánuco supplies being stored in regional granaries. This may have been due to the continuing scarcity of llamas in the northern part of the country, despite the efforts at acclimatization made by the Inca beyond the ecological limits of the *puna*. In peace time, animals in the state herds were also seen as a major source of wool, which was stored and eventually distributed among peasants and the retainers of the king, to be woven into cloth, which was in ever growing demand for state purposes.

Still, in Inca thinking, the primary use of state animals was apparently military. Army llama trains carried burdens and food and were themselves eaten in emergency. Before king Wayna

Qhapaq would set off on a military campaign, he awaited a report on his herds in Qollasuyu (Cieza, [1550], bk. 2, ch. 62; 1943, pp. 235–237). In describing the looting of king Atawallpa's camp during the invasion, Xérez said there were so many llamas following the Inca army that they cluttered up the place, and Pizarro ordered their release, along with the demobilization of the Inca army (Xérez, [1534], 1853, p. 334; Anónimo Sevillano, [1534], 1937, p. 83). A few months later, a general who organized Inca resistance after the murder of his king, fielded an army, which, Zárate was told, had llamas by the thousand in the main body of the force. When he had to withdraw suddenly from the road, he was supposed to have left behind not only thousands of prisoners, but 15,000 llamas (Zárate, [1555], bk. 2, ch. 12; 1853, pp. 482–483).

Border outposts facing the *montaña* also had access to llamas. Near Cochabamba, in eastern Bolivia, a frontier zone where skirmishes were frequent, the garrison could draw on herds which according to Morúa were administratively assigned to the Sun (Morúa, [1590], bk. 4, ch. 14; 1946, p. 410). This could be an error of Morúa's informant, as we hear elsewhere that the army was supplied from state herds (Polo, [1571], 1916b, p. 59), but it could also be right, since there is ample evidence that in the Andes war was viewed as a magico-religious as well as a political matter. War preparations included starving black llamas and dogs so that the enemy's heart would wither away as did the hungry animals. They were later sacrificed along with highland birds, and their entrails studied for military omens (Morúa, [1590], bk. 3, ch. 53; 1946, p. 292; Garcilaso de la Vega, [1604], bk. 6, ch. 21; 1960, p. 221; Cobo, [1653], bk. 13, ch. 22; 1956, p. 202). During a campaign, llamas not only carried the army's burdens but were used in the monthly ceremonies that greeted the new moon. At such times, military operations were interrupted and sacrifices offered which included llamas. The Europeans took advantage of this battle rhythm when they were besieged at Cuzco by Manqo Inka.

Llamas sacrificed came sometimes from the state, although usually sacrificial bucks were provided from church herds (Polo, [1561], 1940, p. 135; [1571], 1916b, p. 95; Román, [1575], bk. 1, ch. 9; 1897, p. 122). As in the military context, it is not always possible to distinguish readily, at this distance, between the two kinds of flocks, nor can we compare them quantitatively. Presumably, state and church had their own *moya* or pastures and their own herders (Polo, [1571], 1916*b*, pp. 87–88), but data on how such divisions actually worked out are not available. Morúa was told that the kings granted the best of ranges (Morúa, [1590], bk. 3, ch. 43; 1946, p. 264) to the church, but his own ecclesiastic status and his distance from the events encourage skepticism.

All that can be stated now is that animals were assigned to the various state cults: Sun, Thunder, and Wiraqocha Pachayachachi, the Creator deity introduced by king Pachakuti, each had herds of its own (Santillán, [1563–1564], chs. 16, 102; 1927, pp. 21, 94; Polo, [1571], 1916*b*, p. 95). There was apparently a pre-Incaic model for this, since we hear of Pachakamaq, the coastal shrine, having llamas "in every town": its local place of worship in Huarochirí was at Checa, and its animals grazed at Suciahuillca (Avila, [1608], ch. 22, f. 89r; 1942, p. 116). Cult herds were carefully separated by color; each deity had its own preference, reflected in the ceremonial calendar. One hundred brown beasts were sacrificed in August-September to ensure the survival of the newly planted maize fields against frost and drought. Wiraqocha also preferred brown. To encourage rain in October, one hundred white llamas were killed, and some black ones starved; the Sun also preferred white ones. One hundred white alpacas would encourage the Sun to shine and promote growth, and one hundred "of all colors" were best for the maize harvest in May.[12]

The Inca royal kindreds shared this interest in color. They told Sarmiento de Gamboa in 1572 that "our main symbol of lordship" was the *napa,* a white llama "dressed in a scarlet shirt, golden earrings, and a necklace of red seashells." Whenever the king left his house, he was preceded by the *napa.* It had played a significant role in dynastic history: one of the legendary four brothers who founded the dynasty had brought with him the "seeds of the cave," presumably maize, and the *napa.* This close association was re-

[12] Polo, [1559], ch. 6; 1916*a*, pp. 15–16. For modern practice, see Tschopik, 1946, p. 521.

enacted during the initiation of adolescent royals in November: midst races, fasting, and ear piercing, the initiates and their families sacrificed llamas, plucked their wool, smeared themselves with their blood, walked with some of them to and from the city, and ate others raw or cooked (Molina "de Cuzco," [1575], 1943, pp. 46–62). The mummies of dead kings had llamas of their own: these allocations of royal herds and others of lands supported the custodians of the mummies. Such royal beasts should be distinguished from state herds, on the model which distinguished royal lands from those of the state. However, the ethnocentric bias of our sources does confuse them.

The legal conditions and personal status of Inca crown herders are also difficult to assess at this distance since we have no source as detailed for state herds as the Lupaca report. Most of our references indicate that herders of church and state flocks were full-time custodians (Falcón, [1580?], 1918, pp. 147–148; Valera, [1590?], in Garcilaso de la Vega, [1604], bk. 5, ch. 13; 1960, p. 165; Román, [1575], bk. 1, ch. 9; 1897, p. 122; Poma, [1615], 1936, p. 890 [904]. They were held accountable for the animals in their care and for a variety of chores which in Andean thinking are associated with *puna* wild life: hunting of deer and buck huanacos, whose meat was dried into *charki*; gathering of multicolored feathers to be woven into military garments; fishing, and the like (Poma, [1615], 1936, pp. 349 [351], 890 [904]). Supervision and audit were provided through special administrative officers (Borregán, [1562–1565], 1948, p. 45; Morúa, [1590], bk. 3, ch. 15; 1946, p. 200). Polo was amazed at the thoroughness of the records kept: in Qollasuyu, the appropriate officials knew "exactly" how many llamas had been raised since the area had been conquered by the Inca and how many had been "given" to the king. If the *khipo* knot record showed a successful season, herders were rewarded beyond subsistence through bonuses of food and clothing (Molina "de Cuzco," [1575,] 1943, p. 60; Morúa, [1590], bk. 3, ch. 20; 1946, p. 212). Conversely, carelessness and decrease in the size of the herds brought whipping and a loss of shirts.

Bookkeeping and accounting of the herds took place in a ceremonial framework. In November, after shearing, and toward the end of royal initiation rites in which llamas played a continuous and very important part, a census was taken of all beasts in the flocks of the church and the state. The census coincided with a ceremony and sacrifices which took place all over the kingdom, intended to increase the herds; the royal mummies were consulted about the welfare of the herds in the year to come, libations were offered, and successful herders received their rewards (Cieza, [1550], bk. 2, ch. 29; 1943, p. 115).

A final possibility should be mentioned. It is likely that the *yana*, hereditary herders of the Lupaca lords, were matched at the state level by royal *yana*, also hereditary and devoting full time to the flocks of the king or one of the royal kindreds (Ortiz, [1562], 1920, p. 165). This cannot be demonstrated fully, since the chroniclers did not distinguish between the various kinds of *yana*, nor did they hesitate to take over and modify the institution for their own benefit, so that their accounts of servile strata in the population are not reliable.

Nevertheless, there is an indirect guide to *yana* herders. Some of our soundest accounts, those of Santillán and Polo, are categorical: llamas from community herds were not contributed as tribute to the state (Polo, [1561], 1940, pp. 135, 165; [1571], 1916*b,* p. 128; Santillán, [1563–1564], chs. 73, 74; 1927, p. 68). Yet, even Polo hesitates; as elsewhere in the same administrative report, he states that no does were so contributed, implying that buck llamas may have been, and in a sacrificial context, he says simply that animals were offered to Incas and to the shrines (Polo, [1561], 1940, p. 135; [1571], 1916*b,* pp. 62, 100). An independent account, describing the village of Alca, in Condesuyo, claims that the peasants "gave" llamas in tribute (Jiménez de la Espada, [1586], 1885, vol. 2, p. 18). But as we read the account we find that the villagers were "adjudicados" to king Pachakuti and his descendants; the chaotic sentences of page 102 of Polo's account indicate that the "tribute" animals to be sacrificed already belonged to the Inca and the Sun, so that the "payments" were probably not made by peasant owners in these two cases, but were deliveries of state animals by their custodians.

If this interpretation is correct, it would indicate that in animal husbandry, as in other aspects, serious changes were looming in the Inca economy at the time of the European invasion. The basic Andean organization of self-sufficient, ethnic communities of cultivators and herders, conceiving of their resources as kinship holdings, is amply confirmed by the Lupaca data from the heart of the llama-breeding area. Access to llamas as a basic right of the peasant household was still a keystone of the economy in the early 1500's. When the breeders became peasants after the Inca conquest, the system that arose had strong continuities with pre-existing arrangements with the Lupaca lords: no contributions in kind came from the peasant household; it owed only time and energy on rotation at state chores, including the crown herds. And yet, just as the township of Xuli had contributed ten households (less than 1 per cent) to full-time, hereditary "service" for lord Cari, so the state, by the opening of the sixteenth century, was no longer satisfied with a *mitta* definition of herding obligations. What role llama tending, through its isolation from and low status within the peasant community, played in the emergence of such new, servile strata in Inca society cannot be stated now. But the very existence of such herding *yana*, plucked from their ethnic community, is a hint of major transformations still to come, had the European invasion not interrupted the course of Andean development.

REFERENCES

ACOSTA, JOSÉ DE. 1940. *Historia natural y moral de las Indias . . .* [1590]. Fondo de Cultura Económica, México.

ANÓNIMO SEVILLANO. 1937. *La conquista del Perú* [1534]. Cuadernos de Historia (R. Porras Barrenechea, editor), vol. 2. Paris.

ARRIAGA, PABLO JOSÉ DE. 1920. *Extirpación de la idolatría en el Perú . . .* [1621]. Collección de Libros y Documentos referentes a la Historia del Perú, ser. 2, vol. 1. Lima.

ARROYO PONCE, GAMALIEL. 1953. Literatura oral de Tarma. *Archivos Peruanos de Folklore*, vol. 1, no. 1. Lima.

AVILA, FRANCISCO DE, editor. 1942. *De Priscorum Huaruchiriensium . . .* [1608]. Bibliothecae Nationalis Matritensis edidit Hippolytus Galante. Instituto Gonzalo Fernández de Oviedo, Madrid.

BANDERA, DAMIÁN DE LA. 1881. *Guamanga* [1557]. Relaciones Geográficas de Indias (Marcos Jiménez de la Espada, editor), vol. 1. Madrid.

BENNETT, WENDELL C., and JUNIUS BIRD. 1949. *Andean Culture History*. American Museum of Natural History, Handbook No. 5. New York, N. Y.

BERTONIO, LUDOVICO. 1879. *Vocabulario de la lengua Aymara* . . . [1612] (Julius Platzmann, editor). 2 vols. Leipzig, Germany.

BETANZOS, JUAN DE. 1880. *Suma y narración de los Incas* . . . [1551]. Biblioteca Hispano-Ultramarina, vol. 5. Madrid.

BIRD, JUNIUS. 1954. *Paracas Fabrics and Nazca Needlework*. Textile Museum, Washington, D. C.

BORREGÁN, ALONSO. 1948. *Crónica de la conquista del Perú* [1562–1565]. Escuela de Estudios Hispano-Americanos de Sevilla, vol. 48, ser. 7, no. 3. Seville, Spain.

BOWMAN, ISAIAH. 1916. *The Andes of Southern Peru*. American Geographical Society, New York, N. Y.

CABELLO VALBOA, MIGUEL. 1951. *Miscelánea antártica* [1586]. Universidad Nacional Mayor de San Marcos, Instituto de Etnología, Lima.

CARDICH, AUGUSTO. 1958. *Los yacimientos de Lauricocha; nuevas interpretaciones de la prehistoria peruana*. Centro Argentino de Estudios Prehistóricos, Buenos Aires.

CARDICH, AUGUSTO. 1960. Investigaciones prehistóricas en los Andes peruanos. In *Antiguo Perú, espacio y tiempo; trabajos presentados a la semana de arqueología peruana*. Juan Mejía Baca, Lima.

CHÁVEZ BALLÓN, MANUEL. 1958. Informe al Plan del Sur sobre el distrito de Macusani. Unpublished MS. Cuzco, Perú.

CHOY, EMILIO. 1960. Sistema social incaico. *Idea*, Apr.-June, pp. 10–12. Lima.

CIEZA DE LEÓN, PEDRO. 1862. *Primera parte de la crónica del Perú* . . . [1550]. Biblioteca de Autores Españoles, vol. 26, pp. 354–458. Madrid.

CIEZA DE LEÓN, PEDRO. 1943. *Segunda parte de la crónica del Perú* . . . [1550] (A. M. Salas, editor). Buenos Aires.

COBO, BERNABÉ. 1956. *Historia del Nuevo Mundo* [1653]. Biblioteca de Autores Españoles, vols. 91, 92. Madrid.

FALCÓN, FRANCISCO. 1918. *Representación hecha en Concilio Provincial* . . . [1580?]. Colección de Libros y Documentos referentes a la Historia del Perú, ser. 1, vol. 11. Lima.

GARCI DÍEZ DE SAN MIGUEL. 1964. *Visita que se hizo de los Indios de la Provincia de Chucuito* . . . [1567–68]. Documentos Regionales para la Etnología y Etnohistoria Andina, vol. 1. Casa de la Cultura del Perú, Lima.

GARCILASO DE LA VEGA, "EL INCA." 1960. *Primera parte de los comentarios reales* . . . [1604]. Biblioteca de Autores Españoles, vol. 133. Madrid.

GILMORE, RAYMOND M. 1950. Fauna and ethnozoology of South America. In *Handbook of South American Indians*, vol. 6. Bureau of American Ethnology, Bull. 143. Washington, D. C.

GONZALEZ HOLGUÍN, DIEGO. 1952. *Vocabulario de la lengua general de todo el Perú llamada lengua Qquichua o del Inca* [1608]. Universidad Nacional Mayor de San Marcos, Lima.

HELMER, MARIE. 1951. La vie économique au XVI siècle sur le haut plateau andin. Chucuito en 1567. *Travaux de l'Institut Français d'Etudes Andines*, vol. 3, pp. 115–147. Lima-Paris.

HERNÁNDEZ PRINCIPE, RODRIGO. 1923. Idolatrias en Recuay [1621]. *Inca*, vol. 1, pp. 25–49. Lima.

HORKHEIMER, HANS. 1960. *Nahrung und Nahrungsgewinnung im vorspanischen Peru*. Bibliotheca Ibero-Americana. Colloquium Verlag, Berlin.

HURTADO DE MENDOZA, MARQUÉS DE CAÑETE. 1953. Provisión del Gobierno Superior . . . chacos de vicuñas . . . [1557]. *Revista del Archivo Histórico*. Cuzco, Perú.

JESUITA ANÓNIMO. 1950. Relación de las costumbres antiguas . . . [1590?]. In *Tres relaciones peruanos*, pp. 133–203. Editorial Guarania, Asunción, Paraguay.

JIMÉNEZ DE LA ESPADA, MARCOS, editor. 1881–1897. Relaciones geográficas de Indias. 4 vols. Ministerio de Fomento, Madrid.

LATCHAM, RICARDO E. 1922. *Los animales domésticos de la América precolombina*. Publicaciones del Museo de Etnología y Antropología, vol. 3. Santiago, Chile.

LATCHAM, RICARDO E. 1936. Atacameño archaeology. *American Anthropologist*, vol. 38, no. 4, pp. 609–619.

MACCAGNO, LUIS. 1932. *Los auchénidos peruanos*. Ministerio de Fomento, Dirección de agricultura y ganadería, sección de defensa y propaganda, Lima.

MATIENZO, JUAN DE. 1910. *Gobierno del Perú* [1570?]. Buenos Aires.

MOLINA "DE CUZCO," CRISTÓBAL. 1943. *Relación de las fábulas y ritos de los Incas* [1575]. Los Pequeños Grandes Libros de Historia Americana, Lima.

MOROTE BEST, EFRAÍN. 1951. La vivienda campesina de Sallaq. *Tradición*, nos. 7–10, pp. 96–189. Cuzco, Perú.

MORÚA, MARTÍN DE. 1946. *Historia del origen y de la genealogía real de los Incas* [1590] (Constantino Bayle, editor). Consejo Superior de Investigaciones Científicas, Madrid.

MURRA, JOHN V. 1960. Rite and crop in the Inca state. In *Culture in History; Essays in Honor of Paul Radin* (Stanley Diamond, editor), pp. 393–407. Columbia University Press, New York, N. Y.

MURRA, JOHN V. 1962. Cloth and its functions in the Inca state. *American Anthropologist*, vol. 64, no. 4, pp. 710–728.

NÚÑEZ ANAVITARTE, CARLOS. 1955. *Teoría del desarollo incasico. Interpretación esclavista patriarcal de su proceso histórico natural*, vol. 1, pts. 1, 2. Editorial Garcilaso, Cuzco, Perú.

NÚÑEZ DEL PRADO, OSCAR. 1949. Chinchero, un pueblo andino del Sur. *Revista Universitaria*, vol. 38, no. 97, pp. 177–230. Cuzco, Perú.

ORICAÍN, PABLO. 1942. Compendio breve . . . sobre diferentes materias y noticias geográficas . . . [1790]. In Julio C. Tello, *Origen y desarollo de las civilizaciones prehistóricas andinas*. 27th International Congress of Americanists. Lima.

ORTIZ DE ZÚÑIGA, IÑIGO. 1920–1925, 1955–1961. *Visita fecha por mandado de su magestad* . . . [1562]. *Revista del Archivo Nacional del Perú*, vols. 1–3, 19–24. Lima.

POLO DE ONDEGARDO, JUAN. 1916a. Errores y supersticiones . . . [1559]. Colección de Libros y Documentos referentes a la Historia del Perú, ser. 1, vol. 3, pp. 3–43. Lima.

POLO DE ONDEGARDO, JUAN. 1916b. Relación de los fundamentos acerca del notable daño que resulta de no guardar a los Indios sus fueros [1571]. Colección de Libros y Documentos referentes a la Historia del Perú, ser. 1, vol. 3, pp. 45–188. Lima.

POLO DE ONDEGARDO, JUAN. 1940. Informe . . . al licenciado Briviesca de Muñatones [1561]. *Revista Histórica*, vol. 13. Lima.

POMA DE AYALA, GUAMÁN. 1936. *Nueva corónica y buen gobierno* [1615]. Institut d'Ethnologie, Paris.

ROMÁN Y ZAMORA, JERÓNIMO. 1897. *Repúblicas de Indias* [1575]. 2 vols. Colección de Libros Raros y Curiosos que Tratan de América, vols. 13, 14. Madrid.

ROWE, JOHN HOWLAND. 1954. El movimiento nacional Inca del siglo XVIII. *Revista Universitaria*, no. 107. Cuzco, Perú.

ROWE, JOHN HOWLAND. 1957. The Incas under Spanish colonial institutions. *Hispano-American Historical Review*, vol. 37, no. 2.

SANTILLÁN, HERNANDO DE. 1927. *Relación del origen, descendencia, política y gobierno de los Incas* . . . [1563–1564]. Colección de Libros y Documentos referentes a la Historia del Perú, ser. 2, vol. 9. Lima.

SARMIENTO DE GAMBOA, PEDRO. 1943. *Historia general llamada indica* [1572]. Emecé Editores, Buenos Aires.

TELLO, JULIO C. 1942. *Origen y desarollo de las civilizaciones prehistóricas andinas*. 27th International Congress of Americanists. Lima.

TELLO, JULIO C. 1959. *Paracas*. Institute of Andean Research, Lima.

TERUEL, LUIS DE (?). 1918. Idolatrias de los Huachos y Yauyos [1613]. *Revista Histórica*, vol. 6, pp. 180–197. Lima.

TRIMBORN, HERMANN. 1928. Die kulturhistorische Stellung der Lamazucht. *Anthropos*, pp. 656–664.

TROLL, CARL. 1931. Die geografische Grundlagen der andinen Kulturen und des Inca Reiches. *Ibero-amerikanisches Archiv*, vol. 5. Berlin.

TROLL, CARL. 1958. Las culturas superiores andinas y el medio geográfico. *Revista del Instituto de Geografía*, no. 5, pp. 3–55. Lima.

TSCHOPIK, HARRY, JR. 1946. The Aymara. In *Handbook of South American Indians*, vol. 2, pp. 501–573. Bureau of American Ethnology, Bull. 143. Washington, D. C.

TSCHOPIK, HARRY, JR. 1951. *The Aymara of Chucuito, Peru*. Pt. 1. *Magic*. American Museum of Natural History, Anthropological Papers, vol. 44, pt. 2. New York, N. Y.

TSCHUDI, J. J. 1891. Kulturhistorische und sprachliche Beitraege. *Denkschriften der Kaiserlichen Akademie der Wissenschaften*, vol. 39. Vienna.

VALCÁRCEL, LUIS E. 1922. Glosario de la vida incaica. *Revista Universitaria*, vol. 11, no. 39, pp. 3–19. Cuzco, Perú.

VALCÁRCEL, LUIS E. 1937–1941. *Mirador Indio, apuntes para una filosofía de la cultura incaica*. 2 vols. Imprenta del Museo Nacional, Lima.

VALERA, BLAS. 1960. In Garcilaso de la Vega, *Primera parte de los comentarios reales . . .* [1604]. Biblioteca de Autores Españoles, vol. 133. Madrid.

XÉREZ, FRANCISCO DE. 1853. *Verdadera relación de la conquista del Perú . . .* [1534]. Biblioteca de Autores Españoles, vol. 26, pp. 319–343. Madrid.

ZÁRATE, AUGUSTIN DE. 1853. *Historia del descubrimiento y conquista de la Provincia del Perú . . .* [1555]. Biblioteca de Autores Españoles, vol. 26, pp. 459–574. Madrid.

The Myth of the Sacred Cow

MARVIN HARRIS

Department of Anthropology, Columbia University, New York, New York

> We have use for the cow. That is why it has become religiously incumbent on us to protect it (Gandhi, 1954, p. 36).

> Social life is essentially practical. All mysteries which mislead theories to mysticism find their rational solution in human practice and in the comprehension of this practice (Marx, 1941, p. 84).

AMONG THE POPULAR MYTHS of cultural anarchy none is more widely accepted than that of the Indian "sacred cow." The alleged mismanagement of India's cattle is a source of comfort for many philosophers and social scientists who promote idealist and antideterminist explanations of socio-cultural phenomena.

The myth of the sacred cow is part of a larger myth according to which culture is equally capable of elaborating itself along any of the lines of imagination, caprice, and illusion of which the human mind is capable (cf. Harris, 1959, p. 194). The effect of this misconception upon the attempt to understand human ecology is clearly visible in Simoons' (1961, p. 3) assertion that irrational ideologies frequently prevent the effective utilization of available food resources. Simoons' claim that food taboos compel human populations to "overlook foods that are abundant locally and are of high nutritive value, and to utilize other scarcer foods of less value" is widely shared. The Indian sacred cow, one of the cases stressed by Simoons, is a favorite instance of ecological caprice. If space permitted, I would argue that, contrary to established

This paper is being published in a more detailed version, under the title "The cultural ecology of India's sacred cattle," in *Current Anthropology*, vol. 7, 1965.

opinion (Lowie, 1938, p. 320), it has rarely, if ever, been shown that "religious or dietary preconceptions" have by themselves prevented any large human population from maximizing metabolic yield to the limit of techno-environmental capacity. I argue here merely that the taboo against the slaughter and eating of Indian cattle is consistent with an ecological balance in which human material welfare takes precedence over the welfare of animals.

Any examination of the economic functions of Indian cattle must begin by admitting that India's dairy industry is among the least efficient in the world. In India, the average yield of whole milk per year per cow has been reported as 413 pounds as compared with an average of 2000 to 5000 pounds in Europe and the United States (Kartha, 1936, p. 607; Spate, 1954, p. 231).[1] In Madhya Pradesh the yield is as low as 65 pounds, and in no province does it rise higher than the barely respectable 1445 pounds of the Punjab (Chatterjee, 1960, p. 1347). According to Chatterjee (ibid.), the economic loss involved in producing this milk amounts to 6.7 times the amount that India is spending on the importation of food grains. Furthermore, of the 79.4 million cows maintained in 1961, only 20.1 million were milk producers (Chaudhri and Giri, 1963, p. 598). Among the 47.2 million cows over three years old, 27.2 million were dry and/or not calved (ibid.). If we go on to accept the proposition that "India is unique in possessing an enormous amount of cattle without making profit from its slaughter" (Venkatraman, 1938, p. 706), we have almost completed the standard case for the great cattle bungle. It is also frequently reported that "useless" animals wander about at will, impeding traffic and damaging the crops (Mayadas, 1954, p. 28), while in some parts of India, aged cattle are housed in bovine old age homes (called *pinjrapoles* or *gowshalas* and more recently, under the Five-Year Plans, *gosadans*). Hence the conclusion of the Ford Foundation's report on India's food problem:

[1] According to the 1954 U.S. Census of Agriculture, milk production in the United States ranged from an average of 3979 pounds per cow in the Nashville Basin Sub-region to 11,112 pounds in the Southern California Sub-region (Census of Agriculture, 1954, p. 30). Yields of more than 20,000 pounds are not uncommon.

There is widespread recognition, not only among animal husbandry officials, but among citizens generally, that India's cattle population is far in excess of the available supplies of fodder and feed. . . . At least one third and possibly as many as one half, of the Indian cattle population may be regarded as surplus in relation to feed supply (Ford Foundation, 1959, p. 64).

According to Matson (1933, p. 227), it is a commonplace of the "cattle question that vast numbers of Indian cattle are so hopelessly inefficient as to have no commercial value beyond that of their hides." This same conviction is evident in Srinivas' (1952, p. 222) pronouncement: "Orthodox Hindu opinion regards the killing of cattle with abhorrence, even though the refusal to kill the vast number of useless cattle which exist in India today is detrimental to the economy of the nation." These views are endorsed by the government, at least to the extent of insisting that "the large animal population is more a liability than an asset in view of our limited land resource" (Ministry of Information, 1957, p. 243). In view of the perpetual shortage of food for humans in India, refusal to slaughter cattle seems to prove that the mysterious has triumphed over the practical. Some would even have us believe that the individual farmer is prepared to sacrifice his own life in order to preserve that of his cow:

In the tropics, as elsewhere, cattle are essential as a source of food, work, and of many by-products of great value; but with millions of people these considerations, though vital, are secondary to the part cattle play in religion, in social custom, as a reserve of family wealth and as a mark of respectability. The . . . Hindu would rather starve to death than eat his cow (Williamson and Payne, 1959, p. 137).

Such is the myth of the sacred cow.

A better understanding of the cow complex in India involves the answer to the following two questions: (1) Is it true that the rate of reproduction and survival of the Indian population is lowered as a result of the competition between man and cattle for scarce resources? (2) Would the removal of the Hindu taboo on slaughter substantially modify the ecology of Indian food production?

The answer to the first question is that the relation between man and cattle—both cows and bullocks—is not competitive, but symbiotic. The most obvious part of this symbiosis is the role played by male cattle in cultivation. Indian farming is based on plow agriculture, to which cattle labor contributes as much as 46 per cent of the labor cost exclusive of transport and other supporting activities (Chaudhri and Giri, 1963, p. 591). Needless to say, tractors are not a realistic alternative.

Despite the existence of 96.3 million bullocks, of which 68.6 million are working animals (Government of India, 1962, p. 76), India suffers from a shortage of such animals. It is generally agreed (cf. Gupta, 1959, p. 42; Lewis and Barnouw, 1958, p. 102) that a pair of bullocks is the minimum unit for cultivation. But a conservatively estimated 60 million rural households (Mitra, 1963, p. 298) dispose of only 80 million working cattle and buffaloes (Government of India, 1962, p. 76). This would mean that as many as two-thirds of India's farmers may be short of the technical minimum. Some significant degree of shortage would appear to be beyond dispute. In a survey by Diskalkar (1960, p. 87), it was found that 18 per cent of the cultivators had one bullock or none. According to Spate (1954, p. 36), "There are too many cattle in the gross, but most individual farmers may have too few to carry on with." "Even with overstocking, the draught power available for land operations at the busiest season of the year is inadequate" (Kothavala, 1934, p. 122). Moreover, under existing property relations the bullocks cannot be shared among several households without further lowering the productivity of marginal farms. Desai explains why:

> An overwhelmingly large number of bullocks maintained by farmers are of an indigenous breed and undersized; most of the farmers having limited means are unable to feed the draught animals adequately. This robs the bullocks of their working capacity considerably and necessitates the maintenance of a number larger than considered necessary. Secondly, over vast areas, sowing and harvesting operations, by the very nature of things, begin simultaneously with the outbreak of the first showers and the maturing of crops respectively and especially the former has got to be put through quickly during the first phase of

the monsoon. Under these circumstances, reliance by a farmer on another for bullocks is highly risky and he has got, therefore, to maintain his own pair (1948, p. 86).

Shastri (1960, p. 1592) also emphasizes the importance of critical phases of the agricultural cycle as a factor in the utilization of animal traction: "Uncertainty of Indian farming due to dependence on rains is the main factor creating obstacles in the way of improvements in bullock labor." According to Wiser and Wiser (1963, p. 62), when the farmer "needs the help of bullocks most, his neighbors are all using theirs." The same point is emphasized by Dube (1955, p. 84): "The cultivators who depend on hired cattle or who practise cooperative lending and borrowing of cattle cannot take the best advantage of the first rains, and this enforced wait results in untimely sowing and poor crops."

We see, therefore, that the draught animals which appear to be superfluous from the point of view of what would be needed in a perfectly engineered society turn out to be considerably less than sufficient in the actual context of Indian agriculture.

But what of the cows? The first thing to note is again obvious. No cows, no bullocks. Of course, the issue is not so easily settled. Though the need for bullocks establishes the need for cows, it does not establish the need for 80 million of them. We are, however, coming closer to the answer, because we now know that to the value of the milk and milk products produced by the cows, we must add the value of the 69 million male traction animals which they also produce. It is clear that the ecological role of the cows cannot be given adequate expression simply in terms of their efficiency in producing milk. As a matter of fact, if one's principal object is to produce milk in India, it is to the buffalo and not the zebu that one turns. In India, "the buffalo, and not the Zebu, is the dairy cow. There has been little or no conscious effort to improve the inherent capacity of the Zebu to produce milk" (Kartha, 1959, p. 255). Indeed, only 46.7 per cent of India's milk production is accounted for by the cow (Chatterjee, 1960, p. 1347).

Other contributions of the cow immediately present themselves, among which those deriving from dung are most important. In addition to the relatively minor value of dung as plaster in house

construction, this material is India's main cooking fuel. There can
be no question about the importance of cooking or the absence of
alternative combustibles. In the first instance, India's grain crops
cannot be metabolized by human beings without cooking. Secondly, an inverse relation exists between forest areas and dung fuel
consumption (National Council of Applied Economic Research,
1959, p. 11). Coal and oil are, of course, prohibitively expensive
for the peasant family (*ibid.,* p. 20). Thus, dung alone provides
the needed energy, and cattle provide the dung on a lavish scale.
Of the 800 million tons annually bequeathed the Indian countryside, 300 million are consumed in cookery. This amount of dung
is the BTU equivalent of 35 million tons of coal or 68 million
tons of wood (Lupton, 1922, p. 60; National Council of Applied
Economic Research, 1959, pp. 3 ff.; Mujumdar, 1960, p. 743).

Of the remaining 500 million tons of dung, the largest part is
used for manuring. Mujumdar claims that 160 million tons of this
manure is "wasted on hillsides and roads" (1960, p. 743), but it
must be noted that some of this probably re-enters the ecological
system, since, as we shall see in a moment, the cattle depend upon
hillsides and roads for much of their sustenance. Needless to say,
the intensive rainfall agriculture characteristic of large parts of
the subcontinent is dependent upon manuring. So vital is this
contribution that Spate argues that substitutes for the manure
which is consumed as fuel "must be supplied, and lavishly, even
at a financial loss to government" (1954, p. 239).

In the present context, the most important point to note about
the fuel and manure functions of India's cattle is that old, dry,
barren animals do not cease to provide dung. On this score alone,
one might expect more caution before the conclusion is reached
that the sacred cow is a useless luxury.

Two additional contributions of cattle, including cows, remain
to be mentioned. In 1962 India produced 16 million cattle hides
(Randhawa, 1962, p. 322). Much of this output is consumed in
the manufacture of leather products which are vital to the traditional farming technology. In addition, despite the Hindu pro-
scription, a considerable amount of beef is eaten. Those who stress
the quaintness of the beef-eating taboo fail to give proper emphasis

to the fact that India contains millions of people who have no caste to lose. Not only are there some 55 million members of "scheduled" castes (Hutton, 1961, p. vii), many of whom are under no obligation to spurn beef, but there are also several more millions who are pagan, Christian, or Moslem. It seems likely that a high proportion of the 20 million bovines which die each year get eaten. Moreover, it is quite clear that not all these cattle die a natural death. On the contrary, the very extent of the agitation for anti-slaughter bills reveals how widespread the practice remains (cf. Roy, 1955, p. 15).

We see that to the contribution of the cow as a producer of milk, we must add the production of meat, bullocks, manure, fuel, and hides. The extent of the symbiosis between man and cow, however, is not thereby demonstrated. There still remains the possibility that all these needs could be met at a lower energy or monetary cost per peasant household by reducing the number of aged cows which the peasant tolerates in his ménage. To prove that the ecosystem under discussion is essentially positive-functioned, it must be shown that resources consumed by the cows, old and young, do not, from the point of view of the peasant's balance sheet, outweigh the enumerated contributions. This proof is fairly easy to establish.

Note, first of all, that one of the most persistent professional complaints against the sacred cow is that the beasts wander all over the place, cluttering up the markets, railroad stations, and roadsides. Many authorities seem not to inquire why all this wandering takes place from the point of view of the cow, since presumably she has remained uninformed of her sacred privileges. The cow is wandering about because she is hungry and is looking for food—in the ditches, around the base of telegraph poles, between the railroad ties, along the hillsides, in every nook and cranny where something edible has reared its head. "Neglect of the cow, traditionally regarded as 'the mother,' is indeed pathetic . . . the cattle roam about the shrubs and rocks and eat whatever fodder is available there" (Dube, 1955, p. 84). The sacred cow is an exploited scavenger, a mere walking skeleton for most of the year, precisely because her ecological niche is removed from that of human food crops. Speaking of Malabar, Mayer makes this fact quite clear:

At present cattle are fed largely according to the season. During the rainy period they feed upon the grass which springs up on the cultivated hillsides, either being taken there by a cowherd or, when the monsoon rains are too strong for them to leave the cattle shed . . . having cut grass brought to them. But in the dry season there is hardly any grass, and cattle wander on the cropless lands in an often half-starved condition. True, there is some fodder at these times in the shape of rice-straw and dried copra, but it is not generally sufficient, *and is furthermore given mainly to the animals actually working at the time* (1952, p. 70; italics added).

Speaking of Gujarat, Desai makes precisely the same point with some additional insight into the relationship between useless cows and useful bullocks: "A large number of undersized and weak cows is maintained by the farmers principally to insure a regular supply of bullocks needed on the farm. These cows roam about on the wastes for food" (1948, p. 88). The same pattern is confirmed by Diskalkar (1960, p. 92) for the Deccan. According to Gourou (1963, p. 123), cattle in Madras "do not compete for agricultural products; no actual or potential agricultural surfaces are sacrificed in their support." Mohan (1962, p. 43) is also quite explicit: "The bulk of the food on which the animals subsist . . . is not the food that is required for human consumption. . . . Man and animals do not largely compete for foods."

An ecological explanation of why so many cows are kept is now possible: Each farmer needs his own pair of bullocks. Lacking cash, he cannot afford to buy these animals. Rather than risk going into debt at usurious rates, he prefers to try to breed bulls (which he will exchange later for bullocks). Since all the available land is given over to human food crops, the breeding cows must scavenge for their food. Being undernourished, they breed irregularly (cf. Mamoria, 1953, p. 263). The farmer refrains from culling uncalved animals since they convert grain by-products and scrub vegetation into useful dung. Meanwhile, there is always a chance that the cow will eventually conceive. If a female calf is born, the scrub and chaff are converted into milk, while the calf is starved to death (cf. Moomaw, 1949, p. 96; Wiser and Wiser, 1963, p. 70; Gourou, 1963, p. 125). In the long run, the more cows an individual farmer owns, the greater the likelihood that he will be able to replace his bullocks without going into debt.

This explanation does not involve references to *ahimsa*, the Hindu doctrine of the sanctity of life. Instead, the large number of cows and bullocks is seen as the result of ecological pressures generated by the human population's struggle to maintain itself. *Ahimsa* may thus be regarded as an ideological expression of these pressures; in other words, *ahimsa* itself derives power and sustenance from the material rewards it confers upon both men and animals.

In answer to the second question under consideration, it would thus seem that the basic ecology of Indian cattle production is not a mere reflex of the Hindu taboo on slaughter. Removing that taboo might temporarily alter the ecosystem. But, in the long run, the rate at which cattle are slaughtered in India is governed by the ability of the peasantry to slaughter cattle without impairing the production of traction animals, fuel, fertilizer, and milk. It is a well known fact that the least efficient way to convert solar energy into comestibles is to impose an animal converter between plant and man (Cottrell, 1955, pp. 15 ff.). Hence, it is wrong to suppose that India could without major techno-environmental innovations support any large number of animals whose principal function was the supply of animal protein. It has already been shown that the supply of beef is one of the functions of the cattle complex, but this must necessarily remain a marginal or tertiary attribute of the ecosystem. As a matter of fact, it is quite obvious that any large-scale drift toward animal slaughter before the traction, fuel, and manure needs of the productive cycle were met would immediately jeopardize the lives of tens of millions of peasants. We need not rely merely on theory to establish this point. During World War II India was cut off by the Japanese occupation of Burma from an important source of its necessary rice imports. Famine conditions rapidly developed, and the Indian farmer began to send alarming numbers of cattle to slaughter. The situation was stabilized only through direct military intervention:

During the war there was an urgent need to reduce or to avoid the slaughter for food of animals useful for breeding or for agricultural work. For the summer of 1944 the slaughter was prohibited of: 1) Cattle below three years of age; 2) Male cattle between two and ten years of age which were being used or were likely to be used as working cattle; 3) All cows between three and ten years of age, other than cows which were unsuitable for bearing offspring; 4) All cows which were pregnant or in milk (Knight, 1954, p. 141).

According to Roy, the response of the individual Hindu peasant to economic necessity is a conscious and thoroughly institutionalized aspect of Indian society. Under economic pressure many Indians who will not kill or eat cows themselves "are likely to compromise their principles and sell to butchers who slaughter cows, thereby tacitly supporting the practice for other people. Selling aged cows to butchers has over the centuries become an accepted practice alongside the *mos* that a Hindu must not kill cattle" (1955, p. 15).

It may be concluded that the power of the sacra surrounding the Indian cattle complex is thoroughly circumscribed by the material conditions under which both man and beast must earn their livings.

REFERENCES

CENSUS OF AGRICULTURE. 1954. *Farmers and Farm Production in the United States,* vol. 9, pt. 9, chap. 5. U. S. Department of Agriculture, Washington, D. C.

CHATTERJEE, I. 1960. Milk production in India. *Econ. Weekly, 12,* 1347–1348.

CHAUDHRI, S. C., and R. GIRI. 1963. Role of cattle in India's economy. *Agr. Situation in India, 18,* 591–599.

COTTRELL, F. 1955. *Energy and Society.* McGraw-Hill Book Co., New York, N. Y.

DESAI, M. B. 1948. *The Rural Economy of Gujarat.* Oxford University Press, Bombay, India.

DISKALKAR, P. D. 1960. *Resurvey of a Deccan Village, Pimple Sandagar.* Indian Society of Agricultural Economics, Bombay, India.

DUBE, S. C. 1955. *Indian Village.* Cornell University Press, Ithaca, N. Y.

FORD FOUNDATION. 1959. *Report on India's Food Crisis and Steps to Meet It.* Government of India, Ministry of Food and Agriculture and Ministry of Community Development and Cooperation, New Delhi.

GANDHI, M. K. 1954. *How to Serve the Cow* (B. Kumarappa, editor). Navajvan Publishing House, Ahmedabad, India.

GOUROU, P. 1963. Civilisation et économie pastorale. *L'Homme, 3,* 123–129.

GOVERNMENT OF INDIA. 1962. *Statistical Abstract of the Indian Union 11.* New Delhi.

GUPTA, S. C. 1959. *An Economic Survey of Shamaspur Village.* Asia Publishing House, New York, N. Y.

HARRIS, M. 1959. The economy has no surplus? *Am. Anthropologist, 61,* 185–199.

HUTTON, J. H. 1961. *Caste in India,* 3rd edition. Oxford University Press, London.

KARTHA, K. P. R. 1936. A note on the comparative economic efficiency of the Indian cow, the half breed cow, and the buffalo as producers of milk and butter fat. *Agr. and Livestock in India, 4,* 605–623.

KARTHA, K. P. R. 1959. Buffalo. In *An Introduction to Animal Husbandry in the Tropics* (G. Williamson and W. J. A. Payne, editors), pp. 247–262. Longmans, Green and Co., London.

KNIGHT, H. 1954. *Food Administration in India 1939–47.* Stanford University Press, Stanford, Calif.

KOTHAVALA, Z. R. 1934. Milk production in India. *Agr. and Livestock in India, 2,* 122–129.

LEWIS, O., and V. BARNOUW. 1958. *Village Life in Northern India.* University of Illinois Press, Urbana, Ill.

LOWIE, R. 1938. Subsistence. In *General Anthropology* (F. Boas, editor), pp. 282–326. D. C. Heath and Co., New York, N. Y.

LUPTON, A. 1922. *Happy India, As It Might Be If Guided by Modern Science.* G. Allen and Unwin, London.

MAMORIA, C. B. 1953. *Agricultural Problems of India.* Kitab Mahal, Allahabad, India.

MARX, K. 1941. Theses on Feuerbach. In F. Engels, *Ludwig Feuerbach and the Outcome of Classical German Philosophy,* pp. 82–84. International Publishers, New York, N. Y.

MATSON, J. 1933. Inefficiency of cattle in India through disease. *Agr. and Livestock in India, 1,* 227–228.

MAYADAS, C. 1954. *Between Us and Hunger.* Oxford University Press, London.

MAYER, A. 1952. *Land and Society in Malabar.* Oxford University Press, Bombay, India.

Ministry of Information. 1957. *India.* Government of India, Ministry of Information and Broadcasting, Publication Division, New Delhi.

Mitra, Ashok. 1963. Tax burden for Indian agriculture. In *Traditions, Values, and Socio-economic Development* (R. Brabanti and J. J. Spengler, editors), pp. 281–303. Duke University Press, Durham, N. C.

Mohan, S. N. 1962. Animal husbandry in the Third Plan. *Bull. Natl. Inst. Sci. India, 20,* 41–54.

Moomaw, I. W. 1949. *The Farmer Speaks.* Oxford University Press, London.

Mujumdar, N. A. 1960. Cow-dung as manure. *Econ. Weekly, 12,* 743–744.

National Council of Applied Economic Research. 1959. *Domestic Fuels in India.* Asia Publishing House, New York, N. Y.

Randhawa, M. S. 1962. *Agriculture and Animal Husbandry in India.* Indian Council of Agricultural Research, New Delhi.

Roy, P. 1955. The sacred cow in India. *Rural Sociol., 20,* 8–15.

Shastri, C. P. 1960. Bullock labour utilization in agriculture. *Econ. Weekly, 12,* 1585–1592.

Simoons, F. J. 1961. *Eat Not This Flesh: Food Avoidances in the Old World.* University of Wisconsin Press, Madison, Wis.

Spate, O. H. 1954. *India and Pakistan; A General and Regional Geography.* Methuen and Co., London.

Srinivas, M. N. 1952. *Religion and Society among the Coorgs of South India.* Oxford University Press, London.

Venkatraman, R. B. 1938. The Indian village, its past, present, future. *Agr. and Livestock in India, 7,* 702–710.

Williamson, G., and W. J. A. Payne, editors. 1959. *An Introduction to Animal Husbandry in the Tropics.* Longmans Green and Co., London.

Wiser, W., and C. W. Wiser. 1963. *Behind Mud Walls: 1930–1960.* University of California Press, Berkeley, Calif.

The Euro-American Ranching Complex

ARNOLD STRICKON

Department of Anthropology, Brandeis University, Waltham, Massachusetts

THE PURPOSE of this essay is to describe and analyze what seem to the author to be the major structural features of the Euro-American ranching complex, a cultural complex of widespread distribution and of strikingly dramatic visibility. The ranching complex plays, and historically played, a role in parts of North and South America and the oceanic dominions comparable to that of the sugar industry in parts of Brazil and the Caribbean. Yet the cattle ranch, unlike the sugar plantation, has not attracted the attention of the anthropologist to any degree. It is the author's hope that the present exploratory attempt at description and analysis will draw professional attention to this complex and bring forth data to fill out the description and refine or supersede the analysis.

The ranching complex consists of two major elements. The first of these is an economic-ecological pattern built around such features as the grazing of livestock, dependence upon a money market, and the extensive use of land and labor. The second element of the complex consists of a particular content and technological kit which is often, though not always, associated with the economic-ecological pattern. It is, of course, the "cowboy" cultural content and technological kit, deriving chiefly from an Iberian background (Bishko, 1952; Jessen, 1952), which gives the ranching complex its high visibility and its dramatic position in Euro-American folklore.

This paper concentrates upon the economic-ecological features of ranching and deals with the "cowboy content" only briefly. "Ranching" is defined here purely by structural features, not by content. Ranching is that pattern of land use which is based upon the grazing of livestock, chiefly ruminants, for sale in a money market. This pattern of land use is characterized by control over large units of land, extensive use of that land, and extensive use of labor on the land. The adjectives "large" and "extensive" in the preceding sentence describe these elements of the ranching complex in comparison with patterns of tenure, use, and labor by crop growers under the same environmental conditions and within the same level of socio-cultural integration.

Like the sugar plantation (Steward, 1956; Wagley and Harris, 1955), the modern cattle complex can be seen as a child of the commercial revolution and, especially, the industrial revolution. Both the modern ranch and the sugar plantation depend upon the presence of large urban markets. The expansion of these markets was paralleled by the expansion of beef and sugar production. The expansion of sugar production demanded ever larger numbers of workers and intensive use of the land. The expansion of ranching, however, was successful in so far as it did *not* demand large numbers of workers or intensive use of land. Where increasing numbers of potential workers became available to put land to intensive use in any given area (and for whatever reason), this usually signaled the contraction or disappearance of ranching in that area.

Both sugar production and ranching emerged from the Old World and explosively expanded in the New in response to the economic revolutions of the seventeenth to nineteenth centuries. Each, however, expanded into a different kind of habitat, and each was marked by its own characteristic features. In terms of an evolutionary and ecological typology, both can be seen as ecological variants of industrial agriculture (Steward, 1955, pp. 23, 30).

Ranches, of course, exist in a great number of environmental, ecological, and political situations. This paper is concerned primarily with those similarities which crosscut particular situations. It is concerned with those features of ranching which can be attributed to the characteristics which all ranches have in common, specifically the grazing of livestock destined for a money market. Such common features must be highly generalized, hence cannot cover all the details and variations to be found in any particular situation.

Ranches come in all shapes and sizes. Some are purely livestock operations, others include farming. In parts of North America the line between mixed-farm and ranch becomes quite difficult to draw. In order to simplify the data to be handled, the discussion in the present paper will be limited to those ranches on which livestock grazing is the sole or, at least, the overwhelmingly major activity. In effect this means that what will be discussed here is the large ranch, the "livestock plantation" as it were. The smaller ranch which may include a great deal of crop growing, which irrigates its forage land and hand feeds its stock part of the year, and which uses primarily family labor as opposed to primarily wage labor must await consideration at a later date. This type of "family ranch" will be dealt with here only in so far as it may provide, by comparison, some insight into the structure and function of the "plantation ranch."

The data for analysis are drawn chiefly from three areas in which ranching, as defined above, has played a crucial historical role: the western United States (especially before 1900), Argentina, and Australia. In the latter area the major grazing animals are sheep rather than cattle. The resulting structural differences, however, are minor.

The inclusion of Argentina in the paper is critical. At the present time ranching in the United States and Australia tends to be restricted to arid and semiarid areas. Many American students of ranching (Webb, 1931) tend to see ranching as an arid lands adaptation. The assumption is that where land is useless or marginal for crop growing it becomes the ranchers' habitat. The situation is not so simple. In Argentina ranching is carried out in areas which are perfectly good for commercial agriculture, and this used to be the case in the United States as well. It is therefore clear that more is involved in the ranching adaptation than adjustment to arid conditions. Variables other than environmental marginality must be sought to explain the presence or absence of ranching and to delineate the critical features of the adaptation.

The advantage of the ranching adaptation vis-à-vis alternative patterns of land use within the same habitat is determined in the long run almost purely by the return on investment as compared with that from alternative forms of land use. This implies that ranching is not primarily concerned with providing subsistence directly to the rancher and his employees; and it is not. Ranching is a business and can be understood only as such. As long as the extensive pattern of land and labor use provides a better return than alternative adaptations, ranching maintains itself or spreads. If farming, or the test firing of rockets or atomic explosives for that matter, returns a greater profit, then ranching contracts or disappears altogether. Conversely, if commercial grazing becomes potentially more lucrative than alternative adaptations (for whatever reason), ranching will then expand. Although the former situation is historically more common, the latter, as we shall see, occurs as well.

The body of this paper is organized as follows: (a) the livestock themselves and their direct relation to the land they subsist upon are described; (b) the relation of the ranching complex to the world market is considered in terms of the expansion of ranching and its dependence upon a highly industrialized processing and transportation network; (c) the patterns of land tenure and use which characterize the complex are next considered, followed by (d) the patterns of labor, labor control, and community organization associated with the ranching complex. Following these discussions, the structural features already dealt with are used to analyze the adaptive advantage of gross size in ranching. The total model is then applied to an examination of the replacement of ranching by farming on a macrocosmic level in the American West, the Argentine pampas, and the outback of Australia. The replacement of farming by ranching is then analyzed in three microcosms: "Homestead," New Mexico (Vogt, 1955), Bell County, Texas (Lewis, 1948), and "Eleodoro Gomez," in the Province of Buenos Aires, Argentina (Strickon, 1960).

LIVESTOCK AND LAND

Horned cattle are not the most efficient animals for converting vegetable matter into meat. The pig holds this distinction; it converts one-fifth of what it eats into food for human consumption. A beef steer converts only one-twentieth or less of its food into meat. The pig, however, subsists almost entirely on concentrated carbohydrates and proteins, foods which could be consumed, at least in theory, directly by man. Though cattle need more food than pigs to yield the same number of calories, the double digestive system of the ruminant, and certain microorganisms within that system, permit cattle to digest cellulose, a food source which is not directly available to man (Phillips, 1958, p. 51; Ritzman and Benedict, 1938, p. 1). When cereals are used as livestock feed, meat is necessarily a far more expensive food per calorie than are the grains on which the cattle feed, since the human consumer could have used the grains directly. The raising of livestock for meat or raw materials is only justified economically when a large part of their feed is derived from forage crops (Ritzman and Benedict, 1938, p. 2).

High-quality beef cattle require between 2000 and 2600 pounds of feed per month (between 12 and 15 tons a year) simply to maintain their body weight between 869 and 1364 pounds (Ritzman and Benedict, 1938, p. 197). These figures are based upon controlled experiments using barn-dwelling, hand-fed animals. Under range conditions food intake must necessarily be higher, owing to energy losses resulting from the need to move around looking for forage and water. Furthermore, the raiser of livestock is not concerned with merely maintaining his animals' weight, but is rather concerned with increasing it as rapidly as possible. It is this which determines how quickly the rancher can turn over his inventory (Phillips, 1958, p. 55).

The need to provide cattle with prodigious amounts of foodstuffs requires a larger land base per calorie of food fit for human consumption than would be needed if that land produced plant foods which could be used directly by man. How much land is necessary to produce the minimum of 15 tons of feed per year will, of course, vary with soil, weather, and other conditions of the natural environment as well as with the degree of technological sophistication of the raiser. Breeders are constantly developing new breeds and improving old ones in order to better adapt them to specific environmental conditions (Malin, 1956, p. 358; Phillips, 1958, pp. 51–52).

The relation of livestock to the land they subsist upon is expressed in terms of the number of acres of land necessary to support one head of livestock for one year. Ideally, no more cattle should be supported per unit of land than can be carried without damaging the plant cover, water, and soil. The minimum number of acres which will support one head for one year without such damage (theoretically) is a measure of the "carrying capacity." Carrying capacity will, of course, vary with environmental conditions. In the northern plains of the United States carrying capacity is estimated at about 20 acres per head (Wilson *et al.*, 1928, p. 24); in the part of Argentina where the author did field work, it was about 2½ acres. Nevada ranchers told the author that they needed as many as 120 acres per head in parts of the Great Basin.

The concept of carrying capacity gives a feeling of "ecological objectivity" which, in fact, may be lacking (Clark, 1956, p. 745; Darling, 1956, p. 781). The number of animals actually grazed on any given area is to a large degree structured by the stability of the livestock market. Land which is considered sufficient if prices are high enough to keep the inventory moving may face dangerous overgrazing if prices decline and the rancher decides to hold all or part of his stock for more favorable conditions. The alternative may be to sell at a loss. Because of this, land which is considered properly grazed one year may be overgrazed the next. Maximum grazing pressure leaves the rancher without flexibility in the face of the market, and he must sell at the price offered.

MARKETS

The ranching complex in the western United States, Argentina, and Australia is a child of the industrial revolution. Before large-scale capitalist markets for cattle and cattle products opened up in the nineteenth century, ranches either did not exist in the areas under consideration here or were limited in extent and number, servicing only relatively small, local demand. Most of what today is ranching country was, through the first half of the nineteenth century, "beyond the frontier."

The modern ranching complex emerged in all three areas at about the same time, the 1860's. Each of the areas, however, first entered into large-scale grazing at a different time: Argentina in the seventeenth century, Australia in the 1820's and 1830's, and the western United States in the 1860's. In each of the three areas the efficient cause for the emergence of the complex was the appearance of a market outlet for livestock products outside the grazing area itself.

Argentina's initial product was hides, which were gathered at first by the hunting of domesticated cattle which had gone feral in the pampas. Only when these were hunted out did it become necessary for the entrepreneurs of Buenos Aires to organize land and labor in order to breed and graze cattle. The market outlet for the hides was in Spain (legally) and the rest of Europe (by smuggling). Later, as methods of salting meat were refined, the slave plantations of Brazil became an important market outlet for the Argentine product (Bishko, 1952, pp. 512–514; Giberti, 1958, p. 259; Strickon, 1960, pp. 30–31, 34–38, 69–72).

The emergence of the modern ranching complex in Argentina was directly motivated by the growing inability of northern Europe to provide meat for its rapidly increasing body of urban workers. Before Argentina (or Australia or the United States) could supply that need, a method of cheap transportation had to be developed. The refrigerator ship fulfilled this need. It first appeared in 1879, and only twenty-three years later 278 of them were running between Europe and the Río de la Plata. During these developments Argentine ranching expanded beyond its old frontiers, the last of the fighting Indians being pacified in the 1880's. Argentina became, and to a large extent still is, the abattoir of Great Britain (Hanson, 1938, pp. 8, 15, 18, 70, 92–95; Strickon, 1960, pp. 114–115).

Before the 1860's, ranching in the United States was oriented to local markets and was of little importance. In the Ohio Valley ranches had a market outlet in the plantations of the South, while ranches in the northern plains depended upon the sale of cattle to mine, army post, or emigrant wagon train (Henlein, 1959; Osgood, 1957, pp. 41–42, 55). In neither the East nor the northern plains, incidentally, was ranching at this time associated with the "cowboy complex."

Before the Civil War most of the western United States was outside the Euro-American economy (i.e., beyond the frontier), except for those areas immediately accessible to river transportation (Malin, 1956, p. 357). Before and immediately after the Civil War, the huge herds of half-wild Texas cattle were, for the most part, unclaimed and unbranded (Webb, 1931, pp. 209–212; Clark, 1956, p. 743; Osgood, 1957, p. 28). By the end of the Civil War the demand for beef in the growing industrial centers of the eastern seaboard and Europe, and the high prices offered there for Texas cattle, resulted in a wild rush to get these hitherto useless animals to market (Osgood, 1957, pp. 28–31; Webb, 1931, p. 216). For the next twenty or thirty years Texas cattle, and with them the ranching complex and cowboy subculture, spread rapidly until they filled the country from Texas to north of the Canadian border and from western Kansas to the Great Basin.

Australia's entry into the grazing industry came about because British flocks were diverted to meat production by the 1820's. The great British woolens industry, therefore, had to look elsewhere for its raw materials. By the 1850's wool was Australia's largest export, and the industry depended upon both British capital and British markets for its expansion (Shann, 1930, pp. 80, 88–89; Allen, 1959, pp. 40–42). As was the case with Argentina, Australia had to await the development of canning and refrigeration before it could break into the world beef and mutton markets to any significant degree.

As necessary to the emergence and expansion of the modern ranching complex as the existence of great numbers of urban workers which consumed its product was the massive complex of processing and transportation, themselves both results of industrialization, which linked producer and consumer. The biologically necessary diffusion of livestock over the grazing area makes it impossible for even the largest ranching operation to supply a modern, heavily capitalized packing house and keep it busy all year. The processing plants were built in positions peripheral to both the source of supply and the centers of demand. In the United States, Australia, and Argentina the packing houses went up in the seaports and in areas accessible to both the source of supply and the market, such as Chicago, St. Louis, Kansas City, or Buenos Aires (Osgood, 1957, pp. 38–39; Webb, 1931, p. 232; Allen, 1959, p. 45; Hanson, 1938, p. 18) .

Since the processing plants had to be removed from the centers of production, the railroad was a vital necessity to the expansion of production, and railroads, both in the United States and in Argentina, followed closely behind the expanding "cattle frontier" and, at times, even ran ahead of it. The railroad also permitted the large-scale development of the complex breeding, grazing, and fattening regional specializations that characterize the modern livestock industry (Malin, 1956, pp. 357, 360–361; Strickon, 1960, pp. 116–117; Osgood, 1957, pp. 23, 32, 43; Webb, 1931, pp. 220–221; Giberti, 1958, p. 326) . The expansion of the railroad further motivated the shift to purebred cattle such as the Hereford, Shorthorn, and Angus and away from the old Longhorns (found also in Argentina and known there as *Criollo* stock) . The long legs, toughness, and hardihood of the Longhorn were adaptive on a cattle drive, but its advantage disappeared in the marketplace, where it could not command the price that purebred stock did.

The regional specializations, and the processing plants located in urban centers (together, of course, with their workers and management) , contrast with the factory-in-the-field organization of a modern corporate sugar plantation (Steward, 1956, pp. 509–510; Wagley and Harris, 1955, pp. 435–436) , equally industrialized and equally dependent on the presence of an industrial market. But where sugar production is land and labor intensive, that of livestock is land and labor extensive. A relatively circumscribed area devoted to sugar cane can keep a sugar factory busy. The same cannot be said in reference to supplying a packing house.

In the period following the Civil War in the United States, the expansion of the livestock industry in the three countries discussed here was extremely lucrative and provided opportunities for almost endless financial speculation. In the United States profits for the ranchers ran as high as 200 per cent. The situation in Australia and Argentina was not far (if at all) behind (Thomas, 1956, p. 428; Osgood, 1957, pp. 49, 83, 139n; Shann, 1930, p. 119; Strickon, 1960, pp. 128–129). A great deal of foreign capital (most of it British) was attracted to all three countries. When late in the nineteenth century meat production finally caught up with the demands of the cities and the bubble burst, it was the larger and more heavily capitalized ranches which tended to survive, for reasons which will be discussed later in this paper (Osgood, 1957, p. 222; Hanson, 1938, p. 18; Allen, 1959, p. 45).

By about the turn of the twentieth century, the modern ranching complex and its interdependence and interpenetration with modern industrial civilization was established. The "frontier" into which the cattle complex had expanded in the second half of the nineteenth century was as much the slums of Manchester and Pittsburgh as it was the empty grasslands of Montana or Santiago del Estero.

LAND TENURE

Ranches tend to be larger units of land ownership or control than do lands in farms under the same environmental and sociocultural conditions. The rancher depends upon the cash sale of his livestock for his subsistence, and, obviously, the more cattle he can graze, the greater is his income. Each of these animals, in turn, requires anywhere from 1 acre to 200 acres of land surface to provide it with the forage it needs to maintain itself and reproduce. The facts of market orientation and livestock physiology are the determinants of the relatively large sizes of ranches as compared with alternative patterns of land use. These ecological requirements have made themselves felt wherever grazing was dominant, often in the face of laws which were meant to prevent the formation of large landholdings.

The unit of land tenure in rural Argentina during the colonial period was known as the *suerte de estancia*. This unit covered about 4600 acres and measured about 1.6 miles across and 4.7 miles long. The streams and bays of the eastern pampas were fronted by a series of these striplike units, which on a cadastral map resembled keys on a piano (Giberti, 1958, pp. 270–271; Oddone, 1936; Outes, 1930, plates XLIV, XLV, XLVII, XLVIII–LII). The purpose of this arrangement was to provide each landholding with a sufficient amount of water and a range of pasture; generally the narrow edge of the strip faced on the water source. Only with the invention in the nineteenth century of the modern wind-driven water pump did the rectangular shape of landholdings give way to a more or less square shape.

The rectangular *suerte de estancia* (though not always known by that name) is found repeated in Mexico and, by way of Mexico, in Texas and the Southwest (Webb, 1931, pp. 425–426; Lea *et al.*, 1957, pp. 102, 378–379). North American "strip" ranches existed whether the rancher owned his land or merely exercised *de facto* control over it. Control of land was based upon control of water frontage. Any land which lacked access to surface water was valueless for grazing purposes: livestock must drink as well as eat. The divide between watersheds marked the boundary between ranches (Webb, 1931, p. 229; Osgood, 1957, p. 18). The resulting unit of land was in all essentials the match of Argentina's *suerte de estancia*.

The pattern of tenure and land use in most parts of the western United States was confronted with a Federal land policy which had been designed with the humid East in mind and which had as its goal the creation of small, family-operated farms (Webb, 1931). Major J. W. Powell in his famous *Report on the Lands of the Arid Regions of the United States* (1878) suggested a minimum land unit for pasture lands of 2560 acres. Each plot was to have frontage on a water source. It was, in fact, merely a recommendation to continue the land pattern already established not only in the arid grazing areas of the United States, but in the humid areas of Argentina as well. In spite of Powell's suggestions, the Congress adopted the 640-acre section as the maximum land unit (Webb,

1931, pp. 419–421, 424). The ranchers could not operate on such a small unit (Osgood, 1957, p. 18), and they did not even try. The methods the ranchers used to foil the maximum size limits imposed by the Congress, such as the buying of alternate sections, the buying of sections which controlled water frontage (and therefore gave them control of the land lying behind it as well), and the purchase of land in the names of employees, have been well documented by such authors as Osgood (1957) and Webb (1931). The stratagems of the ranchers resulted in large landholdings which flew in the face of the intent of the law.

In Texas, which had control over its own public lands, the legislature decreed that family-sized ranches should range in size between 4 and 20 sections (2560 to 12,800 acres). Ultimately the basic land unit in the arid ranching areas of Texas rose to 5120 acres (Webb, 1931, pp. 398, 411, 426–427).

In Australia the situation was similar. Imperial land policy in the earlier period of settlement was based upon the idea of making land difficult to obtain. One of the objects of this was to keep laborers (who were always in short supply) from buying and working upon their own land (Allen, 1959, p. 55). By the mid nineteenth century legislation was passed which did aim to make available small and inexpensive landholdings. The attempt to develop small holdings in Australia failed, according to Allen (*ibid.*, pp. 49–50), because of the aridity of the land, which made it unsuitable for crop growing.

Argentina, too, in the years following its independence in 1810, attempted to create a class of independent farmers based upon small holdings carved out of vast amounts of public lands. But here, too, the attempt failed. The failure of the small-farm philosophy in Argentina was clearly not due to its environmental marginality as a crop-growing region. Beginning in the last two decades of the nineteenth century, and continuing until today, much of the pampas developed into what has become one of the major granaries of the world. The failure of the small-farm philosophy in Argentina in the nineteenth century can be attributed to two factors. First, it was due to the fact that whereas the laws which sought to establish a small-farmer class were promulgated by Buenos Aires liberals, they were enforced (or more accurately not enforced) by the ranchers (*estancieros*), who held effective military and political control of the government. The second factor, and judging from what happened later the more important one, was the fact that there were simply not enough people to put the millions of acres available under the plow. The expansion of ranching in Argentina continued, and the *estancias* became ever larger (Strickon, 1960, pp. 55–61).

LABOR AND POPULATION

The ranch worker, unlike the worker in sugar, cotton, or coffee, has received scant attention from the anthropologist. Where the mounted herdsman and his foot-bound confreres have received notice, it has generally been only in passing. Redfield (1956, p. 32) saw that cowboys were not peasants, but considered them a "quasi-folk" or a "folk community in the process of formation" (Redfield, 1953, pp. 47–48). Kroeber (1948, p. 278) simply dismissed them as one occupational group among many in the modern nation.

It is certainly true that once the romantic encrustations which folklore has attached to the mounted herdsmen are peeled away, they stand revealed as simply a rural proletariat. The only nexus which ties cowboy or gaucho to his employer and the land is that of a cash wage. As is the case with other proletariats, the existence of cowboy and gaucho is "predicated on the existence of other classes who own the instruments of production, provide the work opportunities, pay the wages, and sell the commodities" which are produced (Mintz, 1953, pp. 502–503). The earliest notices we have of the Spanish *vaquero* in the fifteenth century describe him as a free man working for wages (Bishko, 1952, pp. 502–503, 506).

What sets the herdsman apart from other proletariats, urban or rural, is that his way of life is marked by a complex of material traits, work patterns, and values which is unique to his trade. This complex varies only in relatively minor details from region to region, nation to nation, and even continent to continent. Whatever its romantic appeal, the "cowboy subculture" provides the techniques and controls for effectively applying a *very* extensive type of labor to the rearing of grazing livestock.

Early ranching in both the United States and Australia was not coeval with the cowboy complex (Henlein, 1959; Shann, 1930, pp. 89–90). This complex is clearly Spanish in origin (Bishko, 1952, pp. 507–508). Even if historical materials did not substantiate this statement, comparisons of the trait lists of Argentine and Brazilian gauchos with those of American cowboys could lead to no other conclusion (cf. Ward, 1958; Rollins, 1936; Saubidet, 1948; Saenz, 1951; Willems, 1944; Rosas, 1951). Of course, in the case of Australia, the diffusion of the complex is recent enough to be documented (Allen, 1959, pp. 46–78). Even in the United States the diffusion of the complex up the cattle trails from Mexico and Texas is well known (Osgood, 1957, p. 48).

The mounted herdsman has always been a paid worker and legally at least the master of his own person. Attempts in the seventeenth to nineteenth centuries to apply slaves to the labor of ranches generally came to nothing. In the early 1800's the ranches of the bluegrass areas of Kentucky did not apply slave labor to their grazing operations. Many of these holdings also raised hemp, and slaves were used for the growing and processing of this crop. In the 1820's, when grazing expanded at the expense of tobacco and hemp production in this area, Kentucky found herself with a surplus of slaves; "cattle farming could not alone keep this labor force busy" (Henlein, 1959, pp. 43, 69–70).

In Argentina also, slavery and ranching did not mix. In 1744 about 10 per cent of the population of Buenos Aires were listed in the first census as slaves (Oddone, 1936, p. 30), presumably Negro. The most striking thing about this slave population was that it was to be found not on the land, but in the city itself. As such it was removed from direct involvement with the livestock industry, which was the economic base of eastern Argentina. Most of the slaves were involved in household duties and are said to have been well clothed, fed, and treated. Early travelers even tell of slave overseers supervising the work of free Spanish day laborers (Vidal, 1820, pp. 30–32). Whereas slavery was abolished in the British Caribbean in the 1830's and in the plantations of Brazil as late as the 1880's, in Argentina the legal basis for slavery began to be dismantled immediately upon independence in 1810. But even before that, a slave could marry a free woman and their children would be free.

Given the labor requirements of grazing, slavery as a source of labor would be both inefficient and expensive. The diffuse nature of grazing made it literally impossible to keep the workers under constant surveillance, as they carried out their work miles from ranch headquarters and from one another. The herder, in order to do his work, had to be mounted and armed, at least against predatory animals and his half-wild charges and often against fighting Indians as well. The cowboy or gaucho had no disadvantage in mobility or arms as compared with his employer. These men would, in fact, when mobilized become a major factor in the political power of an ambitious rancher. In Argentina they were so used throughout the nineteenth century. With such a diffuse, mobile, and armed labor force necessary for the work to be done, slavery was obviously impractical.

Although differing in some particulars from his gaucho and cowboy counterparts, the Australian sheep worker also represents a rural proletariat working other men's sheep, on other men's land, for wages (Allen, 1959, p. 109; Shann, 1930, pp. 113–119).

The diffuse nature of labor with grazing livestock, plus the necessary physical mobility of the men who perform it, calls for a type of labor control which does not require close supervision. Labor, in ranching, is marked for the most part by internal rather than external controls. The cowboy or gaucho does his work not because he must but because he wants to. His work is defined by himself and most others as prestigeful as compared with the labor of farmer or field hand. Furthermore, the cowboy and the owner of his ranch often share at least some of the values and skills of the "cowboy complex." Interpersonal relations in ranching country are usually fiercely egalitarian, at least on the surface. Anyone not able to compete in the "supermasculine" life of cowboy or gaucho is below contempt. Unlike the mounted herder, the farmer or city man is rooted to one spot, he is not "free," and above all things the herder likes to think of himself as his own man.

I have no wish to enter here upon an extended discussion of the values which characterize the cowboy complex. They seem to be simply an intensified version of masculine values which are widespread in the Euro-American culture area. This complex of values and its close dependence upon the work of herding is best reflected perhaps in the way in which cowboy and gaucho spend their spare time. The rodeo, stampede, or Argentine *domada* (and I mean the small, local ones, not the large commercial undertakings) is simply an extension of the cowman's daily work, but here done for the entertainment of himself and his fellows, as well as for reasons of prestige. I rather doubt whether a sugar plantation worker has ever lived who spent his free time cutting cane just for the fun of it (Bennett, 1946, pp. 21–22, 104–105; Vogt, 1955, pp. 136–137; Strickon, 1960, pp. 101–107, 121–127, 261–262, 357; Willems, 1944, pp. 154–157; Lewis, 1948, pp. 68, 110; see also Frantz and Choate, 1955; Guernsey, 1936; Rollins, 1936).

Many of the material traits and work techniques of the cowboy, specifically those centering about the use of the horse in handling and controlling livestock, permit an even more extensive labor pattern than would the handling of livestock on foot. The rapid expansion of the cowboy complex from Mexico and Texas into the northern plains after the Civil War is a good measure of the superiority of the Spanish handling techniques over those known in the East before the 1860's.

In Australia early sheep ranching was essentially European in pattern up to the 1850's, and, as compared with later developments, labor intensive (Shann, 1930, pp. 89–90). By the 1850's, however, the Victoria gold strikes had drained much of the sheep stations' labor away and driven up wages. As a result, mounted sheepherders (boundary riders) replaced the shepherds; fencing and other technological innovations (many clearly borrowed from New World cattle ranching) were applied. More people per head were required to raise sheep in the mid nineteenth century than in the mid twentieth century. These changes, triggered by a labor crisis, left the Australian sheep raisers in a stronger economic position than before (Shann, 1930, pp. 122–123, 127, 185; Allen, 1959, p. 80).

In both Argentina and the United States the expansion of the railroads, the introduction of barbed wire and of windmill-driven pumps, the replacement of half-wild Longhorns by gentle Angus, Shorthorn, and Hereford, all served (in addition to killing the "Old West" in the eyes of the romantic) to permit, and very probably to reinforce, the labor-extensive pattern of livestock grazing (Sbarra, 1955; Strickon, 1960, pp. 118–121, 123; Webb, 1931, pp. 333–347; E. Z. Vogt, personal communication).

On the northern plains of the United States only one herdsman is necessary per 1000 head of cattle (Wilson *et al.,* 1928, p. 15), a proportion that is matched in Argentina (Giberti, 1958, pp. 270–271). In Australia before the gold rush of the 1850's, one man could take care of between 300 and 1500 head of sheep (Shann, 1930, p. 119). After the gold rush began, and after the reorganization of the sheep stations, one man could care for as many as 2500 head (*ibid.,* p. 123).

Giberti's (1958, p. 295) estimate of total labor requirements (not just the direct herders) in Argentina for various types of grazing activities are as follows (per 1000 head) : range cattle, 2.5 men; sheep and goats, 1.5; milk cows, 3. The labor requirement for 100 hectares (247 acres) of grain is 3 men; for 100 hectares of maize, 4.5 men; and for 100 hectares of vegetables the work of 55 men is required. Whereas the 3 men in grains are putting only 247 acres under the plow, the 2 or 3 men working with range cattle (in the central pampas) are putting some 2500 acres to productive use.

Correlated with the low labor demands of grazing is the fact that regions dominated by a ranching adaptation are always characterized by very low population densities. Population density itself is a meaningless figure which achieves significance only in reference to such variables as settlement pattern, percentage of arable land to total area, and so forth. Ranching country is typically organized into open country neighborhoods, the population being scattered more or less evenly over the habitable parts of the countryside (Webb, 1931, pp. 229, 245; Bennett, 1946, pp. 52–54; Willems, 1944, pp. 157–160; Strickon, 1960, pp. 64–111, 150–371; Arensberg, 1955, pp. 1154–1155; Shann, 1930, p. 117; Argentine Republic, 1947, pp. 69–79; Malin, 1956, p. 359; Wittfogel, 1957, pp. 217–218). In taking figures for Argentina (which means, chiefly, the pampas), we are dealing with an area which is habitable and arable throughout for all practical purposes. Using Giberti's (1958, p. 296) figures (which refer only to rural population), we come up with the following population densities and associated patterns of land use: purebred sheep, 0.5 people per square kilometer; mixed livestock (i.e., cattle and sheep), 2.5 per square kilometer. Compare these figures with the population density for agricultural regions of 4.7 per square kilometer.

These widely dispersed populations, and the communities which they form, are integrated into larger regional and national groupings. This wider integration is effected, for the most part, not through the ranch workers and their families, but rather through other social classes. The integration of the local social and economic system with that of the region and nation is carried out by the businessmen of the villages and towns and by the ranch owners. These men are often as much (if not more) at home in the city as they are on the ranch or in the country village. In addition to their business interests they often play political roles. The large ranch owners often constitute a regional elite and may be part of a national one as well (Hartwell, 1955, p. 55; Lea *et al.,* 1957; Strickon, 1960, pp. 33, 55, 61–63, 194–205, 217–230; Strickon, 1962, pp. 503, 510–512; Vogt, 1955, pp. 136–137; Allen, 1959, p. 44).

RANCH SIZE AS AN ADAPTIVE FACTOR

At this point in the discussion of ranching, it is necessary to look to those ecological and economic factors which provide an adaptive advantage to the larger as against the smaller ranch. This advantage may be summarized as follows: that ranch which uses its land and labor more extensively per head has a better chance to survive price fluctuations than one which makes a more intensive use of land and labor.

A stable ranching operation is one which makes sufficiently extensive use of its land during normal years so that it can, during periods of falling prices, hold its cattle off the market rather than either sell at a loss or risk damage to its range. "With a stable situation for operation, which involves permanent range control, a ranchman can attract capital at reasonable rates of interest to improve his ranch and herd and counteract the effect of lean business years" (Wilson *et al.*, 1928, p. 27) .

Aside from land, the investment in cattle represents the largest single item of capital on most ranches. On those United States ranches which depend heavily upon rented land, the investment in livestock may be even greater than that in land (*ibid.*, p. 30) . Other investment in buildings, machinery, fences, and so on, must also be made. Although as the ranch gets larger investment in such materials goes up, the increase in capital investment is *not* proportional to the increasing size of the ranch. Ranches with over 1000 head have a much lower investment per animal unit than do smaller ranches (*ibid.*, pp. 43, 76–86) .

The situation is similar as regards labor. As the ranch increases in size, more labor is needed and the proportion of labor costs to all costs also rises. The number of days of labor needed per animal unit in such a situation *decreases,* however. In other words, the more cattle there are on a ranch, the less labor is needed per animal (Carpenter *et al.*, 1941, p. 45) .

Since cost per head decreases as the number of head increases, it follows that the rate of return on a given ranch investment increases proportionately to the number of livestock the operation carries. Wilson *et al.* (1928, p. 63) report that whereas a ranch which carries 50 cows (about 100 head in total) or less gets a return of 2 per cent on its investment, the ranch with 450 cows (about 900 head or more) will return 8 per cent on its investment.

The situation in Argentina is much the same as that outlined for the United States. The *estanciero* sees his ranch clearly as a business and is quite consciously aware of the benefits of investing his money in an *estancia* as compared with alternative investment opportunities (Strickon, 1960, pp. 221–223) . Argentine mixed-farmer, small rancher, and *estanciero* are aware of the greater viability of the large ranch. After a severe drought or a drop in market prices, it is invariably the small owner who goes under. The large *estancias* add to their capital during such periods, getting both land and underfed livestock at low prices. During periods of high prices the large ranches may sell land to smaller operations secure in the knowledge that during the next period of adversity they will be able to buy it back at a profit to themselves (Strickon, field notes, 1958–1959).

THE FARMER AND THE COWMAN IN MACROCOSM

It is when the ranching and the farming adaptations begin to compete for the same habitat that the ranching ecology with its pattern of extensive use of land and labor is most clearly seen. The conflict over the plains of the United States between farmer and cattleman has become so laden with folklore that it has become difficult to see the real ecological problems that lay beneath it. In the following pages we shall look at these conflicting adaptations, not only in the United States but in Australia and Argentina as well.

When ranching is displaced or replaced by agriculture, it is commercial, not subsistence, agriculture that does it. Obviously, the factors that motivated the spread of cash cropping into what had hitherto been grazing land were much the same ones that had brought about the expansion of ranching not very many years earlier. The growing urban populations which represented a massive market for the products of grazing did so as well for agricultural products, especially grains. The transportation network and industrialized processing industry which were necessary for the expansion of ranching were necessary, as well, for farmers. The chief difference lay in manpower. Ranching needed relatively little, farming needed a lot. When this last problem was met, the conflict over the plains and pampas began. When the point was reached where the profits to be realized from the land were greater from farming than from grazing, then grazing in any particular area began to contract and perhaps to disappear completely.

In the case of the United States, the very railroads which opened up the plains to commercial grazing also provided an easy route for a population flow from the eastern seaboard and Europe into these same plains. The new population wanted to farm, not ranch, and government land regulations, as we have seen, supported this desire. The folklore aside, the ranchers' land, even when they held legal title to it, was not ripped from them at gunpoint. With the coming of the farmers, land values rose, "and the rancher cut up another pasture which he turned over to the farmers mostly on credit" (Webb, 1931, p. 243). The rancher, as a businessman, had one measure of the land: the money it could produce. If more could be made by selling it to the farmer, then that is what he did.

The influx of farmers occurred in different parts of the American West at different times. Western Kansas was flooded by them soon after the Civil War. The northern plains did not receive the full impact of the "granger" invasion until the last couple of decades of the nineteenth century. Associated with the spread of agriculture and the growing population was the appearance of new towns throughout the previously empty plains (Osgood, 1957, p. 243). These towns, in turn, became the centers for political and economic groupings which undercut the virtual political monopoly that the ranchers had enjoyed over these areas (*ibid.*, p. 245). The conflicting patterns of use of land and labor, and the conflicting economic and political interests which reflected these differences, occasionally left the vocal arena and burst into open violence (*ibid.*, pp. 249–253).

The shift in parts of Argentina away from ranching and toward agricultural use accompanied by increased population densities, growth in service communities, and so on, was similar in pattern to that in the United States. In Argentina, though, it took place within a different environmental and legal matrix and lacked the violent and dramatic confrontation between farmer and cattleman.

Most of the pampas (especially the eastern pampas) are arable throughout. Beginning around the 1880's, these great plains began to be drawn into agricultural production. The mechanism was the need for high-grade feeds and forage crops for the new purebred cattle. The situation differed, however, from that in the United States, where the government supported the concept of the family-owned and -operated farm; most of the arable pampas were firmly and legally in the hands of the *estancieros* (Taylor, 1948, p. 177; Strickon, 1960, pp. 55–61), as was the government.

The gauchos would not perform the new farming operations (Strickon, 1960, p. 102) even if there had been enough of them, which there were not. It was necessary to encourage immigration. The farmer was typically a Spanish or Italian immigrant. These farmers were brought onto the *estancias* as renters and sharecroppers. Their primary duty, from the point of view of the ranch, was to plant forage crops. But in addition to these, and as part of the policy of rotating pastures, grains were grown as well (*ibid.*, pp. 121–122). The grains were aimed primarily at the export market to Europe. The introduction of commercial agriculture into Argentina was explosive. In 1865 there was less than 400 square miles (256,000 acres) of tilled land in the pampas. Five years later Argentina was still an importer of grains. By 1895, with 7875 square miles (4,940,000 acres) in wheat, Argentina had become (and remains) one of the major grain exporters of the world (*ibid.*, pp. 123–125).

In the thirty years between 1869 and 1899, 3,500,000 immigrants entered Argentina. Most of these remained in the region around Buenos Aires, the area that was being put under the plow (Strickon, 1960, pp. 125–127). The province of Santa Fé was pastoral in 1869 and had a population density of 0.7 per square kilometer. In the years following the 1869 census, Santa Fé turned into a primarily agricultural region; its population density in 1947 was 12.9 per square kilometer. The province of Santiago del Estero has remained a grazing area. Its population density increased only from 0.9 per square kilometer in 1869 to 3.3 in 1947 (Argentine Republic, 1947, p. 7).

What had started out as a supplement to ranching became, in many parts of the eastern pampas, the major pattern of land use. As in the United States, the coming of the railroads and the farmers drove up the value of the land. But whereas the American rancher sold his land, the *estanciero* rented his. The end result, ecologically, was the same. Great areas of the pampas became primarily agricultural (Hanson, 1938, pp. 98, 112).

The story in Australia differs from that in the United States and Argentina. Here the chief problem remained a lack of labor, and the spread of agriculture was limited to a few coastal districts. Attempts at agriculture, up to the early years of this century, were limited to the east coastal districts. Attempts to introduce farming elsewhere generally failed, as grazing would return larger profits with less investment in either time or labor. Farmers would not settle. It was difficult, if not impossible, to get farmers to practice proper rotation of crops, since as a field was worked out there was always more land to be had. Wheat farming became important in Australia only with the introduction of mechanized farm machinery, the use of which permitted an approach to the utilization of as large units of land with as few workers as was possible with grazing (Allen, 1959, pp. 49, 55–57, 59; Shann, 1930, pp. 215–216, 220–222).

THE FARMER-COWMAN CONFLICT IN MICROCOSM

In the three areas which have been considered in this paper, the general trend has been one wherein the ranching complex has been replaced by some kind of agricultural production. The situation is reversed, however, when we consider the three studies available which deal directly with a grazing community or with farming communities closely tied to the ranching complex. In all three communities ranching was replacing agriculture at the time the studies were made. Here the processes which were to be seen at work in the previous section are seen operating in reverse, as it were. In these cases extensive land and labor use becomes advantageous over intensive use, towns contract in size or disappear, and population decreases. The three communities to be considered are "Homestead," New Mexico (Vogt, 1955), Bell County, Texas (Lewis, 1948), and "Eleodoro Gomez," Province of Buenos Aires, Argentina (Strickon, 1960).

Until the early 1930's, land which now supports Homestead was used for grazing by Anglo-American and Spanish-American ranchers (Vogt, 1955, p. 37). The farmers who settled Homestead in the early thirties came from Texas, and their livelihood depended upon the cultivation and sale of pinto beans. Even after the settlement of the farmers, however, the area of Homestead remained surrounded by ranches which ranged in size from 1300 to 115,000 acres (*ibid.*, p. 40). In 1935 the farming community reached its maximum population of 375 and its maximum area, controlling some 130 sections or 83,200 acres (*ibid.*, p. 41). This region is marginal, at best, for agricultural production, and crops can be expected to be bad about one-third of the time (*ibid.*, pp. 57–58).

Of the original holding by the farmers of 130 sections in 1935, 30 sections had been lost by the farmers up to the time of Vogt's stay in the community. Ten sections had been reclassified by the government as unsuited for farming and returned to the public domain as grazing land. The other 20 sections were lost owing to outright purchase by the surrounding ranches (*ibid.*, p. 41).

The smaller landowners among the Homesteaders are full-time farmers; those with two or more sections "tend to farm less and to become livestock ranchers" (*ibid.*, p. 42). In spite of the Homesteaders' complaints about the "rancher-nester" conflict, once they begin to ranch they are as driven to acquire more and more land as are the ranchers themselves (*ibid.*, p. 42). Furthermore, as they acquire more land, and therefore as they switch more and more to grazing, there is a greater chance for a family to survive and remain in Homestead (*ibid.*, p. 176). The farmer, unlike the rancher, had to spend at least part of his time working for wages elsewhere than in Homestead (*ibid.*, p. 60). The Homesteader who has remained on the land (i.e., who has become more dependent upon grazing) has, on the average, doubled the size of his landholding since 1935 (*ibid.*, p. 41).

The increase in the size of landholdings has meant a population decline for the community, "for when additional land is acquired by either rancher or Homesteader, it does not become a home for another family but is merely added to the existing operating unit" (*ibid.*, pp. 41–42). Between 1935 and 1950 the population of Homestead fell from 375 to 232 (*ibid.*, p. 41). Vogt (*ibid.*, p. 188) believes that this community of farmers is disappearing and that the land will ultimately return to the ranchers who originally grazed their cattle upon it.

Bell County, Texas, straddles two ecological niches. Eastern

Bell County is clearly agricultural, western Bell County is shifting back to an older grazing adjustment. Four of the five "village centered communities" in the county are in the eastern, or agricultural, part of the county (Lewis, 1948, p. 50), and farms in this district are markedly smaller than landholdings in the western (or grazing) sections of the county (*ibid.*, p. 18). These grazing areas of Bell County, says Lewis (*ibid.*, p. 40) are characterized by "broken down rural communities," whereas the agricultural villages are united by ties of kinship, long residence, farm ownership, schools, churches, and the like.

Western Bell County was a grazing area up to 1900. At that time cotton growing spread from the eastern area into the more arid western parts and the grazing lands were plowed up. With the cotton came nucleated villages. The land became exhausted, however, and in the fifteen years up to 1948 landholding units became consolidated and the area returned to grazing. "Families have been forced out of the area, schools and churches have suffered, and community life has greatly deteriorated" (*ibid.*, p. 40). This trend toward the resuscitation of livestock grazing in Bell County is attributed by Lewis (*ibid.*, p. 23) to high beef prices and a shortage of labor. The resulting ecological adaptation ("adjustment to the environment" in Lewis' words) is essentially similar to that of the pioneer days.

In the case of both Homestead and western Bell County, the expansion of grazing was at least partly attributable to the marginality of the environment for the crops grown in the respective regions. This is not the case in Eleodoro Gomez. Throughout the humid (i.e. eastern) pampas the shifting allocation of land to sheep grazing, cattle grazing, and agriculture has been structured chiefly by the market advantage of one land use pattern as against the others at any particular place and time. By retaining ownership of their land, *estancieros* could add or remove tenant farmers as market conditions, and other variables, required.

Central Buenos Aires Province, where Eleodoro Gomez is situated, is peripheral to both grazing and agricultural districts, and both activities can be, and are, carried out there. In 1928, 21 per cent of the adult male population of Eleodoro Gomez (which in-

cludes both the village of that name and the surrounding countryside) were farmers. In 1942, 34 per cent of the adult male population were farmers. By 1957, however, the proportion of farmers
had fallen to only 14 per cent (Strickon, 1960, pp. 349–351). During the forties Eleodoro Gomez was "livelier" and "more progres-
sive" than it is today, according to remaining farmers and village
dwellers. There were parent-teacher groups and charitable associ-
ations, church life was active, there were formally organized ath-
letic teams, and so on. Today almost all that is gone and the community seems to be disappearing. What is happening, of course,
is that an older culture, which was partially obscured by that of
the farmers, is becoming dominant once again (*ibid.,* pp. 351–
353).

The pattern seems much the same as that described earlier for
Homestead and Bell County. But here in Argentina the replacement of farming by grazing was not determined primarily by environmental factors. Rather, the causative element here was ecological in the broadest sense of the word: the political and economic
machinations of the Argentine national government.

In the years following the 1943 revolution in Argentina, rent
and tenure controls were imposed by the government on the
ranchers in order to protect the sharecropper and tenant farmer.
The rents were frozen and were to be paid in cash, not as per-
centages of the harvest. The rancher could no longer order his
tenants off the *estancia,* but had to buy them out. The demands
of world war and reconstruction drove the value of cattle and
grains up. The point was finally reached where it became profitable for the rancher to buy out his renters and sharecroppers. The
largest ranch in the neighborhood of Eleodoro Gomez (90,000
acres), which had some forty farmers in the early 1940's, had none
at the time of the field study (1958–1959). The same story could
be repeated on the other ranches in the neighborhood (Strickon,
1960, pp. 353–354). I saw in Eleodoro Gomez in 1959 a community in many ways more like that of the traditional pampas than I
would have seen if I had gone there twenty years earlier.

The preceding paragraph should not be taken to mean that agriculture is disappearing from Eleodoro Gomez; it is not. Forage

crops must still be planted; pastures must be rotated; the sale of grains is still lucrative. But all this is no longer done on the ranches by renters or sharecroppers using family labor. It is done by wage laborers, using modern farm machinery. Like the grazing operations themselves, this kind of operation is labor extensive and under the control and organization of the ranch. It introduces new activities into the countryside; it does not (or at least has not, so far) brought into being new types of settlements, new institutions, groupings, or values such as emerged when the farmers came into the pampas. In terms of the categories of people in and around Eleodoro Gomez, the new rural proletariat is practically indistinguishable from the gauchos that preceded it (Strickon, 1962, p. 507).

Conclusion

The purpose of this paper has been to describe and analyze livestock ranching as a cultural-ecological type. In order to do this, it has been necessary to isolate specific aspects of the ranching complex—those of marketing, land tenure and use, and labor—and relate these to each other and to the larger socio-economic system of which the ranching complex is a part.

In its absolute dependence upon an industrialized market for its product, in its use of wage workers, in its need for a complex marketing and processing system, the ranching complex is clearly one with other types of commercial, industrial agriculture.

Its particular characteristics can be seen to derive from the fact that mediating between man and his environment, in the case of ranching, are the livestock with their need for relatively large areas to supply their food and the relative lack of care necessary for their well-being. The land- and labor-extensive patterns which are the hallmarks and advantage of the ranching adaptation derive from this biological "given."

Acknowledgments. I should like to thank Professors John W. Bennett and Richard N. Adams for their comments and suggestions. The responsibility for what appears here is, of course, my own.

REFERENCES

ALLEN, H. C. 1959. *Bush and Backwoods; A Comparison of the Frontier in Australia and the United States.* Michigan State University Press, East Lansing, Mich.

ARENSBERG, C. M. 1955. American communities. *Am. Anthropologist,* 57 (6), 1143–1162.

ARGENTINE REPUBLIC. PRESIDENCIA DE LA NACIÓN. MINISTERIO DE ASUNTOS TÉCNICOS. 1947. *IV censo general de la República.* Tomo I. *Censo de población.* Dirección Nacional del Servicio Estadístico, Buenos Aires.

BENNETT, R. H. 1946. *The Compleat Rancher.* Rinehart and Co., New York, N. Y.

BISHKO, C. J. 1952. The Peninsular background of Latin American cattle ranching. *Hisp.-Am. Hist. Rev., 32,* 491–515.

CARPENTER, G. A., M. CLAWSON, and C. E. FLEMING. 1941. *Ranch Organization and Operation in Northeastern Nevada.* Nevada State Printing Office, Carson City, Nev.

CLARK, A. H. 1956. The impact of exotic invasion on the remaining New World mid-latitude grasslands. In *Man's Role in Changing the Face of the Earth* (W. L. Thomas, Jr., editor), pp. 737–762. University of Chicago Press, Chicago, Ill.

DARLING, F. F. 1956. Man's ecological dominance through domesticated animals on wild land. In *Man's Role in Changing the Face of the Earth* (W. L. Thomas, Jr., editor), pp. 778–787. University of Chicago Press, Chicago, Ill.

FRANTZ, J. B., and J. E. CHOATE, JR. 1955. *The American Cowboy; The Myth and the Reality.* University of Oklahoma Press, Norman, Okla.

GIBERTI, H. C. E. 1958. Cria de animales. In *La Argentina, suma de geografía* (F. de Aparicio, editor), vol. 4, pp. 261–492. Ediciones Peuser, Buenos Aires.

GUERNSEY, C. A. 1936. *Wyoming Cowboy Days.* G. P. Putnam's Sons, New York, N. Y.

HANSON, S. G. 1938. *Argentine Meat and the British Market.* Stanford University Press, Stanford, Calif.

HARTWELL, R. M. 1955. The pastoral ascendancy. In *Australia; A Social and Political History* (G. Greenwood, editor), pp. 46–97. Frederick A. Praeger, New York, N. Y.

HENLEIN, P. C. 1959. *Cattle Kingdom in the Ohio Valley 1783–1860.* University of Kentucky Press, Lexington, Ky.

JESSEN, O. 1952. Cosacos, cowboys, gauchos, boers, y otros pueblos a caballos propios de las estepas. *Runa, 5* (1, 2), 171–186.

KROEBER, A. L. 1948. *Anthropology*. Harcourt, Brace and Co., New York, N. Y.

LEA, T., H. McCOMBS, and F. L. FUGATE. 1957. *The King Ranch*, vol. 1. Little, Brown and Co., Boston, Mass.

LEWIS, O. 1948. *On the Edge of the Black Waxy; A Cultural Survey of Bell County, Texas*. Washington University Studies, St. Louis, Mo.

MALIN, J. C. 1956. The grasslands of North America; Its occupance and the challenge of continuous reappraisals. In *Man's Role in Changing the Face of the Earth* (W. L. Thomas, Jr., editor), pp. 350–366. University of Chicago Press, Chicago, Ill.

MINTZ, S. W. 1953. The folk-urban continuum and the rural proletarian community. *Am. J. Sociol., 59* (2), 136–143.

ODDONE, J. 1936. *La burguesía terrateniente argentina; Capital federal, Buenos Aires, territorios nacionales*, 2nd edition. Privately published, Buenos Aires.

OSGOOD, E. S. 1957. *The Day of the Cattleman*. Phoenix Books, Chicago, Ill.

OUTES, F. F. 1930. *Cartas y planos inéditos de los siglos XVII y XVIII y del primer decenio del XIX, conservados en el Archivo de la Dirección de Geodesia, Catastro, y Mapa de la Provincia de Buenos Aires*. Instituto de Investigaciones Geográficas de la Facultad de Filosofía y Letras, Buenos Aires.

PHILLIPS, R. W. 1958. Cattle. *Sci. American, 198* (6), 51–59.

REDFIELD, R. 1953. *The Primitive World and Its Transformations*. Cornell University Press, Ithaca, N. Y.

REDFIELD, R. 1956. *Peasant Society and Culture; An Anthropological Approach to Civilization*. University of Chicago Press, Chicago, Ill.

RITZMAN, E. G., and F. R. BENEDICT. 1938. *Nutritional Physiology of the Adult Ruminant*. Carnegie Institution of Washington, Washington, D. C.

ROLLINS, P. A. 1936. *The Cowboy*, 2nd edition. Charles Scribner's Sons, New York, N. Y.

ROSAS, J. M. DE. 1951. *Instrucciones a los mayordomos de estancias*. Ediciones Peuser, Buenos Aires.

SAENZ, J. P. (HIJO). 1951. *Equitación gaucha en la Pampa y Mesopotamia*, 3rd edition. Ediciones Peuser, Buenos Aires.

SAUBIDET, T. 1948. *Vocabulario y refranero criollo*, 3rd edition. Guillermo Kraft, Ltda, Buenos Aires.

SBARRA, N. H. 1955. *Historia del alambrado en Argentina*. Editorial Raigal, Buenos Aires.

SHANN, E. 1930. *An Economic History of Australia*. Cambridge University Press, London.

STEWARD, J. H. 1955. *Theory of Culture Change; The Methodology of Multilinear Evolution.* University of Illinois Press, Urbana, Ill.

STEWARD, J. H. 1956. *The People of Puerto Rico; A Study in Social Anthropology.* University of Illinois Press, Urbana, Ill.

STRICKON, A. 1960. *The Grandsons of the Gauchos; A Study in Subcultural Persistence.* University Microfilms, Ann Arbor, Mich.

STRICKON, A. 1962. Class and kinship in Argentina. *Ethnology, 1* (4), 500–515.

TAYLOR, C. C. 1948. *Rural Life in Argentina.* Louisiana State University Press, Baton Rouge, La.

THOMAS, W. L., JR., editor. 1956. *Man's Role in Changing the Face of the Earth.* University of Chicago Press, Chicago, Ill.

VIDAL, E. E. 1820. *Picturesque Illustrations of Buenos Ayres and Monte Video, Consisting of Twenty-four Views; Accompanied with Descriptions of the Scenery and of the Costumes, Manners, etc., of the Inhabitants of Those Cities and Their Environs.* R. Ackermann, London.

VOGT, E. Z. 1955. *Modern Homesteaders; The Life of a Twentieth Century Frontier Community.* Belknap Press, Cambridge, Mass.

WAGLEY, C., and M. HARRIS. 1955. A typology of Latin American subcultures. *Am. Anthropologist, 57* (3), pt. 1, 428–451.

WARD, F. F. 1958. *The Cowboy at Work; All about His Job and How He Does It.* Hastings House, New York, N. Y.

WEBB, W. P. 1931. *The Great Plains.* Grosset's Universal Library, New York, N. Y.

WILLEMS, E. 1944. Acculturation and the horse complex among German Brazilians. *Am. Anthropologist, 46* (2), 153–161.

WILSON, M. L., R. H. WILCOX, G. S. KLEMMEDSON, and V. V. PARR. 1928. *A Study of Ranch Organization and Methods of Range Cattle Production in the Northeastern Great Plains Region.* U. S. Dept. Agr. Tech. Bull. 45. Washington, D. C.

WITTFOGEL, K. A. 1957. *Oriental Despotism; A Comparative Study of Total Power.* Yale University Press, New Haven, Conn.

Comments on the Symposium "Man, Culture, and Animals"

HOMER ASCHMANN

Department of Geography, University of California, Riverside, California

THE AUTHORS of the several papers here presented were concerned to answer a considerable diversity of questions, and they do so with varying success and little comparability. Harris' effort to demonstrate that the handling of cattle in Hindu society is rational from an economic standpoint may be compared with Strickon's description of the economic determinants of the ranching complex in Western societies. On the other hand, Murra is attempting to recover from the documents a description of the llama-herding phase of the Andean economies at the time of the Spanish conquest. He can accept as a given that herding occurred and had some economic significance, but his interest then focuses on the nature of the social organization among the groups actively engaged in herding. Again, Downs and Ekvall examine a single and largely non-economic question: How has the use of animals served to unify the culture and society over a vast, sparsely populated region of difficult terrain in Tibet?

Leeds' and Vayda's desire to develop hypotheses dealing with ecologic adjustments associated with animals is in some measure satisfied. The big question as to whether human cultures are rational in economic terms, even if only unconsciously so, has always been especially vexed when data on domestic animals were introduced. Too many observed practices seemed to be costly, even to the extent of reducing food consumption on the part of chronically hungry people. Permanent destruction of resource by overgrazing, first recognized and analyzed by Marsh and his

259

successors (Marsh, 1869), cannot be denied, but we are vitally concerned to learn more about the economic and social pressures that seem to enforce a continuation of such destructive practices.

Two generalizations seem to have validity, but their universality limits their explanatory power. First, societies will carry on activities that produce value for their members, but the value may not be subject to definition in economic or monetary terms. Second, societies which have managed to exist in a particular region for a long time (several generations) will have achieved reasonably stable adjustments between the number of people, their subsistence technologies, and their natural environments.

Uncovering gaps in our knowledge, even in regard to the societies studied, has been one of the more successful results of the symposium. For groups which are nearly self-sufficient in food, or are isolated enough to allow accurate measures of extraregional imports, precise food budgets would be desirable. Knight's data for Algonkian Indians in the Canadian taiga are interesting indeed. The tremendous intake of highly concentrated foods, perhaps three times the per capita amount that is reported for places like India, clearly correlates with the cold weather, but hunger or starvation in the northlands is likely to prove to be quite a different matter from undernourishment in the tropics. Objective and numerical data on either normal or unusual seasonal variations in food supply are virtually nonexistent.

Perhaps because of the frame of reference for which the papers were prepared, relatively little appears concerning the nonsubsistence or noncommercial reasons why domesticated animals may be kept. Meggitt's paper on dingoes among the Australian Aborigines and Murra's on llamas are to some degree exceptions. Any ethnological theory on ecology will have to encompass in comparable terms not only values for subsistence and security, but those for prestige, taste preference and desire for variety in clothing and ornament as well as food, and entertainment, the latter perhaps including most religious activities. Ours is not the only society that invests a large fraction of its effort in producing values quite unrelated to subsistence, even subsistence broadly conceived. The data on dingoes among the Australians, certainly both primitive and economically insecure people, make this clear. We can assign monetary equivalents to most if not all of *our* values, but data now available to us do not permit us to do so for most of mankind through most of time. It is possible to ask for ethnographic data that will permit general value assessments for the societies concerned, even if the nature of the needed data cannot be defined explicitly. The duration and intensity of the labor required to produce the values recognized by the society are likely to yield far more inclusive terms than animal units or food or caloric ones. Clearly little has been collected that would permit such evaluations. If an ecological science dealing with human sustenance is erected which merely shows how to maximize the number of individuals an area can support with a given technology, something less than the reality and wealth of human culture will be its concern.

It seems possible to order the several societies considered individually in this symposium along several discrete axes or continua, and the fact that particular societies find different positions on the several continua is illuminating. One axis might be the degree to which the subsistence economy is dominated by animals. I would place the Chukchi, Bedouin, and Canadian Algonkian at the extreme of maximum dependence on animals. The people of India in general and the Dodos of Uganda are notably less dependent, and such groups as the Apache and Sioux fall in between. One recognizes quickly that animals are of maximum importance where climates are severely cold or dry and thus unfavorable for vegetable growth. In such societies the procedures for handling animals are maximally rational from an economic standpoint within the technological limitations of the society, and the social organization is specifically structured to that end, be it the nuclear family hunting and trapping group of the Algonkian or the tribal section of the Bedouin. The Indian villager with his privately owned over-age or too young bullock and the Navaho clan fit the ecologies of the animals they deal with less well, but other economic and cultural interests are overriding.

The degree to which the society is commercially oriented varies from the American rancher who sells feeder stock and buys all his

beef, as well as everything else he needs, at the store, to the Australian Aborigine who until recently was completely self-sufficient.
It is, of course, a truism that dependence on commercial interchange grows steadily in the modern world, though perhaps less
rapidly in ancient and complex societies such as those of India
than in simpler ones such as those of the American Indians. The
long-run economic rationality of a commercial society may be no
greater than that of a noncommercial one, but it is easier to assign
a monetary equivalent to the values that the society pursues. Overgrazing and moving on to new ranges is too much part of the history of the American West as long as there were new ranges to go
to (Sauer, 1938). Quick accumulation of wealth from herds,
wealth that could then be transferred to other resources, rather
than a stable ecologic adjustment was, and probably still is, the
goal. Another term for it is the politically acceptable and ecologically ridiculous "ever expanding economy."

The degree to which the exploitation of animals is carried on
by all elements in a society, or, conversely, the extent to which
those who use and exploit animals form a distinct class or subculture, is also highly variable. In general the simpler societies,
such as the Australian Aborigines, the several North American Indian groups, the Chukchi, and the Dodos, have fairly unified approaches to the animals they are concerned with. The Tibetans,
the Andean llama herders, and modern ranchers were or are specialized groups serving and dependent on other parts of their societies with other specialized economic patterns. In the Inca empire herding was sustained as a specialized trade without monetary
exchange, but in general such specialized animal-oriented sub-
economies are most likely to be found in the most commercial
economies.

There is a sharp dichotomy among the societies here discussed
between those which control their animals as full domesticates and
those which hunt them. The dingoes of the Australians alone
stand in a somewhat intermediate position. It will be noted, however, that domestication or nondomestication correlates very poorly, in the sample presented in this symposium, with the importance of the animals to the economy. Where people who do not

have domesticates are heavily dependent on animals, the reciprocal ecological relations are simple. If game is overexploited the human population will move away or decline. Domesticates can, to a degree, be protected and sustained and the human populations sustained, but new factors such as overgrazing and long-term environmental impoverishment are likely to be introduced.

If we consider whole societies rather than specialized animal-breeding sections of complex societies, we can predict that the wealthier the society, the more economically irrelevant the keeping of animals may be. The recent rise in the horse population in our own affluent society is an appropriate example. But in societies in which animals are peripheral to the economy we regularly find instances of economically irrational behavior. Australian Aborigines with their dingoes are paralleled by myriads of tropical villages with their gloriously unproductive chickens. Although the Indian cattle, as their maintenance violates rules of economic rationality—and on the basis of uncontrolled breeding alone it certainly does—may constitute both a more important and a more costly instance of getting satisfactions unrelated to subsistence from animals, I believe that the Indian cattle complex can only be understood in relation to the fact that India's subsistence economy is fundamentally horticultural.

Domestic animals can be and often are thought of as commodity. This is clearly the case with the Chukchi, Bedouin, and Apache among the groups treated in this symposium, as it is with the Western rancher, Argentine *estanciero,* or Australian stockman. When he holds such a viewpoint, the owner will use his technology and his knowledge of animal breeding and the environment to maximize the output of that commodity which the animals yield him and minimize the cost in terms of labor or other resources. As opposed to vegetable or industrial commodities, however, animals learn and behave. Some are capable of yielding and reacting to affectionate responses. They are potential pets.

Eduard Hahn's historical insights and speculations on the domestication of animals (most thoroughly elaborated in Hahn, 1896), though they may never be subject to conclusive proof, look better as our knowledge of ethnography, archeology, and comparative psychology increases (Isaac, 1962). According to Hahn, the dog and the pig were pets, members of the household, and often nursed by women. The herd animals were kept for sacrifices, in which milk and its products figured prominently. The sexual, and thus affectionate, aspects of milking, and the tolerance thereof on the part of the animal, fit in the same frame of reference. The economic utilization of animals and their products then would be derived and, genetically speaking, secondary to other values or satisfactions the animals afforded which justified the effort and resources that went into their keeping. There is clearly no tendency toward domesticating their game on the part of the North American Indian groups described by Hickerson and Knight. The game animals were a commodity to be taken and consumed.

Though they may never have heard of money or Adam Smith, all societies have a problem in the allocation of scarce resources, and there is substantial basis for belief that classical economic models have such an intrinsic validity that they will be independently approached by any society even if not formally recognized by that society. If animals are kept for companionship, enough will be maintained to satisfy that want. If they afford food, clothing, or energy, their numbers will be increased until they are so great as to cut in on some other resource or demand too much of the labor time available. It is in this last connection that the institutional organization of the society becomes a significant factor. Where animal husbandry becomes the main base of the economy, however, the social organization is likely to be modified so as to make labor efficiently available for caring for the animals, as it has been among the Chukchi and Bedouin. To some extent the Apache have been able to by-pass a social reorganization which would make them more effective cattle herders by borrowing some of the organization and technology of American commercial grazers.

Their physical and physiological attributes make each species of domesticated animal, and domesticated animals in general, peculiarly distinctive bases for wealth production. Some of these attributes afford the animal breeder an immediate and positive economic advantage over the plant cultivator. Others set in motion ecologic disturbances that may degrade the environment in terms of its ability to support man, or may stimulate conflicts between or within human social groups. Finally, such strictly cultural phenomena as social organization and inheritance practices among herding societies must accord reasonably well with the feeding, breeding, and protection requirements of the species of domestic animals that are important to their economy. Some of these attributes are here considered.

Feed requirements and tolerance. The true domesticates, i.e., house animals such as the pig, dog, and chicken, subsist on just the same concentrated foodstuffs as man, though they are less fastidious about preparation and condition and are not burdened with food taboos. The dog probably is even less capable than man of getting by on a wide range of food, though chickens and other fowls, because of their small size, can glean seed grains and insects occurring in concentrations too sparse to support man. Thus these animals may, under some conditions, be directly competitive with man for subsistence. If they are to be eaten, they may possibly yield as much as one-fifth as much food value to man as that of the feed that was required to rear them, but under anything other than the most modern scientific feeding programs probably less than one-fifteenth as much. Either the companionship the animals provide or the distinctive flavor of their flesh, along with their actual expensiveness, makes these household animals an almost ideal luxury or prestige item. On the other hand, except in appallingly wealthy societies such as our own, they will remain scarce and secondary food sources.

The grazing animals, with digestive systems that are enormous in proportion to their size, do have the capacity to subsist on feeds too bulky and poor to nourish a human. Where the environment, usually because of a growing season shortened by drought or cold, affords vegetable stuffs not directly nourishing to man but capable of sustaining some grazing animal, the adoption of a pastoral economy constitutes an advance in man's capacity to exploit the area. In the steppes, deserts, dry savannas, tundras, and highlands, herding an appropriate animal is the most effective form of land use and areal exploitation, and under especially severe conditions only a single species, such as the reindeer or the camel, can cope with the environment. In all such areas individual animals or herds compete with one another for pasture after they have reached a saturation number, but not with any other type of economy or land use.

Grazing animals are also pastured on land that might grow crops, as in India, certain savanna districts of East Africa and the Sudan, and, as noted by Strickon, in modern United States, Argentina, and Australia. Under such circumstances the land will not yield its maximum amount of food for human support. To a large human population, then, animal products will be luxuries, scarce and prestigeful under ordinary circumstances. There are, however, economic as well as traditional, value-oriented reasons why animal husbandry can compete with horticulture even where it is not the most productive form of land use.

Size of the economic enterprise. Prior to the utilization of extra-human animate or inanimate energy in farming, an increase in the size of the area cultivated by a man or a family would not produce an increase in output. With a given soil quality, technology, and crop assemblage there is an optimum size of farm that one man can till, and it is usually less than a hectare. Where soils are poor, frequent shifting of fields may be necessary to get high enough yields to sustain the cultivating force, but a sparse population occupying good land cannot raise its per capita consumption level by extending the areas cultivated.

With grazing animals, however, even under primitive conditions, there is a great range, 10:1 or even 100:1, between the largest herd a given labor force can care for and the smallest herd that would support that labor force. The level of consumption and security against natural calamity will both be almost directly proportional to herd size. If grazing land is really abundant, or can be made abundant by conquest, pastoralists will all try to maximize their herds, and if they can do so may achieve a higher living standard than the horticulturalist can attain. Shortly, however, the grazing ranges will be saturated and attempts of individuals to maximize herd size will provoke conflicts within a given social group or between social groups.

Increase in herds. The rate at which the seed stock of plant cultivators might be increased if there were no other limiting factors is so great that this capacity becomes irrelevant. The other factors, especially land and the labor available in the normally short seasons suitable for planting and harvesting, almost always set the limits of horticultural production. For the grazing animals, however, there are very definite limits to the rates at which herds can be increased. Regardless of how favorable the range or the season, and even if the herdsman can minimize his need to slaughter animals for food, a number of years must elapse before a small herd can grow into a comfortably large one. The importance of making the herd grow, for that is the fundamental path to success for the pastoralist, seems to be a universal positive value for all herding peoples. It shows clearly in the accounts in this symposium and in all other relevant ethnographies I know.

The rate at which a herd may be increased varies with the species; the principal variables are the number of offspring per cast, the time interval between casts, the breeding life span of a female, and the duration of the period between birth of a female and her first cast. A sex ratio at birth that departed significantly from parity would also affect the rate. Obtaining a generally applicable closed formula for this rate proves to be difficult, but it is clearly exponential and to some degree approximates a Fibonacci series. The point is that though it takes a number of years to build up a herd, if all the females are kept and bred, and losses from accidents, disease, and predators can be kept at a minimum, a herd of even so slow-breeding an animal as the camel will increase to enormous size well within one human lifetime. This growth can be achieved and still permit slaughter of most of the male half of the annual increment. The herder's economic rationale almost always provides for harvesting the excess male animals. There are data on killing male calves in dairying operations even in India.

As a result, in anything but the shortest span of time following entry to a region or a major disaster that has obliterated the herds, the grazing animals of a region will be pressing on its pasture. Territorial expansion against other herders or into nongrazing areas is an almost constantly felt need. Though it may be restrained by legal systems or a balance of power, a vigorously de-

veloped pattern of individual and collective aggression, and supporting institutional and ethical structures, exist in most herding
cultures. Their intricacy and balance are nicely illustrated among
the Bedouin. The landscape, however, may suffer more than the
neighbors. Since each herd manager recognizes no more critical
imperative than maximizing herd size and maintaining his breeding stock against all vicissitudes, overgrazing will be carried on
with ever increasing intensity as the range deteriorates. Selective
impoverishment of the flora and accelerated soil erosion follow.
No primarily herding society has ever achieved a stable ecologic
adjustment except at a lower level of productivity than the one
that existed when pastoralism was introduced. The worst damage
is done where a relatively nonwarlike society of small herd-holders
utilizes both animal aptitudes and energetic human direction to
sustain its animals in bad seasons. Such recently established New
World pastoral traditions as those of the Navaho and of the Guajira of Colombia and Venezuela (Aschmann, 1960) have already
degraded their ranges. The relatively good condition of the
Apache ranges stems in large part from those groups' having
failed, as Kunstadter points out, to accept a real herding tradition.
The Apache have instead accepted the American system of commercial ranching without integrating it into their culture, and
with it they can accept our scientific and economic notions of
range management. The Chukchi have had a less deleterious effect on their landscape than most pastoralists, probably because
recurring natural disasters have been so effective as to keep both
the human and the reindeer populations below the carrying capacity of the range, permitting the long-term range fallowing that
Leeds discusses.

Vulnerability of the capital resource of herds. Because of their
mobility, herd animals can evade climatic vicissitudes that would
result in complete failure of a vegetable crop. Regular trans-
humant migrations are common, and treks to distant pastures in
times of great stress figure in the histories of most if not all pastoralists. Furthermore, under certain circumstances when general
pasture shortage can be foreseen, the herdsman may reduce his
herd by walking it to a market and converting it into money or
another form of good. These advantages, which might seem to

provide the pastoralist with a more stable economic base than the cultivator, are more than canceled by the fact that grazing as a prime economic activity is generally restricted to the marginal lands in which even mild and frequently occurring climatic fluctuations may have a disastrous impact.

If herding is to form the basis for a family's livelihood, the herd must be of at least a minimal size, and starting with a small breeding population it may take several years to bring it up to that size. Thus the small holder whose herd remains near the minimum size level, kept there by sale of animals to obtain necessities and by slaughter for food that consumes virtually all the annual increase, is in a peculiarly vulnerable position. Predation, human or animal, disease, or a natural disaster that destroyed only ten per cent of his herd would make his position economically untenable, whereas the same percentage loss would easily be made up in a year by the owner of a large herd. Having fallen below a viable productive capacity, the small operator has to become a dependent of a larger one; such relationships are almost universal in fully pastoral societies, as noted here among the Chukchi and the Bedouin. On the other hand, the environment is hard, and large herds need consistent personal management. Leeds' Chukchi data are especially illustrative and by no means unique. The owner of a large herd finds a definite upper limit to his holdings; he must follow and superintend closely and cannot adopt a way of life completely alien to that of his herdsmen, as does a landlord as opposed to a renting cultivator in an irrigated valley. The overt egalitarianism of Western ranchers noted by Strickon is a normal phenomenon among pastoralists.

An inheritance pattern which will preserve the integrity of viably large herds is another requisite, though the precise pattern in which it is established can vary widely.

Prestige of the herdsman. If not universally, at least frequently enough to require explanation, where farming and herding groups live in close contact or where the two occupations are pursued by different individuals within the same tribe, the pastoralists enjoy distinctly higher status. An individual may become a cultivator because his herd has become too small to support him, but he does not do so voluntarily just because that occupation offers more

comfort and security. Should he prosper as a farmer, he is likely
to purchase enough animals to return to herding.

Among Indian peasants and to some extent among East African
peoples, where people both till the soil and keep animals, the
owners of more animals will be the richer people, and their prestigeful position is expectable. But those East African groups consisting primarily of herdsmen tend to occupy the poorer land, and
they probably suffer from hunger, privation, and economic insecurity more than their farming neighbors. In some instances the
tradition of conquest by warlike herdsmen and even the exaction
of feudal dues from farmers may provide an adequate explanation,
but certainly not in all. The notion that because of their concentrated value and capacity for being moved to fairly distant markets, livestock are a better medium or standard of exchange than
perishable, nontransportable vegetable stuffs has explanatory
value. One accumulates visible wealth with livestock, wealth con-
vertible into any desired good. In noncommercial societies, except in times of famine, surplus vegetable produce is only food or
something to be given to visitors.

Nonetheless these two suggestions do not seem to me to be a
full explanation of the generality of the herdsman's greater prestige. Why then is there more merit in manipulating animals
rather than plants for a living? Some insights might be gleaned
by a comparative examination of the few localities such as Japan
and India where those who deal primarily with animals for a living seem to experience an inferior social status.

References

Aschmann, H. Indian pastoralists of the Guajira Peninsula. *Ann.
    Assoc. Am. Geographers, 50,* 208–418.
Hahn, E. 1896. *Die Haustiere und ihre Beziehungen zur Wirtschaft
    des Menschen.* Duncker & Humblot, Leipzig, Germany.
Isaac, E. 1962. On the domestication of cattle. *Science, 137,* 195–204.
Marsh, G. P. 1864. *Man and Nature; or, Physical Geography As
    Modified by Human Action.* S. Low, Son and Marston, London.
Sauer, C. O. 1938. Theme of plant and animal destruction in eco-
    nomic history. *J. Farm Econ., 20,* 765–776.

Functional Analyses in the Symposium "Man, Culture, and Animals"

PAUL W. COLLINS

*Department of Philosophy, State University of New York,
Stony Brook, Long Island, New York*

THE COLLECTION OF ANALYSES in this volume appear *prima facie* to be united only by their common concern with the kinds of transactions which have developed between specific human populations and animal populations with which they come into contact. Nevertheless, examination of the procedure by which many of the papers attempt to account for the phenomena under inquiry reveals an interesting and possibly significant similarity. This paper will be concerned primarily to make explicit the source of this similarity and its bearing on considerations of explanatory structure. Those papers primarily concerned with description rather than explanation and those not having the characteristic explanatory premise common to the other papers will not be concentrated upon in spite of their merit. This limitation is unfortunate, but is justifiable on the ground that the apparent methodological unity of the other papers raises a number of important issues deserving fairly close examination.

A tacit functional premise seems common to most of the papers treated here. This premise includes a statement to the effect that a functional system operates with respect to the variables that have been selected for analysis. The attempt to establish that such

systems are in operation for the populations under inquiry, moreover, results in the provision of support for the editors' belief,
stated in their Preface, that the collected papers

indicate the possibility and also the fruitfulness of functional analyses
concerned not only with the interrelation of sociological variables but
also with the operation of mechanisms maintaining environmental
variables at values conducive to the survival or expansion of human
populations.

A brief survey of the papers will indicate clearly enough that
most of the contributors not only took the approach suggested by
the editors, but also were able to indicate the "fruitfulness of
functional analyses" by finding data to show the operation of functional systems possessing mechanisms that include the culturally
patterned behavior of the populations studied. Leeds, for example, shows us how the various institutionalized behaviors of the
Chukchi in combination with certain environmental variables
function to maintain reindeer herd sizes within a certain range of
values; Downs and Ekvall suggest how a cultural, linguistic, and
social homogeneity is maintained in Tibet through the functioning of religious and trading activities in which animals play a crucial role; both Harris and Deshler, for their particular human
populations, show how the various institutionalized behaviors of
their populations serve to maintain a cattle population of a certain
size, which in turn serves to maintain in rather interesting ways
the subsistence of the investigated populations within critical
limits; Hickerson suggests how a deer population was maintained
above minimal levels by the fighting activities of the Chippewa
and Sioux Indian populations; and Sweet shows how effects of
tribal segmentation and institutionalized raiding behavior, among
other things, serve to maintain above a certain minimal level the
number of camels per camping unit of the various Bedouin tribes.
    It must be noted, however, that these analyses have not been
uniformly successful in isolating and quantifying the variables of
the systems indicated. Moreover, a justifiable question could be
raised as to whether some of the systems are genuinely functional
in the sense to be indicated below. Nevertheless, the suggestions

provided and the data submitted may be regarded as important preliminary attempts to relate both cultural and environmental variables in functional systems. As such, the analyses deserve our consideration.

It is now necessary for us to investigate in more detail the nature of a functional system and the explanatory structure that it involves.

A functional system is characterized by what are known, in popular engineering terminology, as "feedback" mechanisms. Its structure has the following form. There is a variable (to be called "R") which possesses a range of values having empirically describable limits. If this R variable is removed from these limits, the system is destroyed. But, in response to factors which tend to remove the R variable from these limits, or which would remove the variable from these limits if not checked in some way, certain other variables of the system alter their values. These alterations, in effect, create sufficient and necessary conditions for the operation of certain compensating mechanisms which in turn serve to counteract the disturbing conditions. The R variable is thereby maintained within its range.

It should be noted that systems whose variables and mechanisms are structured in such a way as to exemplify the form described above are numerous in both physical and biological phenomena. Servomechanisms, such as the automatic pilot and the common thermostat, illustrate this form. Biological phenomena, of course, abound in systems that exemplify relations such as those described above. Perhaps the most noted of these systems is that described and made popular by W. B. Cannon in his book *The Wisdom of the Body* (1932), where the temperature-maintaining system of the human body was given careful analysis. However, numerous similar systems, such as those maintaining the blood sugar level, the red blood cell level, and so on, can be isolated. Functional systems, in short, seem to be ubiquitous in the world of biological phenomena.

A significant contribution of the papers collected here is their presentation of materials indicating that systems consisting of variables and mechanisms that involve culturally patterned human behavior may also operate as functional systems. If such is the case, then we can expect a reassessment of the interpretations of cultural behavior usually favored.

It is unnecessary separately to examine each of the papers referred to in an attempt to isolate the functional systems that seem to be indicated in the course of each author's argument. Nevertheless, it is worth while to select a few of the papers more or less at random in order to suggest how they exemplify the explanatory pattern for a functional system as given above.

Turning to Sweet's paper on "Camel Pastoralism in North Arabia and the Minimal Camping Unit," we see that a variable maintained within a range is the distribution of camels per camping unit, an acceptable distribution being about twenty camels per tent. However, as Sweet's analysis indicates, a number of factors operate that have the effect of upsetting this distribution: failure of the pasturage, disease, and so on. But, in response to the disturbing effects on the maintenance of camel distribution, a number of mechanisms for restoring the distribution can come into operation: redistribution of camels by section chiefs, camel raiding, tribal emigration, seizure of new grazing territory, and so on. A more precise analysis might enable us to predict which of these mechanisms would in fact operate for any given situation.

Similar observations can be made with respect to Leeds' paper on "Reindeer Herding and Chukchi Social Institutions." A variable maintained here is reindeer herd size within specifiable minimum and maximum limits. The operation of the various disturbing factors documented by Leeds is counteracted by a number of mechanisms, some involving such institutionalized human activities as marriage, apprenticeship, herd "fissioning," and herd capture.

Even if we maintain a very cautious skepticism in declaring the systems described in these two papers, as well as in the others similarly oriented, to be indeed functional, it is nevertheless the case that the major defining characteristics of a functional system can be discerned in the papers in question: an R variable, disturbing factors, and compensating mechanisms. It is true that we may desire a more precise and comprehensive specification of the variables of the system before making unqualified judgment. Nevertheless, the data provided in these papers are sufficient to render at least probable the proposition that functional systems are in operation in the situations described.

It is instructive to examine the verification procedure employed by Leeds. Since the system with which he is concerned was in operation around 1900 and cannot be observed by him now, verification of the hypothesis that a functional system was in operation cannot be accomplished by noting present changes in the values of the variables of the system. However, on the basis of his functional hypothesis, Leeds was able to make a number of inferences that were subsequently borne out by the available ethnological data. For example, noting that for the Chukchi "we find a situation in which human survival is fostered by maintaining herd size relatively stable and within defined limits," Leeds makes the inference that "we should expect to find socio-cultural institutions rather than only 'natural' means operating to maintain optimal herd sizes." That his expectations were satisfied can be readily seen in his text. In this manner, Leeds has shown that hypotheses concerning populations that cannot be directly studied through field investigations are nevertheless capable of some substantiation through a careful analysis of available documentary material.

In turning to questions concerning the explanatory structure of the functional analyses in this symposium, we have already indicated that the isolation and quantification of pertinent variables fails to attain the completeness and precision necessary for an acceptable verification of the accounts presented. The practical difficulties involved in data collection are, of course, largely responsible for this situation. Accordingly, we may generally characterize these accounts as "explanation sketches." The term "explanation sketch" was invented by Carl Hempel to designate an account which provides "a more or less vague indication of the laws and initial conditions considered as relevant, and needs 'filling out' in order to turn into a full-fledged explanation." He observes further that this "filling-out requires further empirical research, for which the sketch suggests the direction" (1942, p. 42). Nevertheless, with this point in mind, the simpler term "explanation" will be employed throughout the present discussion for reasons of convenience.

The above remarks, however, should not permit us to overlook the significance of the structure of explanation which the papers generally seem to exemplify. In spite of limitations in empirical content, the logic of explanation employed is formally valid. Therefore, provided the functional system involved has been isolated and given empirical grounding, it is possible to derive propositions having predictive force. This situation may be said to mark a significant advance over previous functionalist formulations in anthropology. Earlier functionalists were often confused with respect to the object of the analysis, that is, with respect to what was being explained. As a consequence, they left themselves open to unanswerable criticisms that came from various directions. The object of explanation for them was, in general, an institution or a "culture trait." However, it has been frequently observed that to show that a given institution functions in a certain way does not by itself constitute an explanation of that institution or trait. In "The Logic of Functional Analysis," Carl Hempel (1959) has very clearly shown the fallacy involved in this type of explanation. This fallacy is exposed by noting the logical form frequently taken in attempts to provide functional explanations in anthropology:

(a) At [time] t, [social system] s functions adequately in a setting of kind c (characterized by specific internal and external conditions).

(b) s functions adequately in a setting of kind c only if a certain necessary condition, n, is satisfied.

(c) If trait i were present in s, then, as an effect, condition n would be satisfied.

(d) (Hence,) at t, trait i is present in s. (Hempel, 1959, p. 280.)

Brief inspection will show this form to be logically invalid. Trait i (i.e., a "cultural trait" or "institution") can never be regarded as the only item that can satisfy condition n. There are, as various students of functionalism have observed, always possible "functional alternatives" to i. Accordingly, the presence of i in social system s has not been explained through this schema.

The logic of explanation that characterizes the "functionalism" exemplified in most of the papers in this symposium, however, escapes the criticism leveled above. In explanations based on functional systems we cannot admit the conclusion to take the form "at t, trait i is present in s." Rather, as we shall see below, the proper conclusion should be "at t, variable v will undergo certain changes in value" (serving to maintain the values of an R variable within specified limits). The *conclusion* cited by Hempel ("at t, trait i is present in s"), on the basis of this approach, appears instead in the *premises* of the explanation as one of the boundary conditions for system s. In short, functional analysis as here conceived explains behavior, or the operation of systems, and not the presence of traits.

For example, although Sweet is certainly concerned to provide an accurate description of the Bedouin institution of camel raiding, she makes no effort to explain its presence in the Bedouin cultural repertory. By carefully noting its presence, she has provided a description that will appear as part of the setting of the system, and this description accordingly forms part of the premises of her explanation. The presence of institutionalized camel raiding in the Bedouin cultural repertory constitutes therefore one of the boundary conditions of the analysis rather than its object.

To provide an explanation of why camel raiding occurs at a given time and place rather than at another time and place is, however, an object of Sweet's analysis. She is, accordingly, explaining changes in Bedouin behavior under given circumstances, and this explanation, moreover, makes reference to a functional system as defined earlier. If her explanation is sound, she should be able to predict specific instances of camel raiding.

In general, therefore, we can say that functional explanation as here conceived depends on the isolation of a functional system, and the explanation provided is of the changes in the values of variables of the system and of the operation of its mechanisms. The "mechanisms" of the system are dependent on the values of certain variables for their operation, and may therefore be stated in terms of the values of these variables.

This type of explanation consists of two discriminable components. The first component is the one justifying the use of the term "functional" in characterizing the type of analysis employed, and can be formalized in the following way:

(a) At t, if s is a functional system, then in a given setting variable v will undergo x change in value (or, mechanism m will operate).

(b) s is a functional system.

(c) (Hence,) variable v will undergo x change in value (or, mechanism m will operate).

This component permits the prediction of changes in the elements of the system, assuming, of course, that the system has been isolated and possesses those characteristics of the functional system outlined earlier. However, the universal conditional (a) is not a law statement, since its scope of predication is limited to a specific spatio-temporal state of affairs. System s is a specific system involving a particular human population, and the conclusion of the conditional is derived on the basis of system-specific laws ("laws of the system"). Accordingly, a second component consisting of the general laws that are exemplified by the changes in variables and by the operation of mechanisms is necessary to complete the explanation. In other words, the system-specific laws must be shown to be derivable from general laws unlimited in scope of predication given the conditions under which the system operates. These laws, however, will in general be only tacitly assumed in anthropological analysis, and, if made explicit, would probably refer to certain types of regularity in collective human behavior (cf. Hempel, 1942; Nagel, 1961, chap. 15). For functional analysis, of course, the establishment of the first, or functional, component will be the primary goal and can be pursued independently of attempts to specify the general laws that may be involved.

Two of the papers of the symposium present negative conclusions in the sense that the traits that they are investigating are indicated to have no functional consequences for the population under inquiry. Meggitt has been able to argue that the association of the Australian Aborigines and tame dingoes has only minimal if any effects supporting a functional system, although wild dingoes can be most useful in hunting. The importance of a negative instance in this context is to underscore the point that the discovery of functional systems is predominantly an empirical affair, and negative evidence with respect to the tame dingo–Aborigine association illustrates the fact that all traits are not necessarily parts of such systems. A trait of this sort may be called "afunctional" in the sense that it neither supports nor has effects detrimental to the maintenance of an R variable. Nevertheless, it should also be noted that the failure to find supporting evidence for a given hypothesis is never conclusive, inasmuch as evidence may appear at a later time.

Knight's paper, on the other hand, shows that under conditions characterized by an absence of subsidies from the government or other sources, the much disputed trait of family hunting territories among the northeastern Algonkian Indians cannot be present, or, if instituted, must disappear. In essence, Knight faces two problems in his paper. The first is that of showing how one functional system involving a caribou population is changed to another functional system involving a moose population. The second is the problem of showing that the institution of family hunting and trapping territories among the Algonkian could not exist in either of these systems in the absence of government control and subsidies.

The second problem involves showing that family hunting territories are dysfunctional with respect to both the caribou and moose systems. Knight attempts to accomplish this aim by showing that family hunting territories in the absence of government subsidy and credit systems would have led to a severe decline in population, since exploitation of resources would have been drastically curtailed. This did not take place, and Knight states that family hunting territories are not an indigenous feature among the Algonkian, but generally appear with the imposition of government controls.

The first problem, that of showing how one functional system has changed into another, involves the difficulty of explaining the appearance of new variables and mechanisms, rather than changes in the values of extant variables. Functional analysis, however, can only explain the latter. Although functional analysis will be necessary to isolate the previous and subsequent functional systems, the additional problem of explaining the origins of the new variables and mechanisms requires recourse to explanatory procedures independent of functional analysis. This recourse is taken by Knight. In addition, however, he is quite successful in underlining the critical difference between the two systems, and in indicating why the older system was no longer able to continue.

Harris' paper on "The Myth of the Sacred Cow" raises some questions concerning the relation of ritual or religious behavior to the ecology of human populations. If we interpret his analysis as involving a functional system, it should be evident that a "regulated" or R variable with which he is concerned is a cattle population that must be maintained above certain limits. This cattle population, in turn, is critical for the continued success of the Indian peasant in maintaining an already marginal subsistence.

The suggestion that the cow in India has important economic value is supported in Harris' paper by a wealth of varied evidence: the dung is a cooking fuel; the bullocks are used for agricultural purposes; beef from cows, either slaughtered or otherwise dead, provides a supplement to the peasant diet, and so on.

Moreover, it can be seen on the basis of Harris' data that the taboo on the consumption of beef does have at least short-run effects supporting the maintenance of the cattle population. Presumably, some Indians with caste do observe the taboo, and consume beef either not at all or only under rare conditions. One possible source for a decline in the cattle population is accordingly eliminated. Furthermore, it may be that the wealthier Indians are constrained by the cow's sacredness to permit the wandering cows of peasants to have access to fields. Generally, non-interference with the wanderings of cows enables the animals to exploit an ecological niche removed from the possibility of direct competition with human beings.

Accordingly, it is possible that the case of the sacred cow can profitably be considered in conjunction with cases studied by Vayda, Leeds, and Smith (1961), O. K. Moore (1957), and others, which direct attention to the possibility of finding "religious" or ritual behaviors having economic consequences of critical importance to the populations under analysis.

The logic of functional analysis makes no prescription concerning the nature of the variables and mechanisms constituting the system. On the basis of methodological considerations, we stipulate simply that the variables have empirical reference, and that changes in the variables be measurable according to explicit rules. Nevertheless, it may be of some significance that many of the analyses in this symposium are concerned with a regulated variable of critical importance to the survival and success of the population under given conditions. With changing conditions, of course, we should probably expect a change in the system, as suggested by Knight's paper. But it does not seem premature to agree with Harris that the "larger myth according to which culture is equally capable of elaborating itself along any of the lines of imagination, caprice, and illusion of which the human mind is capable" is effectively combatted by the type of analysis provided in these papers. Considerable understanding of culture is gained by showing how cultural behavior has effects that maintain systems affording the means of sustenance for the populations concerned. Most of the papers have shown that the systems investigated are "rational" if by "rational" we mean that the variable maintained by a system is critical for the continued survival and success of a population under the conditions specified by the analysis. It would seem, therefore, that the speculation that most if not all human populations receive benefits from the operation of functional systems in the sense defined above is not an idle one. Certainly if this is so, our understanding of human culture will be significantly enriched by analyses such as those appearing in this symposium.

REFERENCES

CANNON, W. B. 1932. *The Wisdom of the Body*. W. W. Norton and Co., New York, N. Y.

HEMPEL, C. 1942. The function of general laws in history. *J. Philos., 39*, 35–48.

HEMPEL, C. 1959. The logic of functional analysis. In *Symposium on Sociological Theory* (L. Gross, editor), pp. 271–307. Row, Peterson and Co., Evanston, Ill.

MOORE, O. K. 1957. Divination—A new perspective. *Am. Anthropologist, 59,* 69–74.

NAGEL, E. 1961. *The Structure of Science*. Harcourt, Brace and World, Inc., New York, N. Y.

VAYDA, A. P., A. LEEDS, and D. B. SMITH. 1961. The place of pigs in Melanesian subsistence. *Proceedings of the 1961 Annual Spring Meeting of the American Ethnological Society* (V. E. Garfield, editor), pp. 69–77. University of Washington Press, Seattle, Wash.

Index of Authors
and Names of Persons

Index of Peoples and Places

After every place name, except a few most commonly known, a familiar geographical area has been entered for identification purposes. All names not so identified are those of peoples.

Aborigines, *see* Australian Aborigines
Acora (Perú), 191, 194, 199
Afghans (Pathans), 9n
Africa, 153
  eastern, 153–168 *passim*, 266, 270
  western, 153
  see also individual countries
Africans, 154, 166
  East, 270; *see also* Dodos; Karamajong
Aitkin County (Minnesota), 50
Alabama (U.S.A.), 78
Alamogordo (New Mexico), 78
Alca (Perú), 210
Algonkian, 27–42 *passim,* 260, 261, 279; *see also* Montagnais-Naskapi
Alice Springs (Australia), 14n
Amdo (Tibet), 181
America, North, 43, 137, 178, 229, 231, 239; *see also* Canada; Indians, North American; United States
America, South, 229; *see also* Aymara; Inca empire; Indians, South American; *and individual countries*
Americans, 78, 124
Anadyr River and area (Siberia), 88 (map), 97, 98
Anaizah, *see under* Bedouin
Anaizah highland (Arabia), 135
Andeans, 185–215 *passim,* 259
Andes and Andean area, 185–215 *passim*

Apache, 67–86 *passim,* 261, 263, 264, 268
  Eastern, 73, 78
    Chiricahua, 73, 76, 77, 78, 79
    Jicarilla, 73, 78, 79
    Mescalero, 67, 68, 69, 73, 75, 76, 78, 79, 82, 83
  southwestern, 68
  Western, 73, 78n
    San Carlos, 73
    White Mountain, 73
Arabia, 133, 134, 136, 146
  central, 142
  north, 129–152 *passim,* 274
  southeastern, 132
  southern, 132, 142
Arabian nomads, 4; *see also* Bedouin
Argentina, 229–258 *passim,* 266
Arizona (U.S.A.), 78
Arkansas River (Colorado-Kansas), 43
Asia
  central, 170, 174, 177
  south, 7, 10
  southeast, 10
  see also Orient; *and individual countries*
Athabaskans, *see* Southern Athabaskans
Australia, 7–26 *passim,* 229–258 *passim,* 266
  Central Australia, 10, 11, 11n, 14, 15n, 16, 20, 22
  New South Wales, 14, 15, 15n, 18, 19, 21
  Northern Territory, 9, 20

Index of Subjects